Medit
Millionar

These playboys are masters of seduction!

By
Request

Mediterranean Millionaires

THE RELUCTANT HUSBAND

by

Lynne Graham

THE MARRIAGE SURRENDER

by

Michelle Reid

FARELLI'S WIFE

by

Lucy Gordon

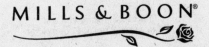

MILLS & BOON®

MEDITERRANEAN MILLIONAIRES
© by Harlequin Enterprises II B.V., 2003

The Reluctant Husband, The Marriage Surrender and *Farelli's Wife*
were first published in Great Britain by Harlequin Mills & Boon Limited
in separate, single volumes.

The Reluctant Husband © Lynne Graham 1998
The Marriage Surrender © Michelle Reid 1998
Farelli's Wife © Lucy Gordon 1999

ISBN 0 263 83587 1

05-0203

*Printed and bound in Spain
by Litografia Rosés S.A., Barcelona*

Lynne Graham was born in Northern Ireland and has been a keen Mills & Boon reader since her teens. She is very happily married with an understanding husband, who has learned to cook since she started to write! Her five children keep her on her toes. She has a very large dog, which knocks everything over, a very small terrier which barks a lot, and two cats. When time allows, Lynne is a keen gardener.

**Don't miss Lynne's sensational
Mills & Boon single title:
DARK ANGEL
Available April 2003**

THE RELUCTANT HUSBAND

by

Lynne Graham

CHAPTER ONE

MATT FINLAY scanned Frankie's shocked face and gave her a bracing smile. 'I happen to think that Sardinia could be a very therapeutic trip for you. You could confront your memories of the love of your life and get it all out of your system—'

'Santino was hardly the love of my life!' Frankie countered between gritted teeth, her whole body tense as a drawn bow.

Matt frowned with pretended concentration. 'I seem to recall that every time you saw the bloke you went weak at the knees and your little teenybopper heart turned cartwheels!'

The evils of alcohol on a loose tongue at the office party, Frankie reflected painfully. One of those times when she had tried a little too hard to be accepted as one of the boys. She should have known Matt would throw that confession back in her face one day when it suited him. 'I spent five of the worst years of my life in Sardinia. You can't blame me for not wanting to go back.'

'You could be off the island again within forty-eight hours and go on to Italy. It wouldn't need to interfere with your holiday plans. Who else is there? Dan's still in France and Marty's wife is due to give birth any day now...'

Frankie wanted to appeal to him again but her sense of fairness would not allow it. Their travel agency, of which she herself owned a sizeable share, specialised in self-catering accommodation abroad, and business had not been that good in recent months. They had lost more

5

than the usual number of properties to competitors. Times were tough in the holiday market.

She squared her shoulders, a tall young woman with the sleek, graceful lines of a thoroughbred, dressed in a sharply tailored black trouser suit, quite deliberately chosen to play down her femininity. She had a fine bone structure, with clear green eyes fringed by ebony lashes and set below equally dark brows. Her burnished hair, a fiery combination of red, copper and gold, was worn in a French plait, embellished by a velvet bow clip. That clip was her one concession to being female.

'And you're a native,' Matt mused with satisfaction. 'That has to be to our advantage.'

'I'm British,' Frankie reminded him flatly.

'Six villas on the Costa Smeralda. You check them out, sign up the owner, go on to Italy and we're in business. And who knows…? By the time you come home from your holiday, you might even be in the mood to celebrate with me over a romantic dinner for two,' Matt suggested with a slow, suggestive smile.

Discomfited by that look, Frankie tensed and coloured. They were friends, but Matt had recently strained their friendship by trying to persuade her into a more intimate relationship. She had already told him as tactfully as she could that she wasn't interested and his persistence was making her increasingly uncomfortable. After all, not only did they work together, they also had to live under the same roof.

'No chance,' she told him with a rather forced grin as she walked to the door.

'Sometimes I hate your brother,' Frankie informed the smiling blonde manning the counter outside.

Leigh just laughed. 'Sardinia?'

'You *knew*?' Frankie felt betrayed and knew she was being oversensitive. Neither of her friends could be expected to understand how threatened she felt by the thought of setting foot on the island again. After all, she hadn't told either of them the full truth of what had happened to her there. 'Why didn't you warn me?'

'Matt thought you'd take it better coming from him, and you'll only arrive for your holiday in Italy sooner,' Leigh pointed out cheerfully as she turned away to answer the phone.

Frankie's long legs made short work of the stairs up to the spacious two-bedroom apartment which she had shared alone with Matt since Leigh had got married. She had moved in with the Finlay siblings three years earlier. Using the proceeds of an insurance policy which had matured when she was eighteen, she had bought into the business. The agency was on the ground floor of the same building. Since Frankie now spent most of her time travelling, spot-checking the standards of current properties and negotiating for new ones, she found the location very convenient.

Or at least she had until Matt had begun acting up, she conceded ruefully. His recent innuendos and familiarities hadn't gone unnoticed by their employees either. The office tongues were already wagging and gossip upset Frankie. A long time ago she had learnt to her cost that careless talk could wreck lives. It had, after all, very nearly destroyed hers once. She shook off that memory with an inner shudder. Did Matt see her as some sort of a challenge? She wasn't even his type. Why were men so infuriatingly contrary? The sooner Matt went back to chasing his trademark tiny blondes, the happier she would be.

She rang her mother's home. The maid answered and put her through.

'Mum? I'm going away earlier than expected,' she said apologetically.

'Frankie...don't you think you're getting rather too long in the tooth to be calling me Mum?' Della snapped in petulant reproof. 'It makes me feel as if I should be collecting my pension!'

'Sorry.' Frankie bit her lip uneasily, a shard of pain that was all too familiar piercing her as Della brushed off the news of her coming absence without comment or indeed any perceptible interest. 'I have to go to—'

'I have an appointment with my manicurist in an hour,' Della interrupted impatiently. 'I'll call you some time next month.'

Frankie replaced the receiver, her hand not quite steady. No matter how many times it happened, it still hurt. All the old excuses came flooding back. Her mother had a very busy social life. She was not a demonstrative person. Those years of separation when Frankie had been in Sardinia had damaged their relationship. But at the back of her mind always lurked the insecure fear that her mother would really not have noticed if her daughter had *never* come home again. And then she felt deeply ashamed of herself for even thinking such a thing.

Frankie's eyes flashed with growing exasperation. It was early evening and she was thoroughly fed up. Today she had expected to be on a ferry to Genoa, in Italy, and what was she doing instead? She was cooped up in a hideously noisy little Fiat, travelling along narrow, steep Sardinian roads that forced her to drive at a snail's pace. Why? Signor Megras, the owner of the villas, had not condescended to meet her at his properties.

She had been given the grand tour by an employee and now *she* had to travel deep into the mountainous interior of the island to negotiate with the owner at his hotel. The drive had already taken far longer than she had anticipated. Of course, she could have taken advantage of the lift she had been offered by the employee, Pietro—he of the sexually voracious dark eyes and the overly eager-to-touch hands. In remembrance, Frankie grimaced. Welcome back to Sardinia, Frankie, home of the macho male and the child-bride...

As swiftly as that designation slunk into her thoughts,

she suppressed it again. She knew what was wrong with her. It was these mountains, the same mountains that had imprisoned her for five unforgettable years. Her flesh chilled at the memories, so why should she let them out? That was the past and it was behind her. She was twenty-one now, and fully in control of her own life again.

But still the memories persisted. The culture shock of being eleven years old, one moment living a civilised life in London and the next being suddenly thrust unprepared into the midst of an almost illiterate peasant family, who didn't even want her. The horror of being told that she would never see London or her mother again. The desertion of her father within days. The loneliness, the fear, the terrifying isolation. All those feelings were still trapped inside Frankie and she knew she would never be free of them.

Her mother had been an eighteen-year-old model when she became pregnant by a handsome Sard photographer called Marco Caparelli. The resulting marriage had been stormy. Her parents had finally separated when Frankie was eight. Her father had stayed in touch but on a very irregular basis, generally showing up when he was least expected and rarely appearing when he was. Once or twice he had even contrived to talk his way back beneath the marital roof again. Frankie's desperate hope that her parents would reconcile had seemed like a real possibility to her on those occasions.

So, perhaps understandably, she had been upset when her mother met another man and finally decided that she wanted a divorce. Della's plans had outraged her estranged husband as well. There had been a terrible argument. One day, shortly after that, Marco had picked Frankie up from school. They were going on a little holiday, he had told her and no, she didn't need to go home to pack, he had laughed, displaying the small case which he'd explained contained everything that she might need for the wonderful trip he was taking her on.

'Does Mum know?' She had frowned.

And then he had let her into the even more wonderful secret. Mum and Dad were getting back together again. It might seem a big surprise to her, but while she had been at school Mum and Dad had made up. Wasn't she pleased that she wasn't going to have a stepfather after all? And wouldn't it be fantastic when Mum joined them in Sardinia at the end of the week?

Bitterly rejecting the memory of that most cruel lie of all, Frankie rounded another corkscrew bend on the tortuous road and saw the sign at the head of a tumbledown bridge. 'La Rocca', it said. At last, she thought, accelerating up the hill into the village, braking first to avoid a goat and then two pigs. Her surroundings gave her a bad case of the chills. A clutch of scrawny hens scattered as she climbed out of the car in the dusty square.

The village was so poor you could taste it, and the taste of that poverty made Frankie shiver. She was reminded of another village even more remote from civilisation. Sienta, that particular cluster of hovels had been called. Birthplace of her paternal grandfather. Sienta had been a dot on the map of another world.

The silence grated on her nerves. Where was the hotel? She hoped it was reasonable, since she was probably going to be forced to spend the night there. Twenty yards away, through an open doorway, she saw a café. Her nose wrinkled fastidiously as she peered into the dim interior. The thick-set man behind the bar stared stonily back at her.

'Could you tell me where Hotel La Rocca is?' she asked in stilted Italian.

'*Francesca...?*'

Gooseflesh broke out on her arms, her every muscle jerking painfully tight. That name she never used, that voice...the soft, mellow syllables as smooth and fluid as honey yet as energising for Frankie as the siren on a police car riding her bumper. There was a whirring in her eardrums. Slowly, very slowly, her feet began to turn, her slender body unnaturally stiff as she fought her disorientation, refusing to accept her instantaneous recognition of that voice.

Santino Vitale fluidly uncoiled his long, lean length from behind the table in the far corner and moved silently out of the shadows. Her tongue welded to the dry roof of her mouth. Her skin felt damp and clammy. For a moment she seriously doubted her sanity and the evidence of her own eyes. In an exquisitely cut silver-grey suit, an off-white raincoat negligently draped across his shoulders, Santino looked shockingly alien and exotic against the shabby backdrop of scarred tables and grimy walls.

'Would you like to join me for a drink?' Dark eyes as stunningly lustrous as black jet whipped over her stilled figure. Smoothly he captured her hand, warmth engulfing her fingertips. 'Ah…you're cold,' Santino sighed, shrugging off his coat to drape it slowly and carefully round her rigid shoulders.

Frankie stood there like a wax dummy, so overpowered by his appearance, she could not react. Shattered, she couldn't drag her gaze from him either. At six feet four, he towered over her in spite of her own not inconsiderable height. Devastatingly handsome, he had the hard classic features of a dark angel and the deeply disturbing sexual charisma of a very virile male. Without warning a tide of remembered humiliation engulfed her, draining every scrap of colour from her cheeks. Everything that Frankie had struggled so hard to forget over the past five years began to flood back.

'*This* is the La Rocca hotel,' Santino murmured.

'This place?' Complete bewilderment and the sense of foolishness that uncertainty always brought made Frankie sound shrill.

'And you are here to meet a Signor Megras?'

'How do you know that?' Frankie demanded shakily.

'Just how do you know that? And what are *you* doing here?'

'Why don't you sit down?'

'Sit down?' she echoed, dazed green eyes scanning him as if he might disappear in a puff of smoke at any moment.

'Why not? I see no Signor Megras.' Santino spun out a chair in silent invitation. The proprietor hurried over to polish the ashtray and then retreated again. 'Won't you join me?'

A faint shaft of sunlight pierced the gloom, highlighting the tattered posters on the wall and the worn stone floor. Every natural instinct spurred Frankie to flight. She reached the door again without the awareness that she had even moved her feet.

'Are you afraid of me now?'

Frankie stopped dead, nervous tension screaming through her rigidity as a rush of daunting confusion gripped her. For an instant she felt like an adolescent again, the teenager who had once slavishly obeyed Santino's every instruction. She had been so terrified of losing his friendship, she would have done anything he told her to do. But no, Santino had not taught her to be afraid of him…she had had to learn for herself to be afraid of the frighteningly strong feelings he aroused inside her.

Was it *his* fault that she hated him now? She didn't want to think about whether or not she was being fair. Instead she found herself turning to look back at him again, somehow answering a need within herself that she could not withstand. And inexplicably it was like emerging from the dark into the light, heat and energy warming her, quelling that sudden spurt of fear and making her bite back her bitterness. Slowly, stiffly, she walked back and sank into the seat.

'What are you doing here?' she asked baldly.

'Signor Megras won't be coming. The villas belong to me.'

As the silence pulsed, Frankie stared back at him incredulously. 'I don't believe you.'

A slashing smile curved Santino's wide, sensual mouth. 'It is the truth. I brought you up here. I wanted to see you again.'

'Why?' Her head was spinning.

'You are my wife. It may be a long time since I have chosen to remind you of that fact, but you are *still* my wife,' Santino imparted with measured emphasis.

A jerky laugh of disbelief fell from Frankie's dry lips. 'Our marriage was annulled as soon as I went back to the UK,' she scorned, tilting her chin. 'Didn't you get the papers?'

Santino merely smiled again. 'Did you?'

Her brow furrowed, her mouth tightening. 'Mum has them. Since I was under-age, she dealt with the formalities—'

'Is that what you were told?'

'Look, I *know* that that ceremony was set aside as null and void!'

'You've been had,' Santino drawled with lazy amusement.

An angry flush washed over her cheeks. His persistence infuriated her. 'When I get home, I'll ensure that you're sent confirmation of the fact. I can assure you that we are no longer married.'

'But then we never were…in the adult sense,' Santino conceded.

Attacked without warning by a cruel Technicolor replay of her last sight of Santino, Frankie paled, her stomach giving a violent lurch. Santino with another woman, locked together in the throes of a very adult passion. A beautiful blonde, her peach-tinted nails spearing into his luxuriant black hair as he kissed her, melding every line of her curvaceous body to the lean, muscular strength of his. Frankie had been ripped apart by that glimpse of Santino as she herself had never seen him, and in that same instant she had been forced to see that they had never had a future together. In leaving, she had set them both free.

Dark golden eyes rested intently on her. 'I deeply regret the manner of our parting. You were very distressed.'

Shattered that he should have guessed what was on her mind, Frankie went rigid. In self-defence, she focused on the table. She couldn't think straight. Her emotions, usually so wonderfully well-disciplined, were in wild turmoil. She could barely accept that she was actually *with* Santino again, but even that bewildering awareness was pounded out of existence by the tremendous pain he had cruelly dredged back up out of her subconscious. With fierce determination, she blocked those memories out.

'Perhaps it was a mistake to mention that so soon but I can feel it standing between us like a wall,' Santino incised very quietly.

The assurance sent Frankie's head flying up again, a fixed smile of derision pasted to her lips. 'And I think you're imagining things. So I discovered that my saint had feet of clay.' She shifted a slim shoulder dismissively. 'All part of growing up, and irrelevant after this length of time. Now, if those villas really are yours, can we get down to business?'

'You have indeed been away a long while.' Santino signalled to the proprietor with a fluid gesture. 'That's not how we do business here. We share a drink, we talk, maybe I invite you to my home for dinner and then, possibly after dinner, we get down to business.'

Frankie's expressive eyes flashed. 'I won't be coming to your home for dinner, I assure you—'

'Strive to wait until you're invited,' Santino traded gently.

Her cheeks reddened, her teeth gritting as wine arrived. 'I find this whole stupid charade juvenile!'

'As I remember it, you love the unexpected.' Santino lounged back indolently in his seat, unconcerned by her growing anger and frustration.

'I was a child then—'

'Yet at the time you kept on telling me that you were *all* woman,' Santino reminded her in a black velvet purr of wry amusement.

The worst tide of colour yet crimsoned Frankie's throat. 'So tell me,' she said sharply, absolutely desperate for a change of subject, 'are you in the tourist trade now?'

'This and that.' Hooded night-dark eyes resting on her, Santino lifted a broad shoulder in an infinitesimal shrug and a half-smile played maddeningly about his mobile mouth.

It was ridiculous that she shouldn't know what business he was in, ridiculous that she should know so very little about this male to whom she had once been married! But years ago all she had known about Santino was that the elderly village priest was his great-uncle and that during the week he worked in a bank in Cagliari, where he also had the use of an apartment.

But, whatever Santino was doing now, he appeared to be doing very well. That magnificent suit simply shrieked expensive tailoring. But then he was a Latin male, and the Latin male liked to look good and was quite capable of spending a disproportionate amount of his income on his wardrobe. Even so, Frankie wasn't used to seeing Santino in such formal attire. When he had come home to her at weekends, he had worn jeans and casual shirts. He looked so different now, like some big city business tycoon, stunningly sophisticated and smooth. The acknowledgement sharply disconcerted her.

Santino was surveying her with veiled eyes. 'I had a good reason for arranging this discreet meeting.'

'April Fool off-season?' Frankie derided brittly.

'I understand that you're on vacation and I would like to offer you the hospitality of my home,' Santino contradicted her evenly.

Frankie stared back at him wide-eyed and then a choked laugh escaped her. 'You're kidding me, right?'

Santino pressed her untouched glass of wine towards her. 'Why should I be?'

'I'm leaving for Italy immediately,' she told him, incredulous that he should advance such an invitation. 'So I'm afraid we do business now or not at all.'

'I don't give a damn about the villas,' Santino countered very drily.

'It's my job to give a damn.' Her sense of unreality was spreading by the minute. Santino here…with her. It felt so fantastically unreal. Why should Santino want to see her again after so long? Simple curiosity? Clearly he had found out where she worked in London. Was that why the villas had been offered to Finlay Travel? But how had Santino discovered where she worked?

From below her lashes she watched him as she drank, easing her parched vocal cords. He was so cool, so controlled…so *calculating*? Her spine tingled, some sixth sense spooking her. She scanned his gypsy-dark features, absorbing the stunning symmetry of each. The wide forehead, the thin, arrogant blade of a nose, the blunt high cheekbones and the chiselled curve of his sensual mouth. Her attention roved to his thick black hair, the curls ruthlessly suppressed by an expert cut, and the lustrous, very dark eyes which flared gold in emotion, and yet still a nagging sense of disorientation plagued her.

Santino both looked and *felt* like a stranger, she acknowledged dazedly, more than that even…a disturbingly intimidating stranger, who wore a cloak of natural authority and command as though he had been born to it. He was not Santino Vitale as she remembered him.

Or was it that she now saw more clearly without adoration blinding her perception? *Adoration?* Inwardly she shrank, but there was no denying that that single word most accurately described the emotions which Santino had once inspired in her.

'Francesca…'

'Nobody calls me that any more,' Frankie muttered waspishly, striving to rise above an ever-increasing sense of crawling mortification.

This encounter *was* a nightmare, she conceded, stricken. At sixteen, she had been so agonisingly, desperately in love with Santino. She had thrown herself at his head and done and said things that no woman in her right mind would want to recall once she reached the age of maturity! She must have seemed pathetic in his eyes, forever swearing undying love and resisting his every move to sidestep the intimacy which she had craved and which *he* had never wanted. It hadn't been Frankie who had locked her bedroom door at night, it had been Santino who'd locked *his*. That particular recollection made her feel seriously unwell.

'Look at me…' A lean brown forefinger skated a teasing path across her clenched knuckles. 'Please, Francesca…' he urged gently.

It was like being prodded by a hot wire. Her sensitive flesh scorched and she yanked her hand back out of reach, shaken by a sudden excruciating awareness of every skin-cell in her humming body. Oh, dear heaven, *no*, she thought as she recognised the wanton source of that overpowering physical response. In horror, she lifted her lashes to collide with glittering gold eyes. Her breath tripped in her throat. Her heart hammered wildly against her ribs.

'What do you want?' she demanded starkly.

'Three weeks out of time,' Santino admitted softly. 'I want us to spend that time together.'

'I'm not spending *any* time with you!' Frankie jerked upright, wide green eyes alight with disbelief.

Santino rose at his leisure, grim amusement curling his eloquent mouth. In a single fluid step he reached her. Lean hands confidently tugged her out from behind the table into the circle of his arms. Frankie was so taken aback she just stood there and looked up at him in open bewilderment. She could not credit that Santino would make any form of sexual advance towards her and uneasily assumed that he was trying to be fraternally reassuring.

'Relax,' Santino urged lazily, brushing a straying strand of bright hair back from her indented brow.

At that careless touch her heartbeat lurched violently, her throat tightening. Suddenly she was struggling to get air into her lungs. He angled his dark head down and she came in conflict with shimmering dark golden eyes. Another wanton frisson of raw excitement arrowed through her. Her head swam. Her knees wobbled. And then, before she could catch her breath again, Santino brought his mouth down on hers with ruthless precision, expertly parting her soft lips to let his tongue hungrily probe the moist, tender interior within.

That single kiss was the most electrifyingly erotic experience Frankie had ever had. Heat flared between her thighs, making her quiver and moan in shattered response. Instinctively she pushed into the hard heat of his abrasively masculine body. He crushed her to him with satisfying strength. Then he lifted his arrogant dark head and gazed down at her, his brilliant gaze raking over her stunned face as he slowly, calmly set her back from him again. 'All this time I wondered...now I *know*,' he stressed with husky satisfaction.

Frankie turned scarlet. Appalled green eyes fixed to him, she backed away fast. 'You know nothing about me!' she gasped, stricken.

In a tempest of angry distress, her only desire to es-

cape from the scene of her own humiliation, Frankie
stalked out into the fading daylight. There she blinked
in bemusement before she raced across the square. It was
empty…empty of her car!

'And now, thanks to you, my car's been stolen!'
Frankie shrilled back at Santino where he now lounged
with infuriating indolence in the doorway of the bar.

He straightened fluidly and strolled towards her. 'I
stole it,' he informed her, seemingly becoming cooler
and ever more dauntingly assured with every second that
made her angrier.

'You did *what*?' Frankie enunciated with extreme difficulty.

'I am responsible for the disappearance of your car.'

The sort of blinding rage Frankie had honestly believed she had left behind in her teens swept over her.
That cool, utterly self-possessed tone affected her like
paraffin thrown on a bonfire. 'Well, you just bloody well
get it back, then!' She launched at him, both of her hands
closing into fists of fury. 'I don't know what kind of a
game you think you're playing here—'

'I don't feel remotely playful,' Santino slotted in
smoothly.

Frankie took a seething stride forward and grabbed
him by the lapels of his jacket. 'I want my car back
now!'

'The Caparelli Curse,' Santino remarked softly, reflectively, quite unmoved by the spitting frenzy of her
fury. 'To think I thought rumour exaggerated. No longer
does it surprise me that your grandfather was so desperate to marry you off.'

And that was it. At the mention of the hated nickname
she had acquired in her grandfather's village Frankie
shuddered, and when Santino went on to remind her that
he had been virtually forced into marrying her her last
shred of control went. 'You swine!' she hissed, and drew
back a step the better to take a swing at him.

But Santino was faster on his feet than she had anticipated, and as he sidestepped her the heel of her shoe caught on the lining of the long raincoat still hanging from her shoulders. She lost her balance and went down with a cry of alarm, striking her head. There was pain…then darkness, then nothing as she slid into unconsciousness.

CHAPTER TWO

FRANKIE had a headache when she drifted back to wakefulness with a frown. But worse was to come. She lifted her heavy eyelids and focused not on her familiar bedroom but on a completely strange room. It was the most disorientating experience of her life.

Stone walls…*stone* walls? Massive antique furniture with more than an air of gothic splendour. Her mouth fell wide as she took in the narrow casement windows, for all the world like the windows of a castle. It was a vast room and the bed was of equally heroic proportions.

And only then did splinters of disconnected imagery return to her. She recalled a nun…a *nun*? She remembered feeling horribly sick, and being so. She remembered being told firmly that she had to stay awake when all that she wanted to do was sleep because her head ached unbearably. All the pieces were confused but one particular image, which had strayed in and out of her hazy impressions, struck her afresh with stunning effect…*Santino*!

A flicker of movement at the corner of her vision jerked her head around. A lithe, dark male figure stepped out of the shadows into the soft pool of light by the bed. Everything came back at once in a rush. Planting two hands on the mattress beneath her, Frankie reeled up into a sitting position, a tangle of multicoloured hair flying round her flushed and taut face. *'You!'* she exclaimed accusingly.

'I'll call the doctor,' Santino responded, reaching forward to tug the tapestry bell-rope hanging beside the bed.

'Don't bother!' Frankie asserted between clenched teeth, throwing back the sheet with the intention of getting up and then swaying as a sick wave of dizziness assailed her.

As she pressed her fingers to her swimming head, a pair of strong arms enclosed her and she was pushed firmly back down again on the pillows.

'Get your hands off me!' Frankie bit out, refusing to surrender to her own bodily weakness.

'Shut up,' Santino said succinctly, bending over her with a shockingly menacing expression stamped on his vibrantly handsome features. 'Bad temper put you in that bed and it might have killed you!'

Frozen by outrage, Frankie gaped at him, emerald-green eyes almost out on shocked stalks that he should *dare* to speak to her like that. 'Your crazy games put me in this bed!'

'Your injuries could have been far more serious,' Santino told her with a most offensive edge of condemnation. 'Had I not managed to break your fall, you might have suffered more than a sore head and concussion. You were unconscious for many hours!'

'It's your fault that I got hurt!'

'*My* fault?' Santino repeated incredulously. 'You took a swing at me!'

'The next time, I won't miss! Where the heck am I?' Frankie flared back furiously. 'I want to go home!'

'But you are home. You are with me,' Santino drawled in a soft tone of finality.

'You're nuts…you are absolutely stark, staring mad!' Frankie exclaimed helplessly, huge, bewildered eyes pinned to him. 'What did you do with my car?'

'As you were no longer in need of it, I had it returned to the hire firm.'

The door opened, breaking the thrumming silence. A tall, distinguished man in his fifties entered the room. 'I am Dr Orsini, Signora Vitale.' He set a medical bag on the cabinet by the bed. 'How are you feeling now that you have had some sleep?'

'I am not Signora Vitale,' Frankie said shakily, beginning to feel like somebody playing a leading role in a farce.

The doctor looked at Santino. Santino smiled, raised his lustrous dark eyes heavenward and shifted a broad shoulder in a small shrug.

'What are you looking at him like that for?' Frankie launched suspiciously. 'I am not this man's wife, Dr Orsini. In fact I have never seen him before in my life!' she concluded with impressive conviction.

The doctor studied her with narrowed eyes and a frown. Frankie looked with expectant triumph at Santino, but Santino was already lifting something off the enormous dressing table and extending it to the older man.

'What's that? What are you showing him?' Frankie demanded jerkily, falling fast into the grip of nervous paranoia.

'One of our wedding photographs, *cara mia*.' Santino shot her rigid stillness a gleaming glance from beneath luxuriant black lashes and tossed the silver-framed photo onto the bed for her perusal.

Without reaching for it—indeed her fingers chose to clutch defensively into the bedspread instead—Frankie stared down fulminatingly at that photograph. Her throat closed over, the strangest lump forming round her vocal cords. There she was in all her old-fashioned wedding finery, sweet sixteen and so sickeningly infatuated that she glowed like a torch for all to see, her face turned up to Santino's adoringly. Shame she hadn't had the wit to notice that Santino's smile had more than a suggestion of stoically gritted teeth about it than a similiar romantic fervour!

Quite irrationally, her eyes smarted with tears. Suddenly she appreciated that whether it was fair or not she really *did* hate Santino! He hadn't had to go through with the wedding. When he had realised the gravity of the situation they were in, surely he could have smuggled her back out of the village again and sent her home to her mother in London? She refused to believe that he could not have found some other way out of their predicament, rather than simply knuckling down to her grandfather's outrageous demand that he marry her!

The doctor was opening his bag when she lifted her head again. Throwing Santino an embittered glance, Frankie cleared her throat. 'This man may once have been my husband but he is not any more. In fact—'

'*Cara...*' Santino chided in a hideously indulgent tone.

'He stole my car!' Frankie completed fiercely.

Carefully not looking at her, Dr Orsini said something in a low, concerned undertone to Santino. Santino sighed, contriving to appear more long-suffering than ever.

'Did you hear what I said?' Frankie's voice shook.

The older man was too busy shaking his head in wonderment.

Santino strolled to the foot of the bed. 'Francesca...' he murmured. 'I know I am not your favourite person right now, but these wild stories are beginning to sound a little weird.'

Her jaw dropped. She flushed scarlet and experienced such a spasm of frustrated fury that she was dimly surprised that she did not levitate off the bed. She slung Santino a blazing look that would have felled a charging rhino. It washed over him. For the very first time she recalled Santino's wicked sense of humour. His sensual mouth spread into a teeth-clenchingly forgiving smile, white teeth flashing against his sun-bronzed skin. '*Grazie, cara...*'

'You will be relieved to learn that the X-rays were completely clear,' Dr Orsini told her in a bracing voice.

He didn't believe her; the man did not *believe* a word she had said!

'X-rays…what X-rays?' she mumbled.

'You were X-rayed last night while you were still unconscious,' Santino informed her.

'*Last* night…?' she stressed in confusion.

Santino nodded in grim confirmation. 'You didn't regain consciousness until the early hours of this morning.'

'Where was I X-rayed?' she pressed.

'In the infirmary wing of the Convent of Santa Maria.'

Am I in a convent? Frankie wondered dazedly, her energy level seriously depleted by both injury and shock upon succeeding shock. In a room kept for the use of well-heeled private patients?

'Your husband was most concerned that every precaution should be exercised,' the older man explained quietly. 'Try to keep more calm, *signora.*'

'There's nothing the matter with my nerves,' Frankie muttered, but she couldn't help noticing that nobody rushed to agree with her.

Her head was aching and her brain revolving in circles. While she endured a brief examination, and even answered questions with positive meekness, on one level she was actually wondering if she was still unconscious. All this—the strange environment, the peculiar behaviour of her companions—might simply be a dream. It was a most enticing conviction. But there was something horrendously realistic about Santino's easy conversation with the doctor as he saw him to the door, apologising for keeping him out so late and wishing him a safe journey home. Her Italian was just about good enough to translate that brief dialogue.

As Santino strode back to the foot of the bed, Frankie reluctantly abandoned the idea that she was dreaming. With an unsteady hand, she reached for the glass of water by the bed and slowly sipped.

'Are you hungry?' Santino enquired calmly.

Frankie shook her head uneasily. Her stomach felt rather queasy. She snatched in a deep, quivering breath. 'I want you to tell me what's going on.'

Santino surveyed her with glittering golden eyes, his eloquent mouth taking on a sardonic curve. 'I decided that it was time to remind you that you had a husband.'

Frankie froze. 'For the last time...you are *not* my husband!'

'Our marriage was not annulled, nor was it dissolved by divorce. Therefore,' Santino spelt out levelly, 'we are still married.'

'No way!' Frankie threw back. 'The marriage was annulled!'

'Is that really your belief?' Santino subjected her to an intent appraisal that made her pale skin flush.

'It's not just a belief,' Frankie argued vehemently. 'It's what I know to be the truth!'

'And the name of the legal firm employed on the task...it was Sweetberry and Hutchins?' Santino queried.

Frankie blinked uncertainly. She had only once visited the solicitor, and that had been almost five years earlier. 'Yes, that was the name...and the very fact that you know it,' she suddenly grasped, 'means that you know very well that we haven't been married for years!'

'Does it?' Santino strolled over to the windows and gracefully swung back to face her again. 'A marriage that is annulled is set aside as though it has never been in existence. So would you agree that if our marriage *had* been annulled so long ago I would have no financial obligation towards you?'

Confused as to what he could possibly be driving at, Frankie nodded, a tiny frown puckering her brows. 'Of course.'

'Then perhaps you would care to explain why I have been supporting you ever since you left Sardinia.' Santino regarded her with cool, questioning expectancy.

'Supporting…*me*?' Frankie repeated in a tone of complete amazement. '*You?*'

'I was expecting Diamond Lil to show up at the La Rocca hotel. The little Fiat was a surprise. A chauffeur-driven limo would have been more appropriate,' Santino mused silkily.

Frankie released a shaken laugh. 'I don't know what you're talking about. I've been working for the past three years. I support myself. I have never received any money from you.'

Santino spread fluently expressive lean brown hands. 'If that is true, it would appear that *someone* has committed fraud on an extensive scale since we last met.'

Her lashes fluttering in bemusement, Frankie studied him closely. He didn't look as angry as he should have done, she thought dazedly. 'Fraud?' she repeated jerkily, the very seriousness of such a crime striking her. 'But who…? I mean, how was the money paid?'

'Through your solicitor.'

'Gosh, he must be a real crook,' Frankie mumbled, feeling suddenly weaker than ever, her limbs almost literally weighted to the bed. Santino had been paying money towards her support all these years? Even though she hadn't received a penny of it, she was shattered by the news. Feeling as she did about him, she would never have accepted his money. He owed her nothing. In fact she felt really humiliated by the idea that he had thought he did have some sort of obligation towards her.

'*Forse*…perhaps, but let us not leap to conclusions,' Santino murmured, strangely detached from the news that someone had been ripping him off for years.

Frankie was thinking back to that one meeting she had had with ancient old Mr Sweetberry in his cluttered, dingy office. He had looked like a character out of a Charles Dickens novel, only lacking a pair of fingerless gloves. When he had realised that her marriage had taken place in a foreign country, he had looked very confused, as if it hadn't previously occurred to him that people *could* get married outside the UK. In fact he had reacted with a blankness which hadn't impressed Frankie at all. Her mother had then pointed out that Mr Sweetberry didn't charge much for his services and that they could not afford to be too choosy.

'Possibly,' Santino remarked, 'the guilty party might have been someone rather closer than your solicitor...'

Someone in Sardinia, someone on *his* side of the fence, she gathered he meant. Enormous relief swept over her, her own sense of responsibility eased by the idea. She felt incredibly tired but she still felt that she had to say it again. 'I really wouldn't have taken your money, Santino.'

Santino sent her a winging smile, alive with so much natural charisma that her heartbeat skidded into acceleration. 'I believe you,' he said quietly. 'But the culprit must be apprehended, do you not think?'

'Of course,' Frankie eagerly agreed, grateful that he had accepted that she was telling the truth but still highly embarrassed by the situation he had outlined.

Without warning a sinking sensation then afflicted her stomach. All of a sudden she understood why Santino had been so determined to see her. He had obviously needed to talk about this money thing! She was mortified. She might pretty much loathe her ex-husband, but the knowledge that he had been shelling out for years in the belief that he was maintaining her could only make her feel guilty as hell. Had he found it difficult to keep up the payments? The quip about Diamond Lil suggested Santino *had* found it a burden. Frankie wanted to cringe.

'And this greedy, dishonest individual—you...er... think this person should be pursued by the full weight of the law?'

Frankie groaned. 'What's the matter with you? I never thought you'd be such a wimp! Whoever's responsible should be charged, prosecuted and imprisoned. In fact I won't be at peace until I know he's been punished, because this fraud has been committed in *my* name…and I feel awful about it!'

'Not like hitting me any more?'

'Well, not right now,' Frankie muttered grudgingly.

Santino straightened the lace-edged sheet and smoothed her pillows. She didn't notice.

'If only you had explained right at the beginning,' she sighed, feeling suddenly very low in spirits. 'I suppose this is why you invited me to stay. You needed to talk about the money—'

'I am ashamed to admit that I believed that you might have been party to the fraud.'

'I understand,' she allowed, scrupulously fair on the issue, and then, just as she was on the very edge of sleep, another more immediate anxiety occurred to her. 'You'd better have me moved to another room, Santino…'

'Why?'

'My insurance won't pay out for this kind of luxury—'

'Don't worry about it. You will not have to make a claim.'

Santino had such a wonderfully soothing voice, she reflected, smothering a rueful yawn. 'I don't want you paying the bill either.'

'There won't be one…at least…not in terms of cash,' Santino mused softly.

'Sorry?'

'Go to sleep, *cara*.'

Abstractedly, just before she passed over the brink into sleep, she wondered how on earth Santino had produced that wedding photograph in a convent infirmary wing, but it didn't seem terribly important, and doubtless there was a perfectly reasonable explanation. After all, she now knew exactly *why* Santino believed that they were still married. The perpetrator of the financial fraud had naturally decided to keep him in the dark about the annulment so that he would continue to pay.

The sun was high in the sky when Frankie woke up again. She slid out of bed. Apart from a dull ache still lingering at the base of her skull, she now felt fine. She explored the adjoining bathroom with admiring eyes. The fitments were quite sinfully luxurious. This was definitely not a convent infirmary wing. She was amused by her own foolish misapprehension of before. She was so obviously staying in a top-flight hotel! She reached for the wrapped toothbrush awaiting her and then stilled again.

Had this been Santino's room? Had he given it up for her benefit? Was that why the photo had been sitting out? Why would Santino be carrying a framed photograph of their wedding around with him this long after the event? She frowned, her mouth tightening. She could think of only one good reason. And her mouth compressed so hard and flat, it went numb. Masquerading as a safely married man might well prevent his lovers from getting the wrong idea about the level of his commitment, she conceded in disgust. But then if Santino had genuinely believed that he *was* still a married man...?

That odd sense of depression still seemed to be hanging over her. She couldn't understand it. Naturally she was upset that Santino should've assumed that she was happily living high off the fat of the land on his money, but she knew that she was not *personally* responsible for the fraud he had suffered. And he had believed her, hadn't he? He also had to be greatly relieved to know that he wouldn't have to pay another penny.

Diamond Lil... Just how much cash had he consigned into the black hole of someone else's clever little fraud? Weren't people despicable? All of a sudden she felt very sorry for Santino but ever so slightly superior. Evidently he wasn't half as sharp as he looked or he would have put some check on his method of payment.

Her suitcase was sitting in the corner of the bedroom. As she dressed, she sighed. Santino must have been desperate to sort out this money business to go to the lengths of pretending that he wanted her to come and stay with him. Why would he have been staying in a hotel, though, if his home was nearby? And this was some hotel. How could he possibly afford a room like this? Unless this wasn't a hotel but was, in fact, Santino's *home*...

Frankie laughed out loud at that ridiculous idea even though her grandfather, Gino, had told her smugly that Santino was rich and a very good catch. In her eyes too, then, Santino had seemed rich. He had bought the largest house in Sienta for their occupation—an old farmhouse on the outskirts of the village. He had even carted a fancy washing machine home to her one weekend. Not that she had done much with it. She hadn't understood the instructions and, after flooding the kitchen several times, she had merely pretended that she was using it. Of course, Santino had not seemed rich simply because he could afford a house and a car! He had just been considerably better off than anyone else in Sienta.

So therefore this *had* to be a hotel. Without further waste of time, Frankie pulled on loden-green cotton trousers and a toning waistcoat-style top with half-sleeves before she plaited her fiery hair. She discovered two new freckles on the bridge of her classic nose and scowled as she closed her case again, ready for her departure. A knock sounded on the door. A uniformed chambermaid entered with a breakfast tray and then shyly removed herself again. There was no hovering for a tip either.

While she ate with appetite, Frankie found her eyes returning again and again to that silver-framed photo sitting on the dressing table. Finally she leapt up and placed it face-down. Why had Santino kissed her yes-

terday? she suddenly asked herself. Curiosity now that
she had grown up? Or had he actually started fancying
her five years too late? Had her cold and businesslike
attitude to him stung that all-male ego of his? Had he
expected her still to blush and simper and gush over him
the way she had as a teenager?

Frankie shuddered with retrospective chagrin, only
wishing she had found some of that defensive distance
in Santino's arms. But, as for what she had *imagined*
she felt, hadn't she once been hopelessly infatuated with
Santino? Doubtless that adolescent memory had heavily
influenced her response. For a few dangerous seconds,
the years had slipped back and she had felt like that love-
lorn teenager again, a helpless victim of emotions and
longings too powerful for her to control.

And if Frankie went back in time she could easily
remember a much younger Santino, a tall, graceful,
golden-skinned youth, who had looked startlingly akin
to some pagan god of myth and legend. He had only
been twenty then, still a student. While he was visiting
his great-uncle, Father Vassari, the elderly priest had
brought him to her grandfather's house purely because
Santino spoke English and nobody else in the village
did.

In those early days Frankie had picked up little of the
ancient Latin-based dialect her grandfather and his sisters, Maddalena and Teresa, had spoken within their tiny
home. After months of isolation, the sound of her own
language had released a flood of tears and frantic,
over-emotional speech from her. She had begged
Santino to find out where her father was and when he
was returning to take her back to England.

He had suggested that they go for a walk. 'I am not
going to talk to you as if you are a little girl,' Santino
had told her wryly. 'I will be frank. Father Vassari believes that you will be happier if you learn to accept that

this village is now your home, for the foreseeable future at least.'

Scanning her shocked face, he had emitted a rueful sigh. 'He understands that this life is not what you have been accustomed to and that you find your lack of freedom stifling, but you too must understand that your grandfather is unlikely to change his attitudes—'

'I hate him!' Frankie had gasped helplessly. 'I hate everyone here!'

'But you have your father's blood in your veins, and therefore your grandfather's too,' Santino had reminded her, endeavouring to reason her out of her passionate bitterness and homesickness. 'Gino acknowledges that bond. If he did not, he would not have accepted you into his home. You are part of his family—'

'They're *not* my family!' she had sobbed wretchedly.

'Maddalena would be very hurt to hear you say that. She seems to be very fond of you.'

Her shy great-aunt, who was wholly dominated by her sharp-tongued elder sister and her quick-tempered brother, had been the only member of the household to make any effort to ease Frankie's misery. She had never shouted at Frankie when she heard her crying in the night. She had quietly attempted to offer what comfort she could.

'I promise that I will try to locate your father, but in return you must make a promise to me,' Santino had informed her gravely. 'A promise you must study to keep for your own sake.'

'What kind of promise?'

'Stop running away. It only makes your grandfather angrier, only convinces him that you have been very badly brought up and cannot be trusted out of the house. He is a strict man, and your continued defiance makes him much nastier than he would normally be—'

'Did Father Vassari say Grandfather was nasty?' Frankie had prompted, wide-eyed.

'Of course not.' Santino had flushed slightly. 'But Gino Caparelli has the reputation of being a stubborn, unyielding man. What you must do is bite your tongue in his presence and appear willing to do as you're told, even if you don't feel willing—'

'I bet the priest never told you to tell me to act like a hypocrite!'

'You're smart for a twelve-year-old!' Santino had burst out laughing when she'd caught him out. 'My great-uncle is very devout, but he *is* sincerely concerned by your unhappiness. He wanted me to tell you to respect and obey your grandfather in all things—'

'But you didn't say that—'

'Where there is as yet no affection, I think it would be too much to ask of you.'

'I just want to go back to London,' she had mumbled, the tears threatening again. 'To my mum…my friends, my school—'

'But for now you must learn to live with the Sardinian half of your family, *piccola mia*,' Santino had told her ruefully.

He had been so straight with her and, after long, frightening months of being treated like an impertinent child whose needs and wishes were of no account, she had been heartened by Santino's level approach. But then he had been clever. He had known how to win a respectful hearing, and the bait he had dangled in reward for improved behaviour had convinced her that he was on her side. She had trusted him to find out where her father was.

When he had brought instead the news of her father's death in a car crash, she had been devastated. But, in the years which had followed, Santino had become Frankie's lifeline. He had visited his great-uncle every couple of months, more often as the old man's health had begun to fail, and Frankie had learnt to live for Santino's visits for he always made time for her as well.

She had had nothing in common with her father's family. It had been an unimaginable joy and relief to talk without fear of censure to Santino and just be herself. He had sent her English books and newspapers to read and she had started writing to him. His brief letters had kept her going between visits. Learning to love and rely on Santino had come so naturally to her.

As she dredged herself out of the past, Frankie found poignant memories of Gino, Maddalena and Teresa threatening to creep up out of her subconscious. Stiffening, she closed her Sard relatives out of her mind again. Her grandfather had ignored her letters in the last five years and that hadn't been a surprise. He could neither have understood nor condoned the actions of a granddaughter who had deserted her husband. Her father's family had thought the sun rose and set on Santino. In their ignorance of the true state of his marriage, they would have been angry and bitterly ashamed of her behaviour.

Frankie left her room. She emerged into a panelled corridor, lined with dark medieval paintings and beautiful rugs that glowed with the dull richness of age. When she saw a stone spiral staircase twisting up out of sight at the foot of the passageway, she was tempted to explore. Well, why not? If the villas on the Costa Smeralda were not to be made available to the agency, she was now technically on holiday. She really ought to give Matt a call, she conceded absently. He might be wondering why he hadn't heard from her in three days.

Through the studded oak door at the top of the spiral flight of steps, Frankie stepped out onto the roof...or was it the ramparts? With astonished eyes, she scanned the big square towers rising at either end and then, walking over to the parapet, she gazed down in dizzy horror at the sheerness of the drop, where ancient stone met cliff-face far below her, and then she looked up and around, drinking in the magnificent views of the snow-capped mountains that surrounded the fertile wooded valley.

'You seem to have made a good recovery.'

Frankie very nearly jumped out of her skin. Breathlessly she spun round. Santino was strolling towards her and this time he looked disturbingly familiar. Faded blue jeans sheathed his lean hips and long, powerful thighs, a short-sleeved white cotton shirt was open at his strong brown throat. He walked like the king of the jungle on the prowl, slow, sure-footed and very much a predator.

Sexy, she thought dizzily, struggling weakly to drag her disobedient gaze from his magnificent physique. Incredibly sexy. He was so flagrantly at home with his very male body, relaxed, indolent, staggeringly self-assured. She reddened furiously as he paused several feet away. He sank down with careless grace on the edge of the parapet, displaying the kind of complete indifference to the empty air and the terrifying drop behind him that brought Frankie out in a cold sweat.

'I saw you from the tower. I thought you'd still be in bed,' he admitted.

'I'm pretty resilient,' Frankie returned stiffly, thinking that it would mean little to her if he went over the edge but, all the same, she wished he would move.

'One committed career woman, no less,' Santino drawled, running diamond-bright dark eyes consideringly over the plain businesslike appearance she had contrived to present in spite of the heat. 'To think you used to wash my shirts and shrink them.'

Frankie was maddened by the further flush of embarrassment that crept up her throat. It reminded her horribly of the frightful adolescent awkwardness she had once exhibited around Santino. Not that that surprised her. Santino was drop-dead gorgeous. Santino would make a Greek god look plain and homely because he had a quality of blazing vibrance and energy that no statue could ever match. If she hadn't fancied him like

mad all those years ago, there would have been something lacking in her teenage hormones, she told herself.

'Did I really?' she said in a flat, bored tone.

'I always wondered if you boiled them,' Santino
mused, perversely refusing to take the hint that the subject was a conversation-killer.

'Well, you should have complained if it bothered
you.'

'You were a marvellous cook.'

'I enjoyed cooking for you about as much as I enjoyed
scrubbing your kitchen floor!' And she was lying; she
hated the fact that she was lying and that, worst of all,
he had to know that she was lying.

But what else had she known? The formal education
she had received from the age of eleven had been mini-
mal, but her domestic training as a future wife and
mother had been far more thorough. Between them, her
father's family had seen to that. No matter how hard she
had fought to preserve her own identity, she had in the
end been indoctrinated with prehistoric ideas of a
woman's subservient place in the home. Endless back-
breaking work and catering to some man's every wish
as though he were an angry god to be appeased rather
than an equal... That was what she had been taught and
that was what she had absorbed as her former life in
London had begun to take on the shadowy and mean-
ingless unreality of another world.

Her spine notched up another inch, bitter resentment
at what she had been reduced to steeling her afresh. She
had *sung* as she scrubbed his kitchen floor! She had
thought she knew it all by then. She had thought that by
marrying Santino, who said 'please' and 'thank you' and
even, amazingly, 'That's too heavy for you to carry,'
she had beaten the system, but in truth she had joined
it. She had been prepared to settle for whatever she could
get if she could have Santino. For the entire six months

of their marriage, she would not have accepted a plane
ticket out of Sardinia had it been forced on her…

'I did try to persuade you to resume your education,'
he reminded her drily.

'Oh, keep quiet…stop dragging it all back up. It
makes me feel ill!' Frankie snapped, spinning away with
smarting eyes.

He had wanted her to attend a further education college in Florence. *Florence!* The Caparellis had been
aghast when she'd mentioned it. What kind of a husband
sent his wife back to school? She could read, she could
write, she could count—what more did he want? And
Frankie had been genuinely terrified of being sent away
to a strange city where her ignorance would be exposed,
where the other students might laugh at her poor Italian
and where, worst of all, she would not have Santino.

In her innocence, she had actually asked Santino if he
would go to Florence with her, and he had said that he
would only be able to visit because the demands of his
job would not allow him to live there. Of course, in the
kindest possible way, she conceded grudgingly, Santino
had been trying to make the first step towards loosening
the ties of their ridiculous marriage by persuading her
into a separation and a measure of independence. He had
known very well that she was so infatuated with him
that she was unlikely to make a recovery as long as he
was still around.

He hadn't wanted to hurt her. He had even said that,
yes, he would miss her very much but that he felt that
she would greatly gain in self-confidence if she completed her education. And she had accused him then of
being ashamed of her and had raced upstairs in floods
of inconsolable tears. She had refused to eat for the rest
of that weekend, had alternately sulked and sobbed every
time he'd tried to reason with her. No, she reflected painfully, nobody could ever say that Santino had found mar-

riage to his child-bride a bed of roses…or, indeed, any kind of a bed at all, she conceded with burning cheeks.

'We have a lot to talk about,' Santino commented flatly.

Tension hummed in the air. For the first time, Frankie became aware of that thick tension and frowned at the surprising coldness she was only now registering in Santino's voice. Before, Santino had been teasing her, yet now he was undeniably distant and cool. She didn't know him in this mood. The awareness disconcerted her and then made her angrily defensive.

'On a personal basis we have nothing to talk about, but good luck with your fraud case!' Frankie told him with a ferociously bright smile. 'However, if you want to discuss the—'

'If you mention those villas one more time, I will lose my temper. What are they to me? Nothing,' Santino derided with a dismissive gesture of one lean hand. 'The bait by which I brought you here, but now no more! Their role is played now.'

'I'm afraid I haven't a clue what more you expect from me, and nor do I intend to hang around to find out,' Frankie asserted, colliding with hard golden eyes that were curiously chilling, and, since that was not a sensation which she had ever associated with Santino before, she paled and tensed up even more.

'You will. Your wings are now clipped. No longer will you fly free,' Santino retorted with the cool, clear diction generally reserved for a child slow of understanding. 'We are still married.'

'Why do you keep on saying that?' Frankie demanded in sudden flaring repudiation. 'It's just not true!'

'Five years ago you made only a brief initial statement to your solicitor, who has since retired. I spoke to his son yesterday. He checked the files for me. His father advised you in a letter to consult another solicitor, one more experienced in the matrimonial field. No further action was taken,' he completed drily.

Frankie trembled. There was something horribly convincing about Santino's growing impatience with her. 'If there's been some stupid oversight, I'm sorry, and I promise that I'll take care of it as soon as I go home again—'

'Not on the grounds of non-consummation!' Santino slotted in grimly.

'Any grounds you like, for goodness' sake...I'm not fussy,' Frankie muttered, badly shaken by the idea that they might still be legally married.

'Five years ago I would have agreed to an annulment.' Santino surveyed her tense face with cool, narrowed eyes. 'Indeed, then I considered it my duty to set you free. But that is not a duty which I recognise now. To be crude, Francesca...I now want the wife that I paid for.'

'That you...what?' Frankie parroted shakily.

'I now intend to take possession of what I paid for. That is my right.'

Frankie uttered a strangled laugh that fell like a brick in the rushing silence. She stared at him incredulously. 'You're either crazy or joking...you've *got* to be joking!'

'Why?' Santino scanned her with fulminating dark golden eyes. 'Let's drop the face-saving euphemisms. For a start, you trapped me into marriage.'

Frankie flinched visibly. 'I didn't—'

Santino dealt her a quelling glance. 'Don't dare to deny it. Well do I recall your silence when you were questioned by your grandfather. I had never in my life laid a finger upon you but not one word did you say to that effect!'

Frankie studied the ground, belated shame rising inexorably to choke her. She had been so furious with Santino that awful night for taking her back to Sienta.

She had been running away and, using him as an un-suspecting means of escape, had hidden herself behind the rear seat of his car. It had been an impulsive act, prompted by pure desperation…

Santino's great-uncle, Father Vassari, had died that week. She had known that Santino would no longer have any reason to come to the village. She had been in dis-grace on the home front too. Incapable of hiding her feelings for Santino, she had stirred up the sort of ma-licious local gossip that enraged her grandfather. Furious with her, he had told her that she could no longer even write to Santino.

Santino hadn't discovered her presence in his car until he'd stopped for petrol on the coast. It had been the one and only time he had ever lost his temper with her. His sheer fury had crushed her. Deaf to her every plea for understanding and assistance, he had stuffed her forcibly back into the car and driven her all the way back home, but it had been dawn by the time they got there. In Gino Caparelli's eyes, her overnight absence in male company had ruined her reputation beyond all possibility of re-demption. He had instantly demanded that Santino do the honourable thing and marry her.

'Grandfather *knew* nothing had happened,' Frankie began in a wobbly voice, struggling to find even a weak line of self-defence.

'And I knew that after what you had done your life would be hell in that house if I *didn't* marry you! I let conscience persuade me that you were my responsibility. And what did I receive in return?' Santino prompted witheringly. 'A bride who took her teddy bear to bed…'

Frankie's colour was now so high, she was convinced it would take Arctic snow to cool her down again.

'Hamish the teddy with the tartan scarf.' Santino stud-ied her with grim amusement. 'Believe me, he was a hundred times more effective than any medieval chas-tity belt.'

Intense chagrin flooded her. Her teeth gritted as she threw her head high. 'You said...you said that you wanted a wife—'

'I already have one. I also have custody of Hamish,' Santino informed her satirically as he rose fluidly upright again. 'I'd say that makes my claim indisputable.'

'You don't have any claim over me!'

'Have you packed?' Meeting her stunned scrutiny, Santino repeated his question.

'Yes, but—'

'*Bene*...then, since you are no longer in need of further rest, we will waste no more time.' Santino opened the oak door and, standing back, regarded her expectantly.

The tip of Frankie's tongue slid out to wet her lower lip. She continued to stare helplessly at him. 'Why are you doing this...? I mean, what's going on?'

'Really, Francesca...are you always this slow on the uptake?' Santino chided, an ebony brow elevating with sardonic cool. 'You really shouldn't have lied to me.'

'L-lied?' Frankie stammered as he pressed her firmly past him and down the spiral stone steps. 'I haven't told you any lies!'

'I would have been far more understanding if you had made a complete confession when I confronted you. But lies make me incredibly angry,' Santino drawled softly. 'When I found out the truth this morning, I was very tempted to come upstairs, tip you out of that bed and shake you until the teeth rattled in your calculating, devious little head!'

'What are you talking about?' Frankie exclaimed.

'Your forty-eight per cent share of Finlay Travel.' Santino shot her a glittering look of condemnation from icy cold dark eyes. 'You shameless little bitch... You actually fished your lover out of a financial hole with *my* money!'

Frankie was so taken aback by that insane accusation, she could only gape at him.

'Now, I didn't expect to receive my bride back in a state of untouched virginal purity. Nor did I expect to be greeted with open arms, gratitude or any lingering delusion on your part that I could walk on water!' Santino spelt out with sizzling derision. 'Indeed, I believed that my expectations were thoroughly realistic. But I was *not* prepared to discover that for the past five years you've been in collusion with that greedy, grasping vixen who brought you into the world!'

CHAPTER THREE

FRANKIE tried to swallow and failed. In shock, she had fallen still. Santino was talking about her mother. He was calling Della a greedy, grasping vixen. Why? For heaven's sake, he didn't even know her mother, had never met her!

Why on earth was he making such wild and offensive accusations? It made no sense. She had bought her share of Finlay Travel with the proceeds of an insurance policy. Bewildered green eyes clung to his hard, sun-bronzed features and the cold, steely anger simmering in the depths of his contemptuous gaze.

'When I think of the lengths I went to in my efforts to protect you from having your illusions about Della shattered, I am even more disgusted by your behaviour!' He flung wide the door of her bedroom and crossed the floor to lift her case. Emerging again, he curved a powerful arm against her tense spine and carried her towards the stone staircase that wound impressively down into a big hall. '*Dio mio*...I had to pay your mother to take you back. I had to bribe her to welcome you into her home after you left me!'

'P-pay her...you had to *pay* her?' Frankie repeated in disbelief.

Santino released his breath in an audible hiss. 'I should have insisted on an immediate annulment. I should not have allowed myself to be swayed by the assurance that it would distress you too much to have that last link severed—'

'Distress me...?' Frankie broke in even more shakily as she came to a halt on the uneven flagstoned floor of the hall. Her legs felt appallingly weak and hollow. *Pay her?* He had had to pay her mother? Perspiration dampened her short upper lip. She couldn't get her thoughts into any kind of order. When she continued to hover, Santino pressed her out through the big oak doors spread wide on the brilliant sunlight. Without that forceful male momentum Frankie would very probably have fallen at his feet.

'I was a complete fool,' Santino grated. 'Without question I paid out a vast amount of money for you to live in comfort and complete your education, and what have I got back? A wife who still speaks Italian like a tourist with a bad phrasebook! But that is the very least of the deception, is it not? You're so appallingly mercenary, you chose to live in sin with your lover sooner than give me *my* freedom back!'

'Santino—' Frankie mumbled dizzily.

'Keep quiet. The less I hear out of that lying little mouth right now the better!' Santino cut in with ruthless bite. 'I let myself be taken in yesterday. ''Are you in the tourist trade now?'' *Dio mio*…give me strength! But I thought, That is *so* sweet. She still doesn't know who I am… But that charade about there being a bill for your medical care—that was overkill! You know damned well you married a bloody rich man! Only a bloody rich man could have kept you and your mother in the style in which I have kept you both for the past five years!'

With that final ringing and derisive assurance, Santino yanked open the door of the black Toyota Landcruiser parked in the cobbled courtyard, and while she stood .there in a speechless daze at all the revelations being hurled at her at once he swore with impatience. Circling her with strong arms, he swept her bodily off her feet and, after settling her into the passenger seat, he slammed the door on her.

Frankie found herself sucking in oxygen as frantically

as someone coming up for air after almost drowning. She pressed trembling fingers to her throbbing temples.

'So don't look at me with those big green eyes and tell me I'm joking when I say I intend to have what I paid for!' Santino continued fiercely as he swung in beside her. 'One more argument out of you and I pull the rug out from under Finlay Travel and ruin both you and your lover! And then I take Della to court for all the fake bills that have been submitted on your behalf while I was still under the impression that you were a student. By the time I'm finished with you, the sight of a Vitale bank draft with my signature on it will make you feel sick. I'm going to treat you to aversion therapy!'

Frankie was fighting to reason again, but she was in so much shock it was extraordinarily difficult. Somehow she couldn't get past that very first devastatingly painful assurance that he had had to pay her mother to give her a home. 'You've...you've actually met Della?' she heard herself question weakly but incredulously as he fired the engine of the powerful car.

'What sort of stupid question is that?' Santino shot her a glinting glance of enquiry. A sardonic frown line divided his ebony brows as he absorbed her stark pallor. 'Of course you know I've met her! Don't tell me that while the two of you were cheerfully ripping me off all these years she somehow neglected to mention where all the money was coming from!'

'Mum received a very generous divorce settlement from her second husband,' Frankie mumbled tremulously, her throat convulsing as she tried to steady herself. 'That's where the money was coming from, and as for my share in Finlay—'

'Your mother dumped Giles Jensen when his nightclub went bust. He didn't have the means to make *any* kind of settlement. When you went back home to Mum, she was in major debt. I was the sucker who pulled Mum out of it and put a roof over your heads!'

'I don't—'

A plastic folder landed squarely on her lap. 'I own your mother's home. I had no objection to maintaining my mother-in-law when it meant that you shared her comfortable lifestyle. I'm angry now because it's obvious that you were in on the whole scam from the beginning!'

There was a thick legal deed inside the folder. It bore the address of her mother's smart house in Kensington and Santino's name as the current owner. It was the kind of irrefutable proof that stole the very breath from her lungs. It made argument on that count impossible. Her stomach succumbed to nauseous cramps.

'If there hadn't been a recent query about the lease, I wouldn't even have had that here to show you!' Santino gritted. 'But I have a stack of receipted bills a foot thick in my office in Rome. Fakes! Tell me, did you ever actually go to that fancy boarding school I paid for?'

'I went to the local tech for a while, took a few classes…' Frankie told him numbly as the horror of what he was telling her and the source of his very real anger began slowly and inexorably to sink in.

'*Per meraviglia*…no riding, music and skiing lessons? No language tutoring? No finishing school? No educational trips or vacations abroad? You haven't spent a single term at university, have you?'

Dully, Frankie shook her head. Piece by awful piece, it was falling into place. Della was the fraudster Santino had been talking about. Not someone on his side of the fence, but someone a great deal closer to Frankie than a solicitor she had only once met. Her mother, her *own* mother. She felt sick. Della enjoyed an entirely hedonistic existence of shopping and socialising. She didn't work. She had an exquisitely furnished house, a fabulous designer wardrobe and took frequent long-haul holidays abroad. The realisation that Santino must have been paying for that lifestyle devastated Frankie.

'I didn't know…you've got to believe that!' she burst out.

'Fine. Then you can sit back and relax while I prosecute your mother for misuse of funds intended to be spent solely for your benefit.'

Frankie went white.

'And I eagerly await your explanation for the thousands *you* put into Finlay Travel—'

'That *definitely* wasn't your money!' she protested feverishly. 'That came from an insurance policy that Dad took out for Mum and I when I was still a baby—'

'Marco, the compulsive gambler, took out insurance?' Santino murmured very drily. 'Money burned a hole in his pocket. If your father had taken out a policy like that, he would have been trying to cash it in again within months. He certainly wouldn't have kept up the payments.'

Frankie was concentrating hard now. She had never seen any proof that that money had come from an insurance pay-out. She had been only eighteen, had had no reason to question her mother's story or the welcome feeling of security created by that most unexpected windfall. Della had simply paid the money into her account. And by the passing on of that one very substantial payment, Frankie registered painfully, Della had ensured that her daughter was bound up in her dishonesty. Had that been her mother's intention all along? A safeguard so that if Santino ever found out what was really happening to his money he would believe that Frankie had been involved in the deception? Her stomach gave another horrible twist.

'You see, at first I *did* believe that you were telling me the truth. I believed that you had been blissfully unaware of my financial backing until I found out about your stake in Finlay Travel. I was annoyed that you didn't appear to have enjoyed the material and educational benefits that I had believed I was paying for, but

I could have lived with that. What I will not accept with good grace is that you are as big a cheat and a thief as your mother!'

'Stop the car…I feel sick!' Frankie suddenly gasped in desperation.

She almost fell out of the four-wheel drive in her haste to vacate it. As she gulped in fresh air and swayed, she hung onto the car door.

'You do look rough,' Santino acknowledged grudgingly as he strode round the bonnet. 'I thought it was a ruse.'

Frankie couldn't even bring herself to look at him. As the nervous cramps began to settle in her stomach, she was wondering sickly just how much cash Della had contrived to run through in five long years. Given an inch, Della would have taken a mile. Indeed, she wondered if her mother's demands had grown so excessive that Santino had finally become suspicious.

'Sit down…' Lean, surprisingly gentle hands detached her from the death-grip she had on the door and settled her very carefully back into the passenger seat. 'Put your head down if you still feel dizzy,' he urged, retaining a firm grip on her trembling hands when she tried to pull away.

She focused on his hand-stitched Italian loafers and slowly breathed in again.

'Better?' Santino prompted flatly, releasing her from his hold.

Dully, she nodded, glancing up unwarily to collide with brilliant dark eyes fringed by luxuriant spiky black lashes. Close up, those eyes had the most extraordinary effect on her. They made her feel all weak…and sort of quivery deep down inside. Without even realising it, she was staring like a mesmerised rabbit, and then Santino vaulted lithely upright again, leaving her looking dazedly into space.

Had the shock of her mother's deceit deranged her

wits? she asked herself angrily. What was the matter with her? If there had ever been a time she needed to concentrate, this was it. So Santino was still possessed of spectacular good looks; surely she was mature enough to handle that without behaving in the midst of a crisis like an adolescent with an embarrassing crush?

He owned Della's house, she reminded herself in desperation, so most probably all the rest of it was true as well. Then by rights her share in Finlay Travel belonged to Santino. She could sign it over to him, but it would still only be a tenth of what was owed. And wasn't she in many ways responsible for what her mother had done?

If she hadn't been so willing to believe her mother's assurance that the annulment had been a mere technicality, if she hadn't been too ridiculously sensitive to even want to discuss or be forced to think about her marriage, Della wouldn't have found it so easy to fool her. They would have got that annulment years ago, Santino would have had his freedom back and he would have stopped supporting her mother and herself. But had Frankie asked him to support them? Resentment stirred in her. She had wanted *nothing* from Santino!

'You seem to think you own me, and now I know why.' A jagged little laugh fell from her lips as Santino drove on. 'Well, I'm sorry, but you can't buy people—'

'No, it's love you can't buy. Buying people is surprisingly easy,' Santino drawled. 'You only need to know what they want to hook them.'

Frankie shivered and shot a helpless glance at his lean, dark profile, the hardness of his jawline. 'And what do I want?'

'Most?' Santino queried softly, reflectively. 'To be loved. I saw that in you when you were no age at all. You had a desperate need to be loved. But you were so stubborn you looked for it in the wrong places and couldn't recognise it when you did find it.'

Frankie lost colour. He had answered her ironic question seriously, cutting her to the heart by reminding her of the all too many disappointments and rejections of her growing-up years.

'That's one reason why I certainly wasn't expecting to meet an angel yesterday. A lot of people in your life have let you down. I knew that I, too, had lost your trust, but somehow I still expected you to be the extremely honest girl you used to be. I should have known that Della would mess you up—'

'Don't talk about my mother like that!' Frankie bit out defensively.

'I think it's time someone did. You moved in with Finlay when you were…what…only eighteen years old?'

'Where did you get that information from?' Her voice shook.

'It wasn't difficult. Finlay…' he murmured again. 'Tell me, when you sank that money into his business, were you trying to buy his affection?'

Frankie went rigid. 'How dare—?'

'I've never believed in avoiding the issue. It's a reasonable question. Most teenagers with a large sum of money in their possession could think of a hundred things to do with it, but not one of those hundred exciting possibilities would entail investment.'

Frankie pinned her lips together tightly, reluctant to reply. She had wanted to do something secure with that windfall. Until she had married Santino, every person she had ever depended on had lived on a frightening financial seesaw. Her parents had had violent arguments about money. One day it had been treats all round, the next bitter dispute over an unpaid bill. She had gone from that to the very real poverty of her grandfather's home, where there had been absolutely nothing to spare for extras. And those 'extras' had been everyday necessities which she had taken for granted in London.

'So you *were* buying him—'

'No, I blasted well wasn't!' Frankie flared. 'I even took some advice before I did it.'

'Finlay's advice? I ask because that investment is anything but safe right now. You're in a crowded market and the travel agency is financially over-extended.'

'I'm quite content with the returns I've received—'

'A place in his bed that isn't exclusively yours? I know you're not the only woman in his life...'

Frankie was becoming angrier and angrier with every second that passed. 'Well, maybe he's not the only man in mine.'

'Few women settle for an open relationship at your age. Are you that much in love with him?'

Frankie abruptly spread both hands in a gesture of furious frustration. 'I am not in love with Matt. We're friends and I'm the junior partner—'·

'Why live together, then?'

'I have as much right to live in that apartment as he has, or didn't your snoop tell you that? Finlay Travel owns the building!'

'Correction...the bank owns it.'

'So now *you* have a share of what the bank owns!'

'Smart move, Francesca. I quite understand why your lover has suddenly become your platonic friend. But if you think I intend to move in and refinance your boyfriend you're insane,' Santino asserted very drily. 'That is one ship which will sink without any help from me!'

'Do whatever you like. If it was your money to begin with, it's your investment now! But don't make Matt pay for something that has nothing to do with him,' Frankie argued vehemently. 'The agency needs those villas. He'd have no trouble keeping them fully booked right through the season. We badly need more quality properties.'

Santino vented a distinctly chilling laugh. 'You're unbelievable. You rip me off and then you expect me to come to your assistance?'

'I didn't rip you off…I honestly didn't know about the money… And I don't think it's my fault anyway,' she reasoned with steadily mounting resentment. 'You went behind my back to make some stupid arrangement with Della which *I* didn't know about, so how can you now blame me for it going wrong?'

'*Santo cielo*…the rats are jumping ship fast,' Santino murmured sardonically. 'It would appear that it's every woman for herself now. Don't worry about it. I'm very even-handed when I deal out rough justice. I assure you that Della's getting her share of grief today too.'

Frankie tensed. 'What do you mean?'

'She will be served with an eviction notice by the end of the day.'

Frankie surveyed him in horror. Santino indolently drew the car to a slow halt and climbed out. Frankie leapt out at speed. 'You can't do that to her!'

'Give me one good reason why not.'

Frankie hovered on the edge of the dusty road, thinking hard, but her mind was a complete blank. Sheer shock was resounding through her in dizzy waves.

Santino slung her a grimly amused look from veiled golden eyes and calmly removed a basket and a rug from the back of the car. 'It's a challenge, isn't it?' he agreed.

'It's not that… I just can't believe you could be that cruel!' Frankie admitted helplessly.

'But then you've never met with this side of me before. Only with you was I ever a pussycat and, sadly for you, those days are past,' Santino delivered with hard dark eyes that glittered like golden ice in the sunlight. 'I'm lethally unforgiving in business, Francesca…and I'm sorry to say that both you and your unlovely mother fall very much into the category of business now.'

The tip of her tongue snaked out to moisten her dry lower lip in a flicking motion. She just couldn't believe that this was Santino. He was correct about that all right. She didn't recognise the warm, teasing, tolerant male she remembered in this tall dark man with his savagely hard and unfeeling eyes. Her attention fell on the basket he held and total bewilderment seized her. 'What are you doing with that?'

'It's for our picnic,' Santino divulged gently.

Her generous mouth opened and shut. As yet it hadn't even occurred to her to wonder why he had stopped the car and got out.

'Our…picnic?' she questioned unevenly. 'Let me get this straight… Just after you announce that you're having my mother served with an eviction notice, you expect me to join you for a picnic?'

'And the thought of that eviction notice has whetted my appetite,' Santino confided without remorse as he swung fluidly on his heel.

In stunned disbelief Frankie watched him stride down the grassy, rutted track on the far side of the car. It led down the sloping ground into the thick cover of trees. Within a minute, that dark, imperious head was out of sight. Gritting her teeth, Frankie abandoned her pride and chased after him. She passed by the tumbledown shell of a little stone house, long since given over to the weeds and the undergrowth, and just beyond it, beneath the dappled shade of an ancient gnarled tree, she saw that the rug and the basket had been abandoned.

Santino was poised on the brow of the sun-drenched hillside, looking down at the village which straggled untidily over the slopes below them. As she drew level with him, he turned his head.

'Santino,' she began tautly, 'my—'

'That's La Rocca down there,' he cut in informatively. 'My grandmother was born in the bar where we met yesterday. It was called a hotel in those days too. Her father had aspirations which were never fulfilled.'

Frankie frowned uncertainly. 'I—'

'Keep quiet and listen.' Brilliant dark eyes lanced into

hers, his sensual mouth hardening. 'What else can you see from here?'

She swallowed hard and looked around herself with blank, uncomprehending eyes, wondering what on earth he was driving at.

'My grandfather was born in that ruin,' he supplied with studied patience. 'One of eleven children, only six of whom survived to adulthood. He brought me here when I was eight years old and he told me that this is where the Vitale family has its roots. Humble beginnings but, believe it or not, I'm very proud of them.'

'Yes, I can see that,' Frankie muttered abstractedly. 'But—'

'No, you do not *see* at all!' Santino grated with driving derision, and strode away from her.

Frankie just couldn't concentrate; she was too shaken up by all that had burst upon her. Her temples were pounding with tension. But she seemed to be suffering alone, for Santino was uncorking a bottle of wine, his hands deft and sure, stray arrows of light skimming over his chiselled golden profile and the lean, fluid sweep of his lithe masculine body as he knelt on the rug.

'She's got visitors staying right now…Mum, I mean,' she began helplessly, unable even to organise her thoughts, never mind her speech. 'And I'm not trying to excuse what's been done, but she hasn't had it easy—'

'Until *I* came along—'

Frankie flushed and stepped off one foot onto the other. 'She could have been a top model if she hadn't been saddled with me. And then Dad took me and she couldn't find me, and she ended up marrying Giles and he—'

'Was bankrupted by her extravagance.'

Frankie stiffened. 'That's not the way I heard it.'

'I don't suppose she would have told it that way. You're wasting your breath,' Santino informed her drily as he slid upright. 'Della's the very soul of avarice. I tied her into a strict legal agreement—even then I had few illusions about her character—and, believe me, she exercised considerable criminal talent in all the fraudulent claims for cash that were made... You can't expect me to listen to sob-stories on her behalf when you took your cut too.'

'Are you planning to prosecute us both?'

'Can you really see me dragging my wife into court? But your mother...' Santino met her wide, fearful eyes in a head-on collision that slithered through her like a hard physical blow. 'I have no inhibitions about punishing her.'

'But if you consider me equally at fault that wouldn't be fair!' Frankie protested, utterly appalled by the idea of her mother being taken to court and prosecuted like a criminal.

'Are you telling me that you were in on it too, from the start?' Santino demanded very quietly. 'I had received the impression that Della ensured that you received only a small percentage of the money.'

Frankie's heart was pumping at feverish speed behind her breastbone. She could hardly breathe. 'I knew exactly what Della was doing *right* from the beginning,' she lied with fierce emphasis, reasoning that if she forced him to share out the blame it might somehow lessen his fury with her mother and persuade him to direct it at her instead.

Santino was very still, his spectacular bone structure rigid below his golden skin, his eyes hooded. 'You're changing your story now?'

'I knew that taking your money was wrong but I...I hated you after I saw you with that woman in Cagliari!' Frankie shot her last bolt in her determination to give her mother what protection she could.

'That I can believe...but I also once believed that you would sooner starve than knowingly accept my support. Hence the original secrecy. Was I really that naive?'

Santino surveyed her with narrowed dark eyes of grim enquiry, his beautiful mouth taking on a uniquely cynical twist. 'That protective, that romantic? It seems you're not the only one who needed to grow up five years ago. I set out to be a hero and fell at the first fence!'

Frankie wasn't listening to him. 'Please don't do this to Mum,' she whispered pleadingly. 'Give her the time to move out of the house with dignity—'

'And what would I get in return for such undeserved restraint?'

The silence lay thick and oppressive in the stillness. There wasn't the slightest breeze. The heat of midday was like a cocoon. It dampened her skin beneath her clothing. As she breathed in deeply, her distraught green eyes locked into that lancing look of ruthless challenge.

'I don't know what you want...'

'Don't you?' A derisive smile of disagreement twisted Santino's sensual mouth. 'I want you in my bed.'

'I can't believe that...' Frankie muttered unsteadily, unable to accept that he could be serious. 'I can't believe that that's what you want.'

'Isn't that what every man wants from a beautiful woman?'

'I'm not beautiful—'

Santino advanced in one long, graceful stride. He stared down at her with brooding dark golden eyes that burned hotly beneath her skin. And then he lifted his hands and with cool, deft fingers detached the clip from her plait. 'I like your hair loose.'

With disturbing patience he threaded out the multiple strands one by one, and the whole time Frankie stood there trembling, barely breathing, but with every brush of those brown fingers against her cheekbone, or her scalp, or even the nape of her neck, her heart raced faster and her pulses pounded even harder, leaving her dizzy.

'Very beautiful, very sexy,' Santino stressed huskily as he drew her closer.

Instantly she tensed, the sun-warmed, eerily familiar male scent of him flaring her nostrils. Her breasts felt languorously full and heavy, the nipples taut buds of swollen sensitivity pushing against the rough cotton that bound them. There was no thought in her dazed mind as she connected with shimmering golden eyes, only a powerful, drugging awareness of every throbbing skin-cell she possessed.

'And so incredibly submissive all of a sudden too. And you might tell yourself it's to save Della from her just deserts, but really that wouldn't be honest, *piccola mia*. There's a streak of wildness in you. There always was,' Santino breathed in a harshly amused undertone as he released her again. 'And right now you're more likely to expire from excitement than petrified reluctance!'

In shock, Frankie fell back from him, outraged by that assurance but silenced by a sudden sense of intense shame as she acknowledged the truth of it. Her own weak body betrayed her with wanton efficiency. For an instant she had wanted him with a desperate physical yearning over which she had absolutely no control. And it had nothing to do with any echo from the past, nothing to do with what she had once felt…it had been an instinctive craving born very much of the present.

Santino bent down and, drawing two glasses from the basket, he passed her one. 'I'm not complaining, you understand,' he murmured smoothly. 'A sacrificial lamb wouldn't appeal to me. But then what you've become doesn't have any *lasting* appeal either…'

Her skin as hot as hellfire, angry pain sparking in a raw surge through her taut length, Frankie stood her ground. 'What are you trying to say?'

'That at this moment I believe three weeks will suit me fine.' Dense black lashes screening his gaze, Santino treated her to a gleaming scrutiny that was coolly derisive. 'Three weeks will be quite long enough.'

Three weeks was the span of the vacation she had planned to spend touring Italy. Her hand shook slightly as he let clear sparkling wine splash down into her glass. 'You're asking me to spend that time with you?'

'Only this time around Hamish gets to sleep alone,' Santino spelt out lazily.

'I had gathered that,' Frankie gritted, but she couldn't meet his eyes.

'At the end of it, we go our separate ways and get a divorce. Della moves out of the house and I wipe the slate clean. It's a very generous offer,' he asserted softly.

It didn't feel generous to Frankie; it felt horribly humiliating and degrading. She recalled the derision in his gaze and shrank inside herself. Santino had seemed almost like a stranger in the café, but that impression had melted away when she'd seen flashes of the Santino she remembered. Only now he was a stranger again.

'The choice is yours.'

'I don't see a choice.' If she didn't stay, he would prosecute Della. She could not bear to think of her mother being dragged through court on a charge of serious fraud, even if that was very probably what she deserved, she allowed painfully. 'I have no option but to agree,' she breathed tightly.

'Don't pluck violin strings,' Santino advised very drily as he dug a mobile phone out of his pocket, punched out a number and proceeded to speak to someone in Italian too fast for her to follow. Retracting the aerial, he slung the phone aside. 'The eviction order will not be served.'

In a silent daze of disbelief at the agreement he had forced on her, Frankie sank clumsily down on the rug and tipped the wine to her parched lips with a trembling hand.

CHAPTER FOUR

A FIRM hand shook Frankie's shoulder and she opened her eyes. The sun had changed position in the sky.

'It's time to leave.' Reaching down to close his hands over hers, Santino pulled her upright with easy strength.

It was afternoon. Her last recollection was of setting down that empty wine glass. She had slept for a couple of hours. Awkwardly smoothing down her creased trousers, Frankie straightened and finger-combed her wildly tumbled hair out of her drowsily bemused eyes. 'Why didn't you wake me up?'

'I assumed that you still needed some extra rest.' Santino swept up the rug and folded it. The picnic basket had already gone.

'Why did you bring me to this place anyway?' Frankie demanded with helpless curiosity.

'Perhaps I was foolishly attempting to resurrect fond memories of the family you abandoned on this island.'

At that charge, Frankie froze in shock. 'I beg y-your pardon?'

'Gino, Maddalena and Teresa,' Santino enumerated with cutting precision. 'Although you have yet to ask, your grandfather and your great-aunts are all alive and well.'

Santino swung fluidly on his heel and strode back up the grassy track towards the road. Turning a furious pink at that censorious assurance, Frankie raced after him. 'I wrote several times and my grandfather never replied once!'

'Don't tell me any more lies,' Santino advised with an icy bite in his tone as she drew level with him. 'You didn't write. I would've been the first to hear of it if you had.'

'I did write…I *did*!' Frankie protested defensively, but then in her mind's eye loomed the memory of Della taking the letters from her and assuring her that *she* would post them. Her heart sank like a stone. Had those stilted communications she had sweated blood and tears over ever been posted? After all, any exchange of news between Frankie and Gino Caparelli might have endangered Della's plans to enrich herself at Santino's expense.

'I bet Mum didn't post my letters!' she exclaimed.

Santino skimmed her a look of silent and crushing contempt.

Frankie turned her head away, conscious that he didn't believe her and that her excuse sounded pitifully weak. Yet she *had* written several times to her Sard relatives. But those first months back in London had also been a period of frightening disorientation and readjustment for Frankie…

Suddenly plunged back into the world her father had taken her from, she had felt utterly lost and had holed herself up in her mother's flat like a wounded animal, surrendering to both depression and self-pity. Finding Santino with that other woman in Cagliari had devastated her. Santino had been her whole world then—the focus of her love and trust, the support she leant on in times of crisis and the source of all her self-confidence.

And then, in one appalling moment of revelation, she had finally been forced to face the demeaning reality that their marriage had never been anything other than a cruelly empty charade and a burden on his side of the fence. Well, no matter how badly Santino thought of her now, she certainly wasn't about to tell him how she had fallen apart after leaving him or how long it had taken her to pull herself back together again!

She climbed into the four-wheel drive. 'A bloody rich

man', he had called himself. Vitale…the bank in Cagliari… *Vitale*. She could even recall seeing that name a couple of years ago in a glossy magazine, recognising it because it had once so briefly been her name as well. The story had been about a banking family, a great and legendary Italian banking family, who shielded their privacy to such an extent that photographs of any one of them were rare. And that extreme caution had stemmed from the kidnapping of a family member thirty years earlier.

Two months after her very first meeting with Santino, he had come to tell her grandfather that his son, Frankie's father, Marco, had been killed in a car crash in Spain. Frankie had been savaged by the news, not least because by that stage she had begun thinking resentfully of the father who had deserted her as being no better than a kidnapper. In her guilt-stricken distress, she had admitted as much to Santino.

'When your father lied to you and told you that he and your mother were reconciling, when he brought you here and chose to leave you with a family who were strangers…*yes*, that was irresponsible, selfish and wrong,' Santino had responded fiercely. 'But don't you ever say that you were kidnapped, *piccola mia*. I have an uncle who many years on still bears the scars of that crime. Kidnappers are cruel and violent criminals who deprive innocent people of their freedom for profit!'

Sinking back to the present, Frankie stole a shattered glance at Santino's hard classic profile as he ignited the engine of the powerful car and drove off. What was it he had said earlier? That the sight of a Vitale bank draft with his signature on it would make her feel sick? He had also mentioned having an office in Rome.

'Why were you working in that bank in Cagliari?' she asked in a wobbly voice, because even though she had had it hurled in her teeth by him already she just found it so incredibly hard to believe that the man she had married at sixteen might always have had a life far removed from hers which he'd chosen to keep secret.

'I was the manager there. My father believed that it would be useful practical experience for me before I took my seat on the board. However, he did think that choosing to bury myself in a small branch of our bank in Sardinia was going to severe extremes. But he was not then aware that I had other reasons for making that curious choice of locality...not least a child-bride stashed away in the mountains!'

Our bank. Frankie gulped, realisation dawning. 'And all the time you owned a blasted castle at the other end of the island!'

'I only took possession of the *castello* last year,' Santino contradicted her. 'Before that it belonged to my father, and he had leased it out as a hotel for over twenty years.'

'It doesn't matter. You told me nothing about yourself—'

'I told no lies and I gave you as much information as you could cope with. You were perfectly content within your own little world just playing house. Measure the level of your maturity then by recalling how much you ever asked me about what I actually *did* for a living,' Santino suggested drily. 'As I remember it, your sole angle of interest then was that working kept me away from you all week!'

Flames of mortified colour burnished Frankie's complexion. 'What was I supposed to ask you? I'd never been in a bank in my life and I just didn't want to expose my ignorance! Look, where are we going?' she demanded abruptly. 'This isn't the way we came—'

'We're heading to Sienta for a long-awaited Caparelli family reunion,' Santino delivered levelly.

At the news that they were heading for her grandfather's village, Frankie's soft mouth dropped open. '*Sienta?*' she gasped strickenly.

'I hope your family never learn that you would've come to Sardinia and left again without even treating them to a brief visit—'

'Damn you…don't you dare turn pious on me!' Frankie flared back at him in furious reproof. 'You know better than anyone how miserable I was in that village! My grandfather could've written to my mother at any time and she would've flown over and taken me home, but she never got the chance because she didn't know where I was…'

Santino drew the car to a halt again. Then he turned to survey her angry, resentful face. His expressive mouth compressed. 'I will tell no more lies or half-truths to protect you. You're old enough to deal with reality. Your mother made *no* attempt to regain custody of you.'

'How could she when she didn't know where I was? My father was always on the move, and naturally she assumed I was with him!'

Santino emitted a pained sigh. 'After he learnt of his son's death, Gino gave me his permission to make contact with your mother—'

'I don't believe you!' Frankie cried feverishly.

'Your grandfather said, "Let my daughter-in-law come here and talk to us and then we will see what is best for the child." The next time I was in London I visited Della and informed her of Gino's invitation and your unhappiness. Your mother did nothing.'

'That's not true…that *can't* be true!'

'I'm sorry, but it is,' Santino asserted steadily, his veiled dark gaze meeting her appalled eyes and then skimming with cool diplomacy away again. 'Your mother had always known where you were because your father phoned her the day he took you, to tell her that he was bringing you to live with his family. Della has little maternal instinct, and by the time I caught up with her she was out partying every night with her second husband. Even when I told her that Marco was dead, she saw no reason why you shouldn't stay where you were.'

Frankie twisted her bright head sharply away from him, tears smarting below her lashes. A beautifully shaped masculine hand closed over her convulsing fingers and she tore free of his touch in a stark gesture of repudiation.

Santino released his breath in a raw hiss that sliced through the screamingly tense silence. 'In telling you the truth I chose the lesser of two evils. At the time, Gino could not bring himself to hurt you with that truth, and his reward was your resentment and bitterness. After your father died, you blamed your grandfather for keeping you in Sardinia. I could not let you return to your family still harbouring that grudge.'

Santino had unveiled the murky core of something Frankie had always secretly feared. Her young and beautiful mother had indeed just got on with her life once her daughter was gone—content, possibly even relieved to be free of the burden of childcare. And ever since Frankie had come home at sixteen that awful truth had been staring her in the face…hadn't it? Her fond hopes and expectations had never been met by the detached and uninterested parent she had foolishly idealised throughout her years away.

'Thank you for telling me,' Frankie breathed, tight-mouthed, falling back on her pride with fierce determination. 'But I should've been told the facts a long time ago.'

Santino drove on. 'That was not my decision to make.'

A distraught sob clogged up Frankie's throat. She despised and feared the very intensity of her own emotions. Yet it was a weakness she had learned to live with and conceal. Unfortunately that felt like an impossible challenge in Santino's presence. And just at that moment it seemed to her that in all her life she had never been loved...

Not by her emotionally cold mother, not by her feckless father, who had stolen her purely in the vengeful hope of punishing his estranged wife, not by her father's family, who had had no choice but to keep her...and certainly not by Santino, who had already admitted to marrying her because she'd been on his conscience and he'd pitied her.

A tiny gulping sound escaped her compressed lips.

'Cry...it always makes you feel better,' Santino suggested, with the disturbing cool of a male who had suffered through countless impassioned sessions of weeping while she was in her volatile teen years.

'I hate you, Santino...' And she despised herself even more then, for sounding like a sulky adolescent.

'But you still look at me like a starving kid in a candy shop. That hasn't changed.'

A shaken surge of outrage swept over Frankie.

'What *has* changed,' Santino murmured with velvet-smooth emphasis, 'is that I no longer feel that I will be taking unfair advantage of an innocence which I now assume to be long gone...'

As his imperious dark head turned slightly, as if in question on that point, Frankie snarled, 'What do *you* think? Do you fondly imagine that the sight of you snogging the life out of that brassy blonde tart put me off sex for ever?'

Santino froze.

Frankie straightened her shoulders like a bristling cat, all danger of tears now banished. 'Yes, I expect you did think that. I suppose you think you broke my heart too...well, you didn't! I got over my crush on you in one second flat and, believe me, I didn't waste any time in finding a man who *did* want me—'

'Let's skip the gory details of your deflowering,' Santino interposed glacially.

Frankie flushed and dropped her head, ashamed of that outburst, particularly when it was all lies. Santino's rejection of her love had savaged her ego and made her extremely wary of trusting any man again. She had had boyfriends, of course she had, but physical intimacy had featured in none of those brief relationships. She had never met anyone she wanted as much as she had once wanted Santino and, quite frankly, she had been in no hurry to make herself that vulnerable again.

'Your family believe that you have been pursuing your education in the UK.'

Frankie was startled. 'You kept in touch with them?'

'Naturally. As far as they're concerned, I'm still your husband; I'm family too,' Santino extended gently.

Her husband. The designation and the awareness of the devastating choice he had forced on her earlier tensed every muscle in Frankie's body. Three weeks in Sardinia with Santino. Her brain went into stunned suspension. She swallowed hard. She just could not imagine going to bed with Santino. She could not even imagine Santino *wanting* to go to bed with her. This was, after all, the same male who had held her at arm's length and treated her like a kid sister during the six months they had lived under the same roof as man and wife.

Frankie had been tormented by the awareness that they were not properly married until the legal bond was consummated in the flesh. From the outset, Santino had slept in the bedroom next door. She hadn't been able to understand his extraordinary reluctance to do what Teresa had once sourly warned her all men were all too willing to do given the opportunity. And she had been too ashamed of her own obvious lack of attraction to share the humiliating secret of their separate sleeping arrangements with anyone else.

But in her innocence it had still not occurred to her that Santino might simply be satisfying his sexual appetite elsewhere. Her trust had been absolute. And she would never have found out that he had another woman in his life had she not decided to surprise him by showing up to visit him mid-week in Cagliari.

A neighbour had given her a lift to the railway station and she had caught the train the rest of the way. But she had been too intimidated by the bank to go in and actually ask for Santino. It had been lunchtime, and while she had hung around outside, trying to pluck up the courage to go inside, Santino had emerged, laughing and talking with a beautiful blonde woman. He hadn't even noticed Frankie and, disconcerted by the presence of his companion, Frankie had let them walk past. Then, scolding herself for her hesitation, naively assuming that he was merely chatting to a colleague, she had set out after them and followed them across the street. They had vanished into an elegant apartment block.

Intercepted by the security guard who asked her to explain her business, Frankie had watched in frustration as Santino and his companion strolled into the lift. And then she had watched in sick, disbelieving shock as their two bodies had merged and they'd kissed with the passionate impatience of lovers eager to be alone and out of sight of prying eyes. A split second before the doors had glided shut, Santino had lifted his beautiful dark head and seen Frankie. She would never forget the look of angry, guilty regret that had flashed across his savagely handsome features…

Dear heaven, she reflected now, five years older and wiser, and cringing from the memory of her own stupidity. Until that moment in the lift, she had sincerely believed that their marriage was a real one and that Santino had made a genuine commitment to her. But from the start Santino had naturally been planning on an annulment to regain his freedom. 'A child-bride stashed away in the mountains', he had called her. An embarrassing secret and, without doubt, an often exasperating and much resented responsibility…

*   *   *

Afternoon was fading into evening as they passed through the sleepy hill villages with their olive groves and vineyards enclosed by prickly pear hedges. As the mountain road climbed higher, the tree cover grew steadily more sparse. The pasture land took on a wild and desolate grandeur enlivened only by wandering sheep and the shepherds' rough brushwood pens. They finally reached the bare plateau and then slanted off the road onto the long, rough, steeply descending track which eventually led down into Sienta.

Stiff as a broom handle, Frankie stared out at the familiar sights all around her. Apple orchards and mature chestnut and oak trees ringed the village in its sheltered valley setting. Tiny terraced houses, their walls covered with vines, lined the sloping, twisting single street. Santino parked outside Gino Caparelli's home in the centre of the village and turned to look at her expectantly.

'Well, what are you waiting for?' he asked.

Frankie climbed out with the slowness of extreme reluctance. Then she saw her great-aunt Maddalena peering anxiously from the open doorway. Momentarily unsure of herself, she stilled, and then, without warning, a surge of overwhelming emotion engulfed her. Within seconds she was enfolded tearfully in the little woman's arms, crying and struggling to converse in a language which she had believed she had forgotten but which returned surprisingly easily to her lips.

'Come in…come in out of the street,' Teresa urged from behind her tiny sister. 'You will have all our neighbours watching us.'

And then her grandfather was before her, greeting her with a more formal embrace, pressing a salutation to her brow and then setting her back from him, frowning dark eyes below beetling white brows inspecting her. 'I would not have received you back into this house without your husband.' Gino Caparelli admitted he knew the truth behind her long absence without apology. 'But now you are back where you belong, by his side.'

Frankie's days of arguing with her grandfather's lofty pronouncements were far behind her. She coloured and said nothing, overwhelmed by the warm acceptance of her welcome after five years of silence. Right at that moment it felt like more than she deserved and she was humbled by the experience.

Furthermore, she was seeing things she hadn't seen in her teens, when her every thought had been exclusively centred on Santino and escape from Sienta. She saw the suspicious brightness and satisfaction in the older man's eyes and then the hurt look of rejection stiffening Teresa's thin face. Darting over, she wrapped her other great-aunt in a belated and guilty hug.

'Bring Santino a glass of wine,' Teresa instructed Maddalena with a rare smile as she detached herself again. 'I will show Francesca round the house.'

Frankie frowned, not comprehending why that should be necessary until she saw Santino and her grandfather walk out to the little courtyard beyond the parlour. She moved to the doorway, looking out in surprise at the table and chairs and the decorative climbing plants which now beautified the once unlovely space reserved for housing Gino's fierce old sheepdog.

'When the Festrinis sold up next door, your grandfather bought their house and joined it to ours,' Teresa announced with pride. 'We have four bedrooms now.'

'But where on earth did Nonno get the money to do that?' Frankie prompted in astonishment.

'Gino manages all Santino's land round the village and we look after your house,' Maddalena chipped in cheerfully. 'We live very comfortably now.'

In a daze, Frankie let herself be carried through to the enlarged kitchen, with its smart new stove, and on up the stairs to inspect the pristine little bathroom which was clearly Teresa's pride and joy. The tour then took in the bedrooms, all of which were small and very simply furnished.

'This is where you and Santino will sleep tonight,' Maddalena informed her shyly, opening a door on a room mostly filled with a bed.

Prodded over the threshold to admire the pretty flower arrangement on the windowsill and the fresh white cotton spread on an old-fashioned wrought-iron bed that was definitely no more than four feet wide, Frankie found it a challenge to come up with the proper appreciative comments. The prospect of sharing that undersized bed with Santino deprived Frankie of all composure and strangled her usually ready tongue.

'You blush like a bride,' Teresa remarked with a wry shake of her head. 'And so you should. Isn't it time you gave that husband of yours a son?'

'Santino wanted Francesca to finish her education,' Maddalena reminded her sister gently. 'Gino thinks Santino's family must all be very educated people.'

Inwardly Francesca shrank, thinking of her humble quota of three GCSEs, until she appreciated that her lack of impressive academic qualifications scarcely mattered, for she would never meet the Vitale family in Rome. In three weeks' time, possibly even sooner, she would fly back to London and she would never see Santino again. She could not comprehend why that fact should suddenly fill her with the most peculiar sense of panic.

'When Francesca went to school here, her only interest was Santino. Had he written? Was there a letter for her…a parcel? When would he be visiting again?' Teresa was recalling with unconcealed disapproval. 'And when Santino *was* visiting with his uncle you needed eyes in the back of your head to watch her or she'd be wandering round alone with him like a shameless hussy. Oh, the gossip you gave our neighbours, Francesca! We were very lucky that Santino took you…

What other man would have after all the talk there had been?'

Frankie's face burned hotter than ever. Suddenly she was all of fourteen again, being sat down in a corner by an outraged Teresa and lectured about how improper it was for her to still chase after Santino now that she was growing up.

'They're safely married now,' Maddalena piped up soothingly.

Safe, Frankie thought sickly. There had been nothing safe about a marriage forced on a reluctant bridegroom.

Downstairs again, she was drawn into preparations for an elaborate evening meal. The men stayed out in the courtyard drinking aged Nero wine. By then it had sunk in on her that her great-aunts believed that Santino had followed her back to the UK five years ago and healed the breach between them. They thought she had been living in London with her mother solely so that she could complete her education. But then Santino had believed that too, Frankie reminded herself uncomfortably.

And, thanks to *his* generosity and support, her family had prospered as never before. That acknowledgement shamed Frankie. Santino hadn't even sold the farmhouse. He had persuaded her grandfather that his services were needed as a farm manager while his sisters acted as caretakers for the house. Without hurting their pride by offering direct financial help, Santino had given her once desperately poor family the opportunity to improve their lot in life.

From the doorway she found herself watching Santino with compulsive intensity. His luxuriant black hair gleamed in the sunshine. His chiselled profile was hard and hawkish and there was a certain restive edge to his lounging stance by the courtyard wall. Spectacular, sexy, all male. Her *husband*…?

His dark, imperious head turned, brilliant eyes narrowing and closing in on her like piercing golden arrows.

Shock shrilled through Frankie. It was like being thrown on an electric fence. Jolted, her breath caught in her throat. Helplessly she stared back at him. It was Santino who broke that connection first. With a casual word to her grandfather, he straightened and strode forward.

'I'll get your case out of the car,' he murmured huskily.

Frankie's fingers knotted together. 'Can't we go back to the farmhouse for the night?' she whispered urgently.

'And refuse your family's hospitality?' Santino surveyed her hot face and evasive eyes. He laughed softly, as if he understood exactly what was going through her mind. 'I think you know very well that that is out of the question.'

'Santino, *please*—'

He lifted a lean brown hand and let his fingertips trace the taut angle of her delicate jawbone in a fleeting gesture that made her skin tighten and her tense body jerk. 'I'll get your case,' he repeated softly, and walked away again.

Teresa planted a tablecloth and a basket of cutlery into Frankie's dazed hold and shooed her out into the courtyard.

'You have a strong man there,' Gino Caparelli mused, openly amused dark eyes resting on Frankie's tense and flushed profile. 'A strong man for a strong woman makes a good marriage.'

Her wide, full mouth tightened. 'Possibly.'

'You have learnt self-discipline. But then Santino would not tolerate tantrums.'

Frankie's lips compressed even more. When Santino made his mind up about something, he was as unyielding as bars of solid steel. She had come up against that side of Santino the first month they were married, when she had announced that she wanted to spend weekdays in Cagliari with him and he had asserted that he preferred her to stay in Sienta, close to her family. And nothing, not tears, not arguments, not sulks, not even pleas, had moved Santino one inch.

'You don't behave like a married couple of more than five years' standing,' Gino commented with an unexpected chuckle: 'That tale may content my sisters, who have never left this village in their lives…but don't worry, I am so relieved to see you with your husband again that I shall content myself with it too.'

Startled, Frankie had stilled in the act of spreading the tablecloth. Glancing up, she encountered her grandfather's alarmingly shrewd gaze. 'I—'

'You are Santino's responsibility now, and Santino could always manage you very well. With cunning, not a big stick.' Gino nodded to himself with unconcealed satisfaction and pride. 'What a match I made for you, Francesca…I saw his potential as a husband before he saw it himself!'

No truer word had her grandfather ever spoken. Frankie tried not to wince. Five and a half years ago Santino had been entrapped as much by Gino's expectations and her dependency on him as by his own sense of honour. And that same trait had made Santino assume responsibility not only for her security but for that of her Sard relatives as well. Facing up to those hard facts and setting them beside her mother's greedy self-interest, Frankie felt as though she was facing a debt that she could never repay.

'Of course I'm going to help to clear up,' Frankie protested a second time, an edge of desperation roughening her voice.

Piling up dishes with speedy efficiency, Teresa waved her hands in irritation. 'What is the matter with you? You always liked to cook, but when did you ever like cleaning up? Bring your husband more wine…attend to *his* needs,' she urged in reproof.

The candles were burning low on the table outside

and the shadows had drawn in. Tight-mouthed, Frankie hovered with the wine bottle. Santino lounged back, listening to Gino talk but contemplating Frankie with hooded but mercilessly intent dark golden eyes. With a lean hand he covered his wine glass when she would've reached for it.

'You look tired. Go to bed, *cara*. I'll be up soon,' Santino murmured with the most incredible casualness, his deep, dark drawl as smooth as oiled silk.

Frankie set down the bottle and brushed her perspiring palms down over her hips. She went into reluctant retreat, tracked every step of the way by Santino's predatory gaze. He tipped his arrogant dark head back and a dangerous smile of a very masculine tenor slanted his sensual mouth. Her heart jumped as though he had squeezed it and her hands clenched into furious fists of frustration by her side.

Five minutes in that bedroom upstairs and Frankie was convinced that she was looking at the smallest bed for two people she had ever seen in her life. It would barely take Santino, never mind her! Indeed, avoiding Santino in that bed would be an absolute impossibility. She pictured the sheer, frivolous nightwear in her case and almost curled up and died on the spot. Beautiful lingerie was her one secret extravagance, but she recoiled from the prospect of surprising Santino with an inviting display of scantily clad female flesh.

Creeping down the narrow passage into Teresa's bedroom, she extracted a voluminous high-necked cotton nightdress from the corner closet. Only the most ruthlessly determined and lustful male would try to make it past all those billowing folds in a four-foot-wide bed and with the equivalent of in-laws sleeping in the rooms on either side of them. Hugging that comforting conviction to herself, Frankie finally climbed into bed.

About half an hour later, the door opened and the bedside lamp went on. She heard Santino unzip his overnight bag. She breathed in deeply. She opened her eyes just in time to see Santino peel off his shirt. Taut as a bowstring, she studied the long golden sweep of his back, watched the ripple of tightly corded muscles as he stretched. Leaving the door ajar, he strolled barefoot across the passage into the bathroom, and only when she heard the running of water and realised that he was intending to have a bath did she breathe again.

The minutes ticked away, each of them like a saw cutting at her fast-fraying nerves. Frankie lay there getting madder and madder, responding to her own tension with growing rage. Finally the bathroom door opened again. Santino strolled back in and leant lithely against the bedroom door to close it. Frankie studied him like a bristling cat surveying a fully grown tiger invading her patch. Bare-chested, with the button on the waistband of his close-fitting jeans carelessly undone, he lounged there as if he didn't have a care in the world, long straight legs braced slightly apart.

Her mouth ran dry.

CHAPTER FIVE

'WELL, well, well, at least you're not still pretending to be asleep,' Santino commented silkily. 'Perhaps you are at long last beginning to feel just a little *married*?'

'Like heck I am!' With the greatest difficulty, Frankie dragged her attention from the intimidating breadth of his chest and the intensely masculine triangle of rough dark curls hazing his powerful pectoral muscles.

'By dawn I assure you that you will no longer be in any doubt that you belong to me.'

At that assurance, Frankie bridled in outrage. 'I do not belong to you!'

Santino sent her a winging smile that was a shockingly cold threat. 'For the next three weeks, you *do*.'

Something deep down inside Frankie shrivelled up under that chill. That distance, that detachment had been concealed in the presence of her family. Now it sprang out at her from his diamond-hard and incisive scrutiny.

'When you look at me like that, you scare me,' she muttered, and then would've done anything to retrieve that craven admission.

'You're a beautiful woman and I want to make love to you. That has nothing to do with either emotion or temper,' Santino asserted with devastating cool, and ran down the zip on his jeans.

Far from reassured, Frankie sat up with the abruptness of a puppet having her strings jerked. 'Santino…'

Santino slid out of his jeans in one fluid motion and stood there, quite unconcerned, in a pair of black briefs which did spectacularly little to conceal the overt differences between the male and female anatomy.

Hot colour flamed in Frankie's cheeks and she hurriedly averted her attention to the bedspread instead. 'Santino...*no!*' she whispered frantically.

'Why are you whispering?' he demanded, and with an undeniable lurch of dismay she saw the briefs hit the floor.

'Please, whisper back,' she begged, in an agony of embarrassment at the thought of her family hearing him.

The sheet was remorselessly wrenched from her frantically tight hold. 'I wasn't planning to do much more talking,' Santino confessed as he slid into bed with her.

'Not here...not tonight, *please*,' Frankie pleaded from the furthest edge of the mattress.

It wasn't far enough. Santino reached up with two frighteningly powerful hands and simply tumbled her down on top of him. She landed with a strangled gasp and found herself mercilessly pinned to his uncompromisingly hard male physique, startled eyes on a direct collision course with his questioning scrutiny.

'What the hell is this all about?' he enquired grimly. 'If you think you can default on an agreement with a Vitale, you are very much mistaken. What I said earlier I *meant*. What I paid for I fully intend to enjoy, however briefly.'

'But perhaps you're not thinking very clearly right now,' Frankie suggested in breathless dismay as the all-pervasive masculine heat of his naked body began to penetrate even that impregnable nightdress. 'You're still very angry with me...and you don't want to do something you might regret—'

'I want to make love to my wife, Francesca...not commit some violent criminal act,' Santino incised with considerable irony.

'If you wait until tomorrow night, I'll do anything you want!' Frankie gabbled the wildly impulsive promise in desperation.

Frowning, Santino surveyed her through the veil of

his lush black lashes. 'How many glasses of wine did you have over dinner?'

'I...I...*oh!*' Frankie gasped as he rolled her off him again, tumbled her back onto the mattress and pinned one long thigh over her trembling lower limbs.

'*Madre di Dio*...what are you wearing?' Santino enquired with incredulous volume, registering the full effect of the garment for the first time.

Frankie visibly shrank. Disorientatingly, Santino uttered a harsh laugh. He wound one hand into her tousled mane of multicoloured hair and murmured with a cynical twist of his beautifully shaped mouth, 'I wonder who first told you that what is hidden is infinitely more tantalising to most men?'

Frankie's teeth ground together. Her green eyes flashed bright with temper and disdain. 'Right...you want what you paid for...just go ahead and get it over with!' she urged with supreme scorn. 'But don't expect me to join in or pretend I like it!'

Gleaming golden eyes settled on her and flamed with slow-burning satisfaction. 'I *love* to be challenged.'

Since that had not been quite the response Frankie had foreseen, her soft mouth dropped open.

'I'll make you beg me to take you,' Santino promised.

'No...no, you won't,' Frankie mumbled in what sounded even to her own ears a very small, seriously rattled voice.

'You *always* wanted me,' Santino countered with drawling, deeply disturbing assurance. 'I could seduce you with both hands tied behind my back.'

'No...no,' she said fearfully, registering too late that that was what she was truly afraid of. Not Santino, not even the act of sex itself, but the infinitely worse threat that he might have the power to make her lose control over her own body.

'You're shaking like a leaf,' Santino whispered, when

suddenly she wanted him to shout because whispering sounded far, far too intimate.

'I'm not—'

'It's anticipation,' Santino muttered thickly. 'I know it is—'

'It's *not*!'

'Once you could burn up all the oxygen in the room just looking at me. That kind of animal attraction doesn't fade without fulfilment—'

'I grew out of it!'

His ebony brows pleating, his long, lithe body tautening, Santino studied her with sudden flaring intensity. 'Is it possible that the sight of me snogging the life out of that blonde *did* turn you off men?'

'You have the most incredible ego!' Frankie practically spat at him.

'Then there isn't the remotest possibility that you could still be a virgin?' Santino prompted tautly.

'What do you think?' Frankie snarled, at her aggressive and defensive best when it came to falling back on pride for strength. 'Do you also cherish fond hopes about Santa Claus and the Tooth Fairy?'

At her stinging sarcasm, a tiny muscle jerked at the corner of Santino's now fiercely compressed lips. '*Sì*…in this day and age you have every reason to greet such a question with incredulity.'

Over-emotional tears smarting behind her eyes, Frankie jerked her head away and blinked rapidly. She had read that it was often difficult for men to know whether or not a woman was experienced. She prayed that that was true. She could not *bear* Santino to know that she was still such an innocent! Admitting that truth would be horribly humiliating because he would instantly grasp just how deeply he had wounded her self-image with his indifference five years earlier.

Shifting, Santino lowered his dark head, his breath mingling with hers. The clean warn scent of him enveloped her. Her own breath shortened, a nervous tremor racking her.

'You're ridiculously tense...'

'What did you expect?' Frankie flared accusingly. 'This is like waiting to be attacked!'

Santino stiffened and then disconcerted her entirely by bursting out laughing. 'Is it really? And you want me to...what was that wonderful phrase?....*sì*, ''just get it over with''?'

'What's so funny about that?'

With a wolfish smile that challenged, Santino gathered her to him with dauntingly sure hands and pushed her bright hair back from her cheekbones. Drawn into the raw heat of him, Frankie shivered violently. He dipped his head and, instead of directing his attention to the rigidly uninviting line of her mutinously closed mouth, he pressed his lips to the tiny pulse beating out her wild tension in the hollow of her collarbone. Frankie jerked in complete shock, bereft of breath and if possible even more alarmed by that unexpected opening move.

'You will experience only pleasure in my arms. I promise you that. In fact it is a matter of honour that you should relish sharing a bed with me.' Playing the tip of his tongue erotically across the excruciatingly tender skin of her throat, Santino sent her pulses leaping into sensual disarray. 'Open your mouth,' he urged, glittering eyes like scorching shards of pure gold.

Frankie trembled, unyielding as marble, but he brushed her mouth with his and then somehow—and later she genuinely couldn't understand how—her lips softly parted. And without the slightest warning at all Santino was kissing her with slow, deep, shattering intimacy. Her mind was just as suddenly an astonishing blank; her heart pounded in mad excitement with every rawly intrusive thrust of his tongue. What she had never counted on, and what her treacherous body had never before encountered, was that amount of sheer seductive pleasure. It was the pleasure which bowled her over and overwhelmed her.

'San—tino…' she mumbled, coming up desperately for air.

'Nothing but pleasure,' Santino promised in growling repetition.

A hot, melting sensation had begun deep down inside Frankie. Before she knew what was happening to her she was giving back kiss for kiss with frantic, driven urgency.

'You're very passionate,' Santino muttered with hoarse satisfaction, curving a firm hand over the thrust of one full breast and unerringly locating the swollen tender nipple beneath the cotton.

Involuntarily Frankie's spine arched, and a soundless gasp was torn from her as he gently, deftly used that barrier that she had naively hoped would frustrate him to excite her beyond all bearing. As, with his guidance, the coarse grain of the fabric massaged and tormented those achingly sensitive buds, Frankie started burning all over and found it quite impossible to stay still.

An arrow of piercing heat twisted between her restive thighs. He lowered his mouth to the straining peaks and still the screening material failed to lessen the depth of her response. Indeed her whole body jackknifed under that fresh onslaught. A strangled moan was wrenched from her and instantly he covered her mouth with his again, silencing her.

'Hush, *cara*…' Santino instructed in his deep, dark drawl as he ran an exploring and incredibly arousing hand down the quivering length of one securely cotton-shrouded thigh. 'I haven't even begun yet.'

But, whether he had begun or not, Frankie's sensation-starved body was already out of her control, and seething with a feverish, needy passion utterly outside her experience. She clutched at his shoulders with straining fingers, striving to find his mouth again for herself. And then, still quite tormentingly indifferent to the shielding thickness of the nightdress, which was now driving her to the heights of screaming frustration because she wanted so badly to feel her skin naked against his, Santino discovered the most sensitive place of all with an impossibly gentle hand.

A tortured moan of intolerable hunger escaped Frankie. 'Take the wretched thing off,' she pleaded.

'Shush,' Santino soothed, while doing everything possible to ensure that the only way she could keep quiet was either to bite him or bite the pillow. 'I know what I'm doing.'

It was more than Frankie did. Twisting and turning against him, out of her mind with excitement, her entire body was clenched unbearably tight by the burning hunger he had ignited with his touch. Lost and driven without her own volition to a shattering peak of hunger, an explosion of ecstatic pleasure burst without warning inside her, plunging her into wave after wave of drugging sensual delight. At the same moment Santino crushed her under him and sealed his mouth to hers to swallow every gasping cry she made.

When he freed her and she was able to breathe again, Frankie was in so much shock she was a shadow of her usual aggressive self, limp with the satiation of physical gratification and simultaneously devastated by the experience.

In the thundering silence, Santino scanned her shaken face and dazed eyes with a disturbingly shrewd look of satisfaction. 'Now *that* was definitely a first for you.'

Assailed by the most outraged sense of seething mortification, Frankie thrust him away from her with wild and frantic hands. Turning her back on him, she curled up as warily stiff as a hedgehog ready to repel attack. The light went out. She lay there, boiling alive with shame at the awareness that Santino had watched her lose all control while he caressed her wanton, hatefully responsive body. And he hadn't even had to take her nightdress off…though she had actually begged him to remove it, she recalled strickenly, absolutely horrified by her own behaviour.

A long arm plucked her off the very edge of the mattress and drew her remorselessly back into all too physical contact. Frankie went rigid but Santino ignored the fact. Flipping her over, indifferent to the imprisoning folds of the nightdress entrapping her, he sealed her into relentless connection with his long, lithe body. In the moonlight, her eyes flew wide. Against her stomach she felt the shocking proof that he was still very aroused. He had given her the pleasure he had promised but had as yet taken none for himself.

'You said if I waited until tomorrow night you'd do anything I want,' Santino reminded her, with terrifying timing and truly devastating effect. 'A provocative offer…and for me? Pure erotic temptation. So for what remains of tonight I will practise patience and self-restraint…'

Whipped back into life by that tigerish taunting purr, Frankie very nearly exploded with temper. And then she bit her lower lip so hard she hurt herself, but contrived to practise some much needed restraint of her own while she continued to squirm at the memory of him cutting off her whimpers and moans of excitement with kisses.

'Unless you've changed your mind…?'

'No…no, I haven't,' Frankie mumbled, wondering if she had been temporarily insane to say such a thing to a virile male as experienced as Santino. Precisely what would he want her to do? Hurriedly shutting that enervating thought back out again, Frankie breathed in slowly and carefully to calm herself. Tomorrow night felt like a long way away.

Frankie stared into the little mirror propped on top of the chest of drawers and hated what she saw. A woman who had let herself down a bucketful. If she had reacted with revulsion when he'd touched her, Santino would not have persisted. But then what might he have done? Gone back to his original plan to evict Della and prosecute her for fraud? Frankie shivered. No matter how badly Della had behaved, Frankie couldn't bear to think of her mother being humiliated to that extent.

And Frankie was painfully aware that she had betrayed herself to Santino. He had recognised her hunger and chosen a punishment calculated to decimate her pride. And why shouldn't he have? she conceded, with new and bitter acceptance of the situation she had impulsively put herself in. After all, she had stood herself beside Della and had deliberately taken on the guise of a mercenary little confidence trickster.

Now she was reaping the benefit of Santino's angry and vengeful contempt. Santino who knew her so much better than anyone else alive; Santino who knew exactly how much her pride meant to her…Santino who would be quite capable of tearing her to tiny emotional shreds in the space of three weeks. For she didn't know Santino, not as he was now.

She was so vulnerable where he was concerned. And it wasn't just that she still found him wildly attractive. Ninety-nine out of a hundred women would take one look at Santino and go weak at the knees. He had spectacular looks and an electrifying aura of sensual dominance. But Frankie was also threatened by infinitely more subtle and dangerous promptings. For Frankie, Santino had just always been so special. So terrifyingly, hopelessly *special*…

The door opened without warning. In the act of plaiting her hair, Frankie flinched. Santino stilled in the doorway, lean, mean and magnificent in a black shirt and black close-fitting moleskin jeans. 'Breakfast is almost ready.'

As she collided reluctantly with lustrous dark golden

eyes, her entire face burned. It seemed to her that there was a new knowledge in his steady gaze, a sardonic male savouring of her abandonment in his arms only hours earlier. Turning back to the mirror, she said coldly, 'I'll be down in a minute.'

'Don't you have a skirt in that case?' Santino enquired drily.

Frankie skimmed an irritably self-conscious hand down over her navy cotton trousers. 'I don't like skirts.'

'I do…and what I like you have to like for the next three weeks.' Santino delivered the reminder without remorse.

'You think I'm going to turn into some sort of combination sex-slave and dress-up doll?' Frankie enquired, tight-mouthed, breasts swelling with chagrin as she sucked in a deep restraining breath. 'Well, you've got the wrong woman—'

'I don't think so.' Santino appeared behind her in the mirror and she tensed in surprise. He loosened the plait with ruthless cool and planted the brush back into her nerveless fingers. 'You can't suppress that passion in the same way that you strive to conceal that glorious hair. I won't let you.'

Frankie trembled with rage. 'Don't tell me what I can't do—'

'So find out the hard way what happens when you rebel. That seems to be the only way you ever learn,' Santino said flatly. 'Just as you learned last night that the family you spent all those years trying to escape actually love you.'

Choked up by that reminder, temper cruelly squashed by it, Frankie froze. 'I *know*,' she muttered guiltily.

'And when I fade back out of their lives again you will stay in touch,' Santino told her grimly. 'You can blame me for breaking up our marriage and tell them you got the farm in the divorce. They have about as much grasp of the extent of my wealth as you once had.'

'But they're fond of you too…' Frankie heard herself protest shakily.

'I still won't be back,' Santino drawled with flat conviction. 'I think that in your absence I have done everything that could reasonably be expected of me, but my responsibility here is now drawing to an end.'

'For a bigshot like you, it must've been a real drag to come visiting out in the boonies!' Frankie flung, in a distress she couldn't even understand.

Santino's lean hands came down on her taut shoulders to spin her round. Ice-cool dark eyes scanned her over-bright gaze and the sudden intense confusion etched there. 'Keep those emotions under control,' he advised harshly. 'I may want that beautiful body but that's the only interest I have now. At the end of this little interlude, I have every intention of walking away.'

Frankie gulped. 'You think that's not what I want too?'

'I think you're programmed to attach yourself to the wrong people, and I really don't want to pay a second time. This is just the settlement of a long-overdue debt, Francesca. Try to keep that in mind.'

Frankie stared into the mirror long after Santino had gone, registered the stricken look in her eyes and closed them because she could not bear to see what he might have seen.

CHAPTER SIX

AFTER lunch, Santino drove Frankie out to the farm-house. She had spent the entire morning with Teresa and Maddalena, making ceremonial calls on several neighbours. In a village where most of the young people left as soon as they were old enough to seek work there was nothing unusual about the length of her absence, and warm hospitality had greeted her everywhere.

However, thunderous tension-filled silence reigned between Santino and Frankie as he turned the Landcruiser up the lane to the dwelling which had once so briefly been their home. Everywhere Frankie looked she was stabbed to the heart by memories with a very raw edge. Her first glimpse of the house with its weathered stone walls and red-tiled roof simply choked her up. Determined as she was not to betray a single emotional reaction, her facial muscles locked defensively tight as she climbed out of the car.

'What happened to my hens?' she enquired stiffly.

'I should imagine someone finally ate them.'

Careful not to look at him, Frankie breathed tightly, 'Angela?'

'Went to that great goat heaven in the sky.'

'Milly and her calf?' Frankie pressed even more tautly.

'Sold.'

Frankie was now rigid. 'Topsy…and Pudding?' she prompted, half an octave higher. 'They've gone too, haven't they?'

'Yes.'

Unable to contain herself any longer, Frankie rounded

on Santino. 'So what did you *do* with my cats?' she demanded rawly. 'Did you eat them, sell them or bury them?'

Brilliant dark eyes rested on her fearful, accusing face. 'I took them back to Rome with me.'

'O-oh…' Reddening with sudden embarrassment and surprise, Frankie folded her arms jerkily and turned away again.

Trembling, she preceded him into the house and walked straight into the cosy, low-ceilinged lounge with its comfortable twin sofas. From the rear window she looked out in dismay at the garden which she had created five years earlier. It had been swallowed up by brambles and scrub. So what? she asked herself. This is not my home any more; this was *never* really my home. None of these changes matter to me in the slightest, the inner voice insisted. But, in spite of that sensible voice, pained regret and a strong feeling of resentful loss still washed over Frankie.

She had adored this house only one iota less than she had once adored Santino. After the cramped and basic confines of her grandfather's home, this spacious house had seemed like a palace. No sixteen-year-old bride had ever been more deliriously happy with her lot. All that bright, innocent hope and unquestioning trust… She felt such a fool looking back on it now, particularly when she thought of the *castello*…

Maids and antique furniture and fancy bathrooms. That was Santino's true milieu. Yet, five years ago, he had valiantly roughed it every weekend in what to him had to have been the equivalent of a hovel. In keeping with Sard tradition he had bought the house and furnished it before the wedding. He had brought her paint cards, picked her favourite colours, become the first person in Sienta to pay someone else to decorate—an extravagance which had had Gino Caparelli shaking his head with appalled incredulity. But in every other way

Santino had done exactly what was expected of a Sard bridegroom.

'I hate you, Santino,' Frankie breathed unevenly, swallowing the great lump threatening her throat. 'If I played house, I played house because *you* encouraged me to do that!'

'What else was I supposed to do with you?' Santino responded to that accusation levelly. 'As you were then, you couldn't have handled my family, and they couldn't have handled you.'

Flinching from that blunt stating of fact, Frankie nonetheless spun straight back to him. 'I don't think there was *ever* any question of my meeting your family,' she challenged in condemnation.

Santino elevated a smooth ebony brow, his vibrantly handsome features impassive. 'It's immaterial now.'

The unspoken reminder of how much time had passed since then silenced her. She had sounded like a woman scorned, she thought in horror. Bitter, accusing. All over what? A marriage that had never been a normal marriage? A husband who had never been a real husband and who had, understandably, at the age of twenty-four, found celibacy too much of a challenge?

Twisting away, dismally conscious of how close her turbulent emotions were to the surface and how great would be the self-betrayal if she voiced those raw feelings, Frankie stalked out of the room and started up the narrow staircase. On the landing, however, her deep sense of injustice overcame her. 'You should've just come to see me in London...you should *never* have dragged me back here!'

She flashed into what should have been and never had been the marital bedroom. Here she had slept alone. At the foot of the bed rested the carved dower chest presented to her by her great-aunts on her wedding day, filled to the brim with exquisite embroidered linen. Teresa and Maddalena had given the chest with such pride and pleasure. Neither of them had ever married, and no Sard woman of their generation celebrated spinsterhood.

She stood at the low window, staring sightlessly out. Santino evoked a dangerously explosive mix of hatred and fierce longing inside her. The hatred she wanted to nourish, but the strength of that fierce longing filled her with fear. Dear heaven, Santino was already tearing her apart. He was forcing her to relive so much that she had deliberately buried.

'Francesca...' Santino murmured from the doorway.

Her hands closed convulsively in on themselves. 'I was so happy here,' she whispered, and then, instantly regretting that lowering admission—for who wanted to admit to having been happy living in a pathetic dream-world?—she added curtly, 'You should have told me the truth about our marriage right from the start.'

'I didn't think you were strong enough to take it,' Santino countered with devastating frankness. 'You had too much invested in our relationship.'

Frankie's restive fingers coiled into tight fists. 'That's not true!' She flipped round to face him. 'I've had my share of hard knocks in life, but none of them has ever sent me to the wall!'

Santino surveyed her with steady, dark-as-night eyes, as if he knew that she was lying, as if he *knew* that he had cruelly ripped her heart out that day in Cagliari and almost destroyed her. 'You were completely dependent on me and extremely vulnerable. You had the body and the emotions of an adult without the maturity or the experience...' Unusually, Santino hesitated, his deep, dark drawl roughening as he breathed, 'After five years of living in such isolation your knowledge of the world barely went beyond the boundaries of this village.'

Frankie paled and veiled her expressive eyes, appalled by an assessment she could not protest at. Too well did she recall the frightening disorientation she had endured when she had returned to London.

'If you hadn't caught the train to Cagliari that day, you would eventually have agreed to continue your education in Florence,' Santino asserted with conviction. 'I would have been able to watch over you there. You would have outgrown your infatuation with me and found yourself becoming more interested in boys in your own age group.'

Frankie bit back a sarcastic shout of disbelief but could not resist prompting, 'And if I *hadn't*...what would you have done then?'

Santino shifted a powerful shoulder in an infinitesimal shrug, brilliant eyes screened by thick black lashes. 'I would have coped with the situation. I was very fond of you.'

Fond. A shudder of revulsion and mortification rippled through her taut length. What a lukewarm, milky *nothing* word, she reflected fiercely.

'But, regardless of that, we couldn't have gone on living as we were. I didn't want to risk ending up in bed with you—'

'Oh, I don't think there was ever much risk of that!' Francesca hissed with the sharpness of unforgotten pain as she tried to brush past him.

Santino snaked out a lean brown hand and closed it round her slender forearm to force her to still. His dark eyes shimmered with flaring gold anger as he gazed down at her. 'You were as wild as a gypsy. Incredibly beautiful and stunningly sexy. You didn't even appear to be aware of your sexual power, but it *was* there and it kept me awake every night I ever spent in this house with you,' Santino informed her rawly. 'You were a temptation that tormented me every day of our marriage.'

Stunned into paralysis by that staggering admission,

Frankie stared up at him, green eyes wide with disbelief, even her breathing suspended.

'I walked a tightrope with you,' Santino recalled grimly, a line of dark colour accentuating the spectacular slant of his hard cheekbones. 'I knew that if I succumbed I'd plunge us both into an impossible relationship. I deserved a medal for staying out of the marital bed…most particularly when you began reminding me at every opportunity that you *were* my wife!'

Oxygen re-inflated Frankie's lungs as she sucked in a shuddering breath. Shock still rolled over her in heady waves, but a surge of deep and abiding anger followed in its wake. Wrenching herself violently free, she raced down the stairs and out of the back door into the fresh air.

All that time he had wanted her; all that time and she had never once suspected. A jagged laugh was wrenched from her. She had loved him *so* much. She had loved Santino with an intensity that had been unashamed and fearless. Unable to imagine a future without him, she hadn't understood how much damage loving like that could do until it was too late to protect herself. But all along Santino had known…

In spite of the heat, her skin chilled. 'You had too much invested in our relationship.' With those bloodless words of detachment, Santino had acknowledged the reality that she had belonged to him body and soul. So he had been physically attracted to her; so he had been tempted by the body she had been so pitifully willing to offer…it meant so little, she conceded painfully. It was like coming in last of all in a race she had once hoped to win.

For Santino had withstood sexual temptation with colossal cool and self-discipline. They had cracked the mould when they made Santino. Lust had warred with intellect…and intellect had naturally won. A strong and shrewd instinct for self-preservation had kept Santino out of the marital bed. He had known that he'd have a hell of a job getting rid of her if he slept with her.

A lean hand came down on her shoulder. Santino turned her round, gleaming dark golden eyes scanning her flushed and expressive face. 'You are still very intense,' he murmured thoughtfully. 'Still remarkably sensitive to the past. And yet why should I be surprised by that? The Sard blood in your veins fuelled your desire for revenge. I hurt you. And you retaliated in the only way you could. You chose to lie and cheat and steal from me.'

Paling, Frankie muttered, 'I...I—'

Santino's strong dark features were hard and unyielding. 'I've already explained why I behaved as I did then. And yet still you show no shame. That explanation should've been unnecessary. No decent man would've bedded an infatuated teenager!'

Frankie's temper sparked. 'No decent man would've broken his marriage vows either! You were unfaithful. Where's your shame, Santino?' she shot at him, unable to silence that angry demand.

Disconcerted by that spontaneous counter-attack, Santino breathed slowly, '*My* shame?'

'I was your wife. Age doesn't come into it. You married me. You made promises to me. You *broke* them!' Frankie enumerated with raw bite. 'Am I supposed to be grateful because you stooped to marrying me in the first place? Well, I'm not grateful. In fact, I blame you for that most of all. You gave me expectations I would never have had otherwise. You allowed me to believe that I had rights when I had no rights! That was cruel and unfair and very short-sighted. How was I supposed to recover from my infatuation when I thought of you as my husband?'

Her outspoken censure provoked an incredulous flash in Santino's hard scrutiny. Satisfaction filled Frankie. He was a self-righteous rat, blind to his own errors of judgement. Marrying her hadn't been a kindness or a damage-limitation exercise. It had been sheer madness to encourage her love and dependency with a wedding ring.

She lifted her fiery head high, the burden of the past lightening, for she had finally got to put her own point of view and pride had been redeemed. Taking advantage of Santino's charged stillness, she crossed with a sinuous twist of her hips through a gap in the prickly pear boundary to the rough pasture land beyond. 'I'm going for a walk,' she announced.

A long while later, she sank down on a sun-baked rock to stare down at the farmhouse, stubborn resolution etched in every line of her lovely face. At last she felt free of that shadowy teenage self who had been relentlessly haunting her. And she had rediscovered the fighting backbone she needed to deal with Santino. Once he had put her through an emotional wringer, but she would never give him the power to hurt her like that again.

Matt—whom she absolutely had to phone, she reminded herself in exasperation—well, Matt had suggested that this trip might be therapeutic. And, astonishingly, he had hit a bull's-eye with that forecast. It *was* time to move on. It *was* time she got Santino out of her system. And, since she had always been wildly attracted to Santino, wasn't it ridiculously old-fashioned to be ashamed of the fact? Everything that drew her to Santino had to have its roots in that physical hunger.

They would have a passionate affair and nobody would ever know about it. Then they would part and, most importantly, she would be *over* him. Santino's indifference had once smashed her ego. That was why she had never been able to put him behind her, where he belonged. That was undoubtedly why she was still so strongly drawn to him. Human nature was perverse. Didn't people always want what they thought they couldn't have?

When curiosity was satisfied, surely she would be

completely cured of this hangover from her past? Convincing herself of that cheered Frankie up immensely.

'I've started a meal. I thought you might like a drink,' Frankie said breezily as she strolled into the room across from the lounge which Santino had always used as an office.

Santino spun round in surprise from the computer, brilliant eyes reflecting the sunlight and momentarily stilling her. Smiling brightly, Frankie set the glass of wine down on the desk, struggling not to cringe at the sight of the large bridal photograph of herself that she had placed on that same desk five years earlier, and which still sat there, an embarrassing rave from the grave.

'Heavens, does nobody ever dump anything around here?' she complained, lifting the frame and treating it to a disparaging glance before she dropped it with a gentle crash down into the waste-paper bin. 'Sorry, but it's really creepy seeing stuff like that still sitting about.'

Relishing the slight frown drawing Santino's winged ebony brows together, Frankie walked back to the door, secure in the knowledge that her behaviour was disconcerting him. 'Dinner won't be ready for ages yet. I thought I should make this a special occasion,' she murmured sweetly, casting her dancing eyes down. 'What a pity you didn't lay in some champagne…'

Ten minutes later she was standing beneath the bathroom shower, deciding to wear her bathing pareu and possibly her most abbreviated top in which to dine. Santino wanted to see her in a skirt again? She was feeling generous. Santino wanted revenge? Well, Santino was in for a disappointment there. Frankie was the person planning to be empowered by the night ahead. She was going to wash that man right out of her hair and walk away, strengthened and renewed by the experience.

Ironically, Santino had greatly revived her self-image with the astonishing confession that he had found her an almost unbearable temptation at sixteen. *Before* she'd got her slight overbite corrected, *before* she'd got dress sense, *before* she'd become an independent and surely far more interesting adult woman...

So he ought to be a push-over for seduction. And she might be inexperienced but she knew all the mechanics, could hardly fail to be aware of them. The British media surfeit of articles on sensual experimentation was thrust at women from every printed page. And surely knowledge was power in the bedroom?

Downstairs in the lounge she lifted the phone and belatedly tried to ring Matt, but her business partner was out. She left a brief message on the answering machine at the apartment, explaining that so far she had been unable to reach agreement with the owner of the villas. Strictly true, not a lie, she thought ruefully.

The fridge in the kitchen was crammed with fresh food and the cupboards were fully stocked. Her great-aunts had been wonderfully thorough. Frankie hummed as she baked *carta da musica* bread, checked the selection of *antipasti* appetisers and the clear soup she had already prepared and went on to make an asparagus salad, *gnocchetti alla sarda* for a main course and a pecorino-based cheesecake to be served with Sard bitter honey.

Gastronomically, Santino would be as putty in her ruthless hands. She had a second glass of wine to fortify herself. Tonight there would be none of last night's craven uncertainty. Tonight she would hold centre stage and *she* would be in control. When she had the table prepared, she called him.

Santino stilled one step inside the dining room. Brilliant dark eyes raked with infuriating impassivity over the candlelit intimacy of the beautifully set table and then lodged on Frankie, where she positively posed, the

colourful pareu knotted at her slender waist and arranged
to reveal a discreet stretch of one long, fabulous leg. His
intent gaze roamed over her flowing mane of vibrant hair
and the strappy green T-shirt which revealed rather more
than it concealed of her high, full breasts.

Frankie held her breath, heartbeat crashing like warning thunder in her eardrums. Her own attention was all
for him. In a dinner jacket and close-fitting black trousers, with a white dress shirt heightening the exotic effect of his black hair and golden skin, he looked alien
and yet alarmingly, wonderfully spectacular. A tingle ran
down her responsive spine.

'Are you planning to poison me during the first
course?' Santino enquired lethally.

Frankie stiffened incredulously. 'Is that supposed to
be a joke?'

'I know you're temperamental, but this scenario is unbelievable. ''Come into my parlour said the spider to the
fly...'''

Feeling foolish, Frankie tilted her chin in challenge.
'Why shouldn't I amuse myself by cooking up a storm
when I've got nothing better to do?'

Santino's sensual mouth slanted with unsettling sardonic amusement. 'A complete volte-face within the
space of hours? Naturally I'm suspicious.'

'Just sit down and *eat*!' Frankie stalked back out to
the kitchen.

She poured herself another glass of wine with an angry hand. So Santino refused to be impressed. Damn him
for having the power to play his cards so close to his
chest, not to mention the dismaying ability to look at
her, in spite of all her efforts, as he might have looked
at a stone statue.

'You could ravish a saint in that outfit,' Santino
drawled with silken mockery from the doorway. 'You
look gorgeous from top to toe. Happy now? But when
you stood there patently expecting me to compliment

you something in me refused to give you what you wanted.'

Frankie focused on him with mortified resentment. He made her sound so naive, so *obvious*. Sidestepping him, she returned to the table. 'That's because you're devious and stubborn, Santino...you always were. I used to not see that, but now I do,' she confided with driven honesty.

'So be warned,' Santino murmured chillingly. 'I have never liked games, Francesca.'

Her lashes lowered, her appetite ebbing. When she glanced up again, Santino was uncorking a dusty bottle of champagne. 'Where did that come from?'

'It was in the cellar,' he revealed. 'Waiting for just such an opportunity.'

Frankie played restively with her food and just watched him eat. Whenever she looked at him her mouth ran dry. In her mind's eye she was trying to picture them in that bed upstairs. Anxiety at the challenge she had set herself and the tingling heat of undeniable anticipation warred like mutual enemies inside her. Every time she went out to the kitchen she drank more wine. As she sank deeper into abstraction, Santino's polished attempts to make conversation earned only monosyllabic responses.

Over the dessert course, she surveyed him and breathed in an abrupt tone of discovery, 'You secretly wanted me to be a virgin, didn't you?'

Santino's superb bone structure tensed, lush black lashes narrowing on fiercely intent but uncommunicative eyes. 'Now why would you think that?'

Frankie propped her chin on the heel of one hand, knowing she had startled him almost as much as she had startled herself with that sudden suspicion. A rather malicious smile formed on her generous mouth. 'I can't explain it, but somehow I know it's the truth. You must be very disappointed.'

'Hardly.' His beautiful mouth curled as he met that

provocative smile head-on. 'I can think of no more te-
dious a start to a brief affair than the need to initiate a
nervous amateur.'

The silence stretched. Frankie had paled.

'I was just self-conscious last night,' she informed
him even more abruptly. 'Usually I'm very confident in
the bedroom.'

'Good...I'm feeling unusually shy tonight,' Santino
imparted silkily.

Involuntarily, Frankie studied him, her heart banging
frantically fast against her ribs. Those incredible mag-
netic eyes of his. She wanted to drown in them. Maybe
that was why her head was swimming and it was taking
such appalling effort to concentrate. 'Coffee?' she asked
jerkily.

Santino watched the tip of her pink tongue snake out
to moisten her dry lower lip. He tensed, and then rose
in one fluid sweep from behind the table. Deftly depriving her of her glass, he drew her up into his arms. 'Not
for me,' he breathed huskily.

A ripple of quite tormented excitement ran through
Frankie. Long fingers curved against her spine and
pressed her closer. Her pent-up breath escaped in a
shaken hiss as she registered the swollen fullness of her
breasts and the urgent sensitivity of her nipples, but the
power of those sensations was somewhat diminished by
the disorientating dizziness assailing her.

'Let's go to bed,' Santino suggested, his deep, dark
drawl fracturing to send a responsive frisson through her
trembling length.

Frankie closed her eyes to block him out and resist
the overpowering pull of his dominance. This wasn't
how she had planned it. *He* was taking control.
'No...you go up...you wait for me tonight,' she urged,
wondering why her words were slurring.

'OK.' She lifted her lashes and caught his faint frown
and then watched him stride towards the stairs.

Swaying slightly, she steadied herself on the chair-back, dismay gripping her. Rather too late she was appreciating that she had had too much to drink and far too little to eat. She was furious with herself for being so stupid. Pouring herself a cup of black coffee, she forced it down and then crept outside to breathe in great gulps of the night air in the hope of sobering herself up again.

Her head a little clearer, she nonetheless plotted a far from straight path up the stairs. She could still do it. She could, she *could*. Santino was waiting for her just the way she had planned it, so she wouldn't risk embarrassing herself with potentially clumsy attempts to undress him. And there he was in the marital bed for the very first time in his life...

At that enervating sight something akin to pure anguish seized Frankie. Santino was a gorgeous vision of raw masculine appeal against the white bedlinen. All tousled and golden and breathtakingly sexy...and she was feeling...she was suddenly feeling so horribly sick, and the room was revolving round her in the most nauseating way.

'What's the matter with you?' Santino demanded as he thrust the sheet back with startling abruptness. '*Dio*...I thought it was my imagination downstairs, but you're—'

Frankie made a most undignified dive for the bathroom across the landing. Her worst apprehensions were fully fulfilled. Afterwards she just wanted to be left alone to die, but no such mercy awaited her.

'You'll feel a lot better after you eat,' Santino asserted drily.

Unconvinced, Frankie stared down at the rather charred toast on the breakfast tray. It was safer than looking at Santino. Severe embarrassment clawed at her, for she recalled almost every awful moment of the previous night. Santino initially incredulous at the state she was in, then impatient, exasperated, but ultimately kind. And *why* had he been kind? It was bred into Santino's privileged bones to be kind towards those weaker or less able than he was. She squirmed, pride choking on a generosity which had only increased her sense of humiliation.

'Thank you,' she contrived between clenched teeth, pushing up the sliding strap of the slinky nightdress she had woken up in, shamed as only a woman could be by the knowledge that she had no recollection of donning the garment.

'There has to be a reason why you got that drunk.'

'I wasn't drunk...I was only a bit tipsy,' she countered, so desperate to escape a post mortem, she even bit into a piece of that unappetising toast while wondering if she ought to preserve it for posterity. Unless she was very much mistaken, this toast was the closest Santino had ever come to cooking.

'Are you in love with Matt Finlay?'

Frankie almost choked on the toast. 'Of course I'm not...he's just a friend!' she spluttered in frustration.

Santino contemplated her with galling cool. 'Then you over-indulged because you were nervous—'

'That's ridiculous! Why do you have to make such heavy weather out of something that was purely accidental?'

Santino's beautiful mouth clenched hard. 'Possibly because the idea of you endangering yourself with such reckless behaviour in the company of a less scrupulous male angers me. You should know better.'

'The days when I looked to you to tell me how to behave are far behind me.'

Santino dealt her a derisive glance from the doorway. 'It *shows*.'

Head lowering, cheeks burning, Frankie swallowed convulsively.

Having believed Santino had left the room, she was startled when the tray was lifted away and he sank down instead on the edge of the bed. Unprepared for that proximity, her pained eyes unguarded, she stiffened defensively as he threaded long, sure fingers through her wildly tumbled hair in a disturbingly comforting gesture.

And then, without warning, Santino smiled, one of those blinding, sudden, charismatic smiles that shook her up and made her treacherous heart race. 'That wasn't a very generous comment when you spent so much time apologising last night,' he conceded huskily.

He was so close she could smell the hot, sun-warmed scent of him, intrinsically male and powerfully familiar. Her nostrils flared, her breath catching in her throat as she raised an involuntary hand and let her fingers rest on one broad shoulder to steady herself, her gaze welded to the shimmering gold of his. She shivered as he eased her forward and bent his dark head. A warm, drugging anticipation trapped her in submissive stillness.

He kissed her very gently, his tenderness a soothing balm to her smarting sensitivities. And it made her want him even more. In fact it made her want to cling. He tasted her lips in tiny hungry forays that sent her arms snaking round him in desperation to pull him closer. Her whole body felt as if it was reaching up and out, craving what only he could give. An explosive charge of hunger burned up inside her, and when his tongue penetrated between her readily parted lips her heart lurched so violently she could barely breathe in the seething excitement that controlled her.

Santino lifted his imperious dark head and absorbed her dazed expression. His strong face impassive, he sprang lithely upright. A tiny pulse flickered at the corner of his compressed mouth but in every other way he looked utterly relaxed and in control. 'I haven't had breakfast yet,' he murmured, and strode gracefully out of the room.

Chilled by that abrupt withdrawal, Frankie flopped back against the pillows, stunned by the passion he had fired and then abandoned. Had he regretted that terrifyingly seductive instant of tenderness at the outset? No matter…he had still cut through her prickly defences as easily as a child knocking down a wobbly tower of building blocks—and, worst of all, he was well aware of the fact.

Her hands trembled as she reached for the tray again. Physical hunger, that was *all* it was, she told herself, and maybe she was more susceptible than he was in her inexperience. Only that didn't explain why she had suffered a great suffocating attack of fear and insecurity as she'd watched him detach himself from her and walk away.

She was emerging from the shower when she thought she heard the knocker sounding on the front door. Snatching up Santino's towelling robe, she pulled it on hurriedly and walked out onto the landing.

'Francesca?' Santino called softly. 'Come downstairs.'

With a frown she moved to the head of the staircase. In amazement she gazed down at Matt where he stood in the hall, equally welded to the spot by the sight of her.

'M-Matt?' she stammered in amazement.

'Yes…*Matt*,' her business partner confirmed thinly as he ran indignant eyes over her flustered and damp appearance in the oversized male garment she wore. 'Would you like to tell me what's going on here?'

CHAPTER SEVEN

THE tension in the hall was so thick it sent a shocking trickle of apprehension down Frankie's spine as she descended the stairs. Matt's fair face was flushed and he looked, to her, incomprehensibly furious and accusing. Her attention skimmed to Santino, who stood with impenetrable eyes and a curiously threatening quality of absolute stillness.

'What on earth are you doing here, Matt?' Frankie began uncertainly. 'How did you even find out where I was?'

'This was the only place left to look,' Matt returned. 'I remembered the name of this village and I knew you had family here... But why the blazes didn't you tell someone where you were going?'

'I left a message on the apartment answering machine yesterday...' Frankie continued to stare at him in astonishment for she could imagine no good reason for Matt to leave the agency and come racing over to Sardinia in search of her. 'I know I was a little tardy with that call, but what made you think you needed to fly over here to track me down?'

'Your mother—'

'My...*mother*?' Frankie interrupted incredulously.

Matt swore, only half under his breath. 'I wasn't unduly concerned about your silence until I called your mother to ask if you'd been in touch with her. The minute she realised that you were in Sardinia and that I hadn't heard from you, she went off into blasted hysterics.'

'Hysterics?' Frankie echoed in a wobbly voice, unable to imagine Della in such an emotional state.

'So naturally that panicked *me*, and when I found out that your hire car had been returned it did look very suspicious. Nobody about to go on a touring holiday dispenses with their only means of transport. It seemed like you had disappeared off the face of this earth!'

Frankie was horribly embarrassed by her own thoughtlessness. 'It honestly never occurred to me that anyone would worry…nobody ever has before—'

'You've never staged a vanishing act before. Your mother's called in the police—'

'The *police*?' Frankie blinked, appalled. 'I'm sorry…I just don't understand what's got into everybody—'

'Yes, well, personally speaking, neither do I.' Matt shot a resentful glance of unease at Santino, who had gone rigid at the reference to the police, his jawline taking on a distinctly aggressive slant. 'But you made the headlines on the television news last night. British tourist missing—'

'Oh, no…' Frankie mumbled weakly.

'Della thinks you've either been kidnapped because of your secret wealthy connections or—'

'Kidnapped?' Santino incised in an outraged growl.

'Or because of some crazy vendetta against you by that same *secret* connection,' Matt completed with considerable sarcasm, surveying Santino with naked antipathy. 'I think we can rule out both possibilities, since you appear to be on such cosy and intimate terms with your estranged husband.'

'Oh, heck, I'd better phone Mum… Matt, I'm *so* sorry… I really don't know what could've made Della carry on like this—'

'Guilt,' Santino ground out grittily.

'You should've told me you were still married. You told me everything else.' Matt glowered accusingly at

Frankie. 'Does *he* know how long you've been shacked up with me?'

'Sh-shacked up with you?' Frankie was thoroughly disconcerted by that misleading description of the terms on which they shared the same apartment.

'Yes…what kind of kinky marital relationship do you two have?' Matt sent Santino a malicious half-smile. 'I hope you appreciate that she runs around with a lot of other men too… Here today, forgets you're alive tomorrow. That's my Frankie!'

Santino lunged off the wall like a ferocious tiger suddenly provoked by a whip. 'You—!'

'Please…!' Frankie yelped in horror, and, grabbing Matt's arm, she yanked the smaller man hurriedly into the lounge with her, speedily slamming the door on Santino's unfamiliar and frightening aggression. 'Why are you behaving like this, Matt? What the heck's got into you?'

Matt stiffened with an angry jerk. 'I thought I *knew* you! I thought we were a pretty successful team. I even thought I would marry you…it certainly would've made good business sense.'

Frankie stiffened at that revealing admission. Seemingly her share of the agency had been her greatest attraction in Matt's eyes. 'But you never showed the slightest personal interest in me until Leigh moved out of the apartment. We were just flatmates. We led separate lives outside working hours—'

Matt wasn't listening. 'So that is Santino…your husband since you were sixteen, according to Della…and all the smooth bastard is prepared to offer you is a dirty weekend reunion in some godforsaken hole in the hills!' Matt sneered. 'Still, if that's what it takes to turn you on, who am I to interfere?'

'You deliberately let Santino think that you and I were lovers…why did you *do* that?'

Matt grimaced and compressed his mouth, the anger

draining out of him to be replaced by sullen resentment. 'You really don't have the foggiest clue how the average male reacts to being made to look and feel like a fool, do you? Hell, I've had enough of this nonsense! You'd better contact the police and sort it all out…and what about those villas?'

Still in shock, and feeling guilty about the trouble he had been put to on her behalf, she muttered, 'I'm still working on that.'

'This set-up is *work*?' Matt opened the lounge door again and shot her a bitter look. 'I'm glad you're OK, but I feel like wringing your mother's neck for all this!'

Santino was no longer in the hall, and in another thirty seconds Matt, too, was gone, striding out stiff-backed to the hire car parked outside.

Frankie breathed in deeply and then, her mind a whirling turmoil of chaotic thoughts, raced back into the lounge and lifted the phone to contact her mother.

A strange woman answered the phone and questioned her identity. Frankie's voice trembled as she realised she was speaking to a police officer. Only then did the genuine gravity of the situation finally sink in.

Della came on the line, breathless and tearful. 'Are you all right…? Are you *really* all right, Frankie?'

'I'm with Santino, Mum,' Frankie framed shakily, because she was beginning to feel pretty emotional herself. 'You shouldn't have got the police involved…for heaven's sake…'

'If you're with Santino, then you'll know everything,' Della gathered in a strained undertone, and then she went off the line to plead audibly for some privacy. 'Frankie?' she began afresh.

'I was shocked enough to find out that Santino and I were still legally married, but I was devastated when I found out about his financial stake in our lives,' Frankie admitted tautly. 'Della, how *could* you?'

'I couldn't just stand back and allow you to have your

marriage annulled. It would've been like encouraging you to throw solid gold back down the mineshaft! I did it all for *your* sake—'

'Della, please,' Frankie breathed painfully. 'Just be honest.'

'How much more honest can I get? Santino broke your heart and then landed me with a seriously depressed teenager! He deserved to foot the bill for hurting you that much—'

'Mum, I—'

But Della was unstoppable. 'Didn't I do my best for you, Frankie? Didn't I use his money to buy you beautiful clothes and ensure that you lived in luxury? Didn't I throw lots of parties so that you could meet the right sort of people? Is it my fault that none of those things mattered to you and you still moved out as soon as you could?'

'No, but—' Frankie tried to interrupt again, but her mother was now in full angry and defensive flow.

'As for all that rubbish you talked about Santino never having slept with you…do you think I *ever* believed that?' Della vented a sharp laugh of cynical disbelief. 'That was just your pride talking—you trying to cover up the fact that he'd just used you and dumped you again. And Santino thought he could get away with doing precisely that, didn't he? Shove some hush money at me and hang onto his reputation—because he certainly didn't want it coming out that a Vitale had a cute little jailbait bride he'd got bored with!'

Della's stark bitterness on her behalf stunned Frankie. 'But it wasn't like that…'

'You were suicidal, Frankie. He *deserved* to be punished—and I just hope Santino and his filthy rich, snobbish family are cringing at the publicity they're getting now!'

'What p-publicity?' Frankie stammered, with a sick, sinking sensation in her stomach, only vaguely register-

ing the faint click on the line that suggested that someone else had picked up an extension somewhere.

'Look, when you disappeared, I was frantic with
worry!' her mother told her. 'Your father told me loads
of horror stories about Sard vendettas. For all I knew,
Santino had found out where his money was *really* going
and had decided to get rid of you, saving himself the
need to get a very public and expensive divorce from a
wife nobody even knew he had.'

'Mum…this is all so totally insane…' Frankie's head
was banging fit to burst.

'You're very naive, Frankie. The Vitales are a very
powerful and ruthless family, and you can only be an
embarrassment to them. That's why I spiked Santino's
guns for you. Bringing the whole sorry story out into
the open meant you were safe. Right at this minute this
house is being besieged by journalists, and quite a few
of them are Italian… What sort of angle do you want
me to take when I speak to them again?'

Perspiration beading her short upper lip, Frankie
groaned out loud.

Unconcerned, indeed her voice now betraying her excitement, for Della loved to be the centre of attention,
her mother continued inquisitively, 'I mean…how *with*
Santino, are you, darling? Do you want me to say his
family forced the two of you to separate five years
ago…or do you want me to badmouth him as a shameless seducer of teenage girls? It might make a difference
to your divorce settlement—'

Shaking her head in mute disbelief, Frankie muttered
weakly, 'Let me worry about my divorce settlement—'

'Della…' Another voice sliced in with icy precision
on the line, making Frankie's eyes shoot wide in sheer
shock. 'This is Santino. If you speak to one more jour-
nalist, or indeed anyone else who might talk to the paparazzi, I will have you thrown out of that house by the

end of the day. And then I might just take you to court for fraud.'

Appalled silence seethed on the line as both women realised that Santino had been listening in on their dialogue.

'But you're my son-in-law!' Della squawked in aghast protest.

'In this case blood is definitely not thicker than water. *Be warned,*' Santino breathed with chilling exactitude, and the line went dead as Frankie's mother put the phone down without saying another word.

Frankie wheeled round in dizzy confusion as Santino strode into the lounge. Removing the receiver from her damp and loosened grasp, he rammed it back down on the cradle and then, as if that wasn't enough to satisfy him, he yanked the phone cord out of the wall as well. He swung round to face her then.

Uncharacteristically, Frankie shrank. Santino was white with rage beneath his golden skin, his spectacular bone structure hard as iron, shimmering golden eyes slamming into her with ferocious anger.

'That was a most educational call.' Santino's derisive distaste was unconcealed. 'You and your mother have to be the best double act since Bonnie and Clyde. She went to the press for you and now you are happily contemplating your divorce settlement. You conniving little vixen... I should've known you would concentrate on the prospect of eventual profit!'

Pale as milk, Frankie backed off a step. 'Santino...this is all a really ghastly misunderstanding. Mum *has* wildly overreacted, but I think that she honestly believed that she needed to try and protect me—'

'From whom? From *me*? Why should Della need to protect you from me in any way?' Santino demanded with seething bite.

'I never realised that Mum didn't believe me five years ago...about us,' Frankie muttered abstractedly.

'She doesn't even date because she distrusts all men, so I suppose I should have guessed that what happened to me would only make her more bitter. She always used to say that my father and Giles between them wrecked her life, and she thinks you did the same thing to me… Of course, in a way, you *did*—'

'Ensuring that you could live like a princess and attaching no strings to my generosity was…*wrecking* your life?' Santino thrust splayed brown fingers through his luxuriant black hair, his lean dark visage set in lines of outrage. Frankie flinched nervously as he growled something raw under his breath. He fixed burning golden eyes to her transfixed face. '*Sì*, perhaps in this instance the truth does lie where I least want to find it. I did wreck your life in the sense that you are now a twisted version of the woman you might have become.'

'I'm not twisted—'

Santino loosed a harsh laugh of disagreement. 'I gave you into the care of a greedy, selfish woman with her own agenda. If I'd kept you at least you would've hung onto a few morals!'

'I'm not suffering from any shortage in that department, I assure you!' Frankie thrust her chin up, angry colour starting to fire over her cheekbones.

Santino treated her to a slow, insolent sexual appraisal that froze her to the spot. Contemptuous eyes roamed over the deep valley of her breasts, now visible between the parting edges of the robe, to rest on the tantalising twin ripe curves that had been partially revealed. 'Even your lover doesn't ascribe to that belief…'

Frantically twitching the garment back into place and tightening the sash, Frankie said angrily, 'Matt is not and has never been my lover.'

Santino's expressive mouth twisted. 'He is certainly no gentleman if he shares your bed and then chooses to tell me how promiscuous you are.'

Struggling to swallow that insult, Frankie snatched in

a deep shuddering breath and then, without warning, it was as though a bright light exploded inside her head. She was sick and tired of being blamed for everyone else's mistakes, and his attack on her morals was the absolute last straw.

'So what if there have been loads and loads of men in my life?' Frankie flared with angry defiance, well aware that Matt had only made that crack because she had never dated any man for long and her short attention span had offended him, a man who saw that kind of behaviour as a peculiarly male requisite. 'That's none of your business, is it?'

A dark flush slowly rose to accentuate the rigid slant of Santino's slashing cheekbones. For the longest moment he stared at her, eyes as dangerous and cold as black ice. He said nothing.

Frankie broke the screaming silence with a jerky laugh of discomfiture. 'Right, so I'm a tart…big deal!'

But she was no longer able to meet Santino's unsettling gaze. Too late she saw that she had thrown down a gauntlet that he had refused to pick up. Childishly she had tried to shock and she had failed. 'Well, now that we've got that thorny question out of the way,' she continued stiffly, 'don't you think that we ought to be informing the police that I'm here and that there's been the most insane storm in a teacup over nothing?'

'I've already done that. The local police are on their way to confirm your presence…and very soon after that the paparazzi will arrive in their wake,' Santino breathed with grim assurance, already striding out of the room. 'We need to clear out of here fast!'

Unfreezing, Frankie trailed after him and hovered in the doorway of his office, listening to him rap out instructions at speed to someone on the other end of his mobile phone. 'This whole ridiculous mess is your fault,' she accused helplessly as he set the phone aside again. 'If you hadn't lured me out here and set me up with those villas, none of this would ever have happened. And when I go home, how am I supposed to explain all this and you to anybody? You saw how Matt reacted…he thinks this is a truly weird set-up—'

'Weird without sex, boringly conventional *with* it,' Santino slotted in with glancing savagery. 'I do believe it's time I did what I came here to do.'

He strode across to her and, without giving her the slightest hint of his intentions, bent and swept her lithely off her feet and up into his powerful arms.

'Santino…what on earth—?' Frankie gasped.

'I brought you here to put you in the marital bed and enjoy that exquisite body,' Santino reminded her as he started up the stairs with raw determination. 'And I'm still going to achieve that feat *before* we leave.'

'But the police are coming!' Frankie reminded him incredulously, too taken aback by his behaviour even to struggle.

'I think it'll take them quite a while to get here…and if it doesn't they'll have to wait.'

'Wait…while *we*…?' Frankie parroted.

'Why not?' Santino countered, kicking the bedroom door shut behind him and dropping her unceremoniously down on the bed in which she had slept alone yet again the previous night.

Frankie sat up, feverishly pushing flying strands of hair out of her eyes. 'Why *not*?' she repeated in a voice that shook with disbelief. 'Are you out of your mind?'

'No…if I told the typical Sard male that I have waited five years to take physical possession of my beautiful bride, they would probably drive back down the mountain and stay there for at least a month,' Santino breathed with sardonic bite. 'Aside from that, assuming you ultimately intend to be as vocal with the paparazzi as your mother, I wouldn't dream of depriving you of your juiciest source of revelation. No doubt you will be eager to flog every minute detail of the coming encounter to some sleazy tabloid when you get home again!'

'You've got absolutely the wrong idea about me...I wouldn't dream of talking about you to the press!'

'Just the way you swore at the *castello* that you wouldn't dream of taking my money?' Santino enquired with splintering and savage condemnation as he ripped off his shirt and dropped it on the floor. 'You continued to lie like a pro about your innocence all through the day. You came up with quite impressive explanations for almost every charge. You pleaded such complete ignorance and then, when I was on the very *brink* of awarding you a second hearing, you announced that you were in on the fraud from the very first day!'

The sight of Santino's bare brown hair-roughened chest drew Frankie's startled eyes like a magnet to iron filings. Turning pink, she looked away again and wet her taut lips with a snaking flick of her tongue. She was appalled by that masterly summing-up of her credibility in his eyes. Santino didn't trust a word she said, which wasn't surprising when she recalled the number of times she had changed her tune that day, before she'd finally shouldered Della's guilt in an effort to protect the older woman from the full onslaught of Santino's cold and deadly fury.

It felt like the worst possible moment to be suddenly wishing that she could now tell him the truth. Santino *had* to despise Della even more since he had heard her talking on the phone in that coy, calculating way. And, where once Frankie had lied to save her parent out of knee-jerk loyalty, now, ironically, she had a stronger motivation. Della might not be the ideal parent she had once longed to have, but today Frankie had learnt something that touched that sore place in her heart.

Evidently her mother had strongly sympathised with her daughter's misery five years ago, and would probably have done so more vocally had Frankie been prepared to confide more fully in her. Had that happened, their relationship might never have become so detached. In that one field alone, perhaps they had something in common.

'I am really not the person you think I am,' Frankie said shakily, tilting back her head again to look at Santino as she sat on the bed. 'I wish I could tell you something more than that, but just at this moment—'

'Just at this moment you would tell me anything it suited you to tell me.'

Breathless, and abruptly shorn of the ability to vocalise, Frankie focused on Santino as he stripped off a pair of silk boxer shorts and stood there magnificently nude and dauntingly uninhibited. The involuntary victim of a scorching attack of shyness, she removed her attention from the most eye-catching male attribute on display, struggling to swallow on shock and failing dismally. She had always wondered, and now she was receiving the opportunity to forever satisfy all female curiosity, and yet she found that she just couldn't look again because she was gripped by such intense self-consciousness.

'Santino…' she croaked.

'Forget it… I won't believe you have a shy or modest bone in your entire body,' Santino delivered fiercely, coming down on the bed and curving strong hands round her forearms to pull her towards him. 'Not a woman who boasts about the number of men she's had and offers me anything I want in bed without even pausing to consider the risk that I might want something she wouldn't be prepared to give—'

'Might you?' Frankie slotted in helplessly, bare inches away from shimmering golden eyes that seemed to burn over every inch of her exposed skin.

'What do you think?' Santino traded with silken scorn. 'I think possibly you could teach me a thing or two.'

'I'm not in the mood right now—'

'I'll put you in the mood, *cara*. I also think I should have tipped you head-first into the horse trough to sober up last night! You suck up sympathy like a vacuum cleaner, you always did, and you don't deserve my care and consideration.'

Releasing her arms, Santino tugged free the sash at her slender waist in one smooth movement.

The robe fell open. Frankie froze, breath feathering in her convulsive throat, heart racing so fast she felt light-headed.

Santino ran burnished and unashamedly hungry eyes over the enticing feminine curves he had revealed. He reached an assured hand up into her tumbling bright mane of hair and slowly, sensually drew her down onto the pillows. She arrived there with a stifled gasp, just in time to see him close one beautifully shaped hand over the pale swell of one full breast. She trembled, wide-eyed, shaken by both sight and sensation. The heat of his rawly masculine body against her cooler, slighter frame, even the fairness of her skin against his lean, sun-darkened length, was as instinctively enthralling as the expert fingers which rose to caress the pouting pink nipple.

A low, jerky sigh escaped her, her head falling back as the sweet ache of her sensitive flesh made her clench her teeth, blanking out her mind to everything but the power of sensation he possessed, and when he bent his dark head and delicately employed his teeth and his tongue on the same straining rosy bud she moaned out loud.

'What a temptress you are, Francesca,' Santino breathed in a tone of roughened discovery. 'You surrender yourself so completely to pleasure.'

The fog in her brain was pierced by sudden shame. Her lashes lifted again just as Santino pushed a supporting arm beneath her and eased her free of her robe, to cast it carelessly aside. He thrust the bedding back, tumbling her onto a crisp white cotton sheet scented with the faint evocative aroma of crushed rosemary.

Santino focused on her intently, his strong dark features taut. 'Rosemary for fertility—not a concern that I assume I need to consider with you…?'

Frankie's gaze was blank, inward-looking. A tide of burning colour washed over her skin because she wasn't listening; she was picturing herself just seconds earlier, a willing, wanton captive to what he could make her feel. And yet wasn't this what she wanted too? This driving hunger of the flesh satisfied so that she could be free again, free as she had never been in five long years? Inwardly she repeated the comforting mantra that had strengthened her only the day before. Making love with Santino would close this chapter in her life and then she would move on.

'And you still blush…a charming if deceptive consequence of that superb English-rose skin,' Santino contended, brushing away the top sheet she had automatically drawn over herself so that he could feast his attention upon her again.

Frankie stared up at him, as entrapped as if he had her in chains, shyness overpowered by her incredibly deep and strong craving for his admiration. It made her feel so good about herself, so happy. Breasts that had seemed too full for her slender stature, hips that had seemed too angular no longer mattered. Her own new and wondrous sense of perfection was born in that instant in Santino's deeply appreciative appraisal.

'You're exquisite, *cara mia*,' Santino murmured intently. 'At this moment, I don't care about anything else.'

'There *is* nothing else,' Frankie whispered, thinking that there would be just this one time and then they would part, for he had already referred to their leaving the village. A hazy image vaguely reminiscent of *Brief Encounter* seduced her with its drama and romance.

Her hand lifted and curved over a broad brown shoulder, fluttering in an instinctive wondering caress over smooth, taut skin covering a spectacular blending of bone and muscle. It felt so daring and yet so right, here in this bed and in this house, the world shut outside, just the way it might have been five years ago—just the way it *should* have been, she reflected helplessly. A spontaneous and natural event because she had never been infatuated, she had been deeply in love. And, just as then, looking at Santino melted her deep down inside. Her breathing fractured, her quivering body clenching on the all-pervasive sense of dissolving liquidity between her thighs.

'When you look at me like that,' Santino confided, his deep, dark drawl like abrasive sand on silk, 'I want to forget every preliminary I ever learned and fall on you like a sex-starved teenager.'

'Do you?' A dreamy smile of satisfaction curved Frankie's generous mouth, the last shred of uncertainty forgotten as she rejoiced in the sheer power of being a woman.

Santino leant over her and kissed her with a plundering urgency that both shook and excited her simultaneously. He wound a ruthless hand into her hair and held her captive, crushing her lips and invading her mouth with an erotic thoroughness that swiftly changed the status quo—because she became a creature of all feeling and no thought, dragged down into shivering excitement by his innate sensuality.

His hands were slightly rough against her softer skin, the knowing exploration of his fingers over her achingly tender breasts a tormenting pleasure as she strained helplessly up to him, her whole body awash with response and reaction to his every tiny move and caress. She felt dominated and confined and she liked it, and she laced her seeking fingers ecstatically into his thick black hair, holding him tightly to her.

He dragged himself free, shone an innately ruthless smile of satisfaction over her confused face. Her treacherous heart contracted in response.

He looked so dangerous, his slashing confidence unhidden. 'I'm not going anywhere, *cara*…your hunger is the one true gift you have to give me and the only thing you cannot lie about or control. The completeness of your surrender will be my triumph.'

Her stomach twisted, apprehension threatening to break through the unstoppable waves of hunger that controlled her as surely as he did. But with a soft taunting laugh Santino kissed her again, with all the fiery carnal expertise she was defenceless against. Her body burned, no longer willing or able to do her bidding. She was possessed by her own need, her own ever more desperate hunger. She wanted to sink inside his skin and share it with him.

His mouth teased at the straining buds of her swollen breasts. Slow, sure fingers skimmed through the damp curls that guarded her femininity to touch where only he had ever touched. The sensitivity of her flesh was almost unbearable and the explosive, agonising pleasure which seized Frankie in its relentless hold made her jerk and twist and whimper in mindless abandonment.

'You're so ready for me,' Santino groaned.

His lean, strong features harsh and intent in passion, he rose over her, lifting her trembling thighs back and settling himself fluidly between them. As she felt him, hot and urgent and alarmingly male against her tender entrance, Frankie gasped and tensed, and yet with every contrary fibre of her being she would have died of frustration had he stopped. Then he moved, and pleasure splintered into shocking pain as he thrust deep and a startled cry was wrenched from her.

For an instant Santino fell still. He surveyed her with

lancing golden eyes that scorched like flames over her hectically flushed and shaken face. 'If ever anyone got the punishment they deserved for lying...' he breathed, unexpectedly deepening his invasion with a powerful twist of his hips. 'I would have been slow and gentle if I had known the truth.'

So intent was Frankie on the alien intrusion wreaking such upheaval inside her tormentingly sensitised body, she barely caught his words. She was afraid to move until the pain faded, and then she gazed up at him in open surprise. 'It feels so strange,' she whispered.

'It gets to feel good,' Santino promised, with a reluctant laugh and a slanting, almost tender smile.

She couldn't imagine that, but then it was happening and suddenly she couldn't concentrate any more and that instant of control was wrested from her again. Her whole being centred on his every movement, over her, inside her, and the raw power of his possession filled her with wild energy and impatience. It was timeless, utterly absorbing, and she lived each second on an edge of excruciating all-encompassing craving and then she was splintering and shuddering, flung in shock to the furthest boundaries of pleasure. With a hungry growl of release, Santino followed her there, and when she surfaced from that drugging languor of satiation she found herself clutching him with a sense of feverish possessiveness.

As he freed her partially of his weight, Frankie yanked her clinging hands from him. That was inappropriate now that the lovemaking was over, she told herself.

Outrageously unfazed by any concept of what was or was not appropriate in the circumstances, Santino rolled her over and contemplated the sheet with impossible cool, not a muscle moving on his vibrantly handsome face. 'Welcome back, Santa Claus and the Tooth Fairy,' he mused softly. 'Miracles do happen against all the odds.'

Silence stretched and strained like an elastic band

drawn to breaking point. With a galling air of expectancy, Santino took in her outraged look and waited.

'I despise you for this most of all!' Frankie shot at him, feeling naked inside and out, exposed as a fraud where she had most wished to pose as an equal.

As she attempted to shoot off the edge of the bed, a strong hand restrained her. 'My bride, the fake seductress. No wonder you got drunk last night. You needed Dutch courage because you weren't quite sure what to do with me,' Santino breathed with grim amusement, stunning dark eyes raking over her hot and furious face.

Without even thinking about it, Frankie swung up a punitive hand and tried to slap him. Instead she found herself pressed back to the mattress, shocked by the speed of his reactions even as he glowered down at her. 'No,' Santino said succinctly. 'Lash out with your tongue, not your hands, and comfort yourself with the knowledge that I only hurt you because you lied to me.'

Shock surged back over the edge into sheer ungovernable rage. Frankie struggled to free herself from his strong hands and failed. 'Let go of me!' she railed at him, her strained voice breaking.

'My wildcat wife.' Santino surveyed her with a disturbing light of understanding in his shrewd assessment. 'When I crack the surface you are as hopelessly volatile as ever you were. Passion will always betray you—'

'Damn you, Santino…shut up!' she hissed.

'As long as I live, I will never forget you shouting across the lobby that day in Cagliari. ''You were mine,'' you screamed. ''Now I wish you were dead!'' And you meant every word of it,' Santino mused reflectively. 'If you had had a gun you would have shot me—because if you couldn't have me nobody else could be allowed to have me. In the space of a heartbeat, love turned to violent hatred…'

Shutting him out with her lashes, all temper quelled by the unbearably painful reminder of her devastation that day, Frankie said unsteadily, 'I want to get up and pack now.'

'Good idea,' Santino conceded, releasing her in a cool, almost careless movement, as if he could not quite understand why he should still have been holding her close. 'The helicopter should be here soon.'

'Helicopter?' she queried, and then she remembered the phone call he had made downstairs and muttered, 'Yes, of course.' A helicopter to whisk them away at speed to the airport, where they would each go their separate ways—for anything else was now impossible. The publicity, the huge furore Della had ignited would follow them both, and Santino naturally wouldn't want to encourage greater media interest by keeping her with him.

She ran a bath for herself and climbed in, wincing at the unaccustomed soreness she could feel. Herself and Santino? It was over, totally, absolutely and for ever over. She would never see him again. Frankie stared for a long, timeless moment into space, and then her eyes prickled hotly and stung and the tears surged up and gushed like a waterfall. Perfectly natural, grieving for the end of an era, she told herself feverishly, snatching up a towel and burying her face in it as a choking sob swelled up inside her constricted chest.

'Mourning your lost virginity?'

Startled by the interruption, Frankie dropped the towel in the bathwater. 'What are you doing in here?' she demanded strickenly.

'I need a shower…only one bathroom.' Making that reminder, Santino gazed down at her, hard dark eyes sharp enough to strip paint. 'If you want to say goodbye to your family in person, you had better hurry. Otherwise you can call them from Rome.'

'R-Rome?' Frankie repeated in a daze, pausing in the very act of plastering the soaking wet towel to her bare breasts. 'But I'm not going to Rome…'

'Oh, yes, you are,' Santino confirmed steadily. 'Where else did you think you might be going?'

'I thought…I thought we were heading for the airport and then splitting up… I thought I was going home—'

'You thought wrong. I haven't had my three weeks yet…and, by the way, the clock only started ticking when we climbed into bed an hour ago,' Santino imparted as he reached into the shower cubicle and switched on the water. 'You get your timesheet docked for nerves and insobriety.'

'You can't want to keep me with you after all the publicity there's been!' Frankie was reeling with renewed shock, a state that Santino appeared equal to keeping her in almost continually. The pressure of never really knowing what was likely to happen next was starting to wear down her nerves.

Santino shrugged out of his robe and let it fall to the floor, gloriously unconcerned by his nudity. '*Cara*…I don't care if I have to pitch a tent at the top of Everest. You're putting in your time…' He glanced back at her, classic profile hard and implacable. 'I can only hope that I don't live to discover that you're likely to be around even longer…'

'I beg your pardon?' Frankie whispered without comprehension.

'Unless I'm very much mistaken we just had sex without precautions.' Santino sent her a charged look, obsidian in its chilling gravity. 'When I asked you if I needed to worry about your fertility, I took your silence for confirmation that I *didn't* need to protect us both from that risk.'

'I don't remember you asking me anything of the sort!' Frankie gasped. 'You mean you didn't…? No, you didn't…' As she answered that question for herself her voice died away, and she shivered in the cold, clammy clasp of the sopping towel, gripped by panic at the threat of an accidental pregnancy by a male who despised her.

That she was actually married to that same male didn't seem remotely relevant.

'And if your misleading silence was less a mistake than a deliberate attempt to prolong a most profitable association with me…you've made a cardinal error which you will undoubtedly live to regret,' Santino assured her, jawline hard as iron.

An almost hysterical giggle feathered dangerously in Frankie's dry throat. She surveyed him with huge, unwittingly fascinated eyes. Right then she was wondering if the blood of the suspicious Borgias ran in Santino's veins. Here she was, still in shock at the realisation that there had been a misunderstanding and that they had made love without contraception, but Santino's serpentine reasoning processes were infinitely darker and more cynical than her own. He already suspected her of having deliberately deceived him into running that risk.

'I won't even dignify that accusation with an answer,' she returned tightly.

'Even if you prove to be pregnant, I will *still* divorce you,' Santino gritted with ferocious bite as he strode into the shower. 'Three weeks and you're out, bag and baggage…no matter what!'

'Santino…' Frankie breathed, and then she stopped because she heard the betrayingly emotional wobble affecting her diction. Reluctant to probe the complex and painfully confusing storm of emotions attacking her, she chose only to voice her impatience with his fatalistic conviction that one little oversight would unerringly lead to conception.

'I'm quite sure that any egg of mine would have more taste than even to consider an approach from anything with the Vitale signature on it…' Frankie countered curtly. 'In fact, I'm utterly convinced that right now your reproductive cells are fighting a pitched and losing battle in hostile territory and wishing very much that they had stayed home!'

'I can only hope…for both our sakes…that you're right,' Santino delivered rawly, ramming shut the doors on the corner cubicle with a suppressed violence that fully illustrated his mood.

As she clambered out of the bath, dashing tears from her eyes, Frankie scolded herself furiously for her own over-sensitivity. It was stupid to feel so totally gutted by Santino's appalled reaction to the risk that she might conceive. After all, how likely was it that they might be unlucky? And why *should* his attitude hurt and wound her? Why should it feel like the ultimate rejection? Goodness knew, she would be climbing the walls too if that misunderstanding of theirs led to such a consequence!

CHAPTER EIGHT

'BUT your passport is in the name of Caparelli, *signora*,' the portly little local police inspector remarked with a frown of surprise. 'Indeed it still carries the designation of a single woman.'

'Francesca applied for a British passport in her maiden name shortly before our marriage.' As Santino spoke, Frankie studied him covertly. He was sheathed in a stupendously well-cut pearl-grey suit that framed his broad shoulders, lean hips and long, long legs to quite spectacular effect, and she was finding it a really horrendous challenge to look anywhere else.

'Perhaps the continued use of Caparelli was intended as a security precaution?' the older man hazarded uncertainly, evidently aware of the kidnapping that had once occurred in the Vitale family. He returned the item to Frankie with a wry shrug of acceptance. 'It should be brought up to date now. Your face has been splashed all over the newspapers and the television screen. It is sadly ironic, *signor*…your illustrious family are famed for their zealous protection of their privacy but your wife couldn't walk down a street anywhere in Italy today without being instantly recognised as a Vitale.'

Santino tensed, his strong face darkening at the assurance. Frankie was certain he had to be appalled by that information. Discretion, yes, he had mentioned the necessity of discretion at their very first meeting in La Rocca, only then she had not grasped his true meaning because she hadn't had a clue that Santino belonged to one of the wealthiest and most newsworthy families in

Europe. Nor could she even believe as yet that she was really to fly to Rome with him.

'It's crazy to force me to accompany you back to Rome,' Frankie contended half under her breath as she watched the policeman climb back into his car, his subordinate, who had played no part in the interview, taking the wheel.

'When you steal a ride on someone else's rollercoaster, Francesca, you can't expect it to stop just because you find it scary that events are moving out of your control.'

Frankie lost colour at that perceptive stab, her stomach twisting. The tension between them nagged like toothache at her raw nerve-endings. The racket of a helicopter coming in low over the valley broke the silence and she turned towards the lounge window, eager to make use of any distraction. But long brown fingers closed with ruthless precision over one slim, taut shoulder and prevented her retreat.

Her head whipped round, tilting back to look up at Santino. 'I *am* in control!' she informed him doggedly, digging her unsteady hands deep into the pockets of her loose ankle-length summer dress. 'And I am not scared—'

'But you *should* be,' Santino emphasised, his rich, dark drawl feathering down her rigid spine like a dangerous storm warning that ironically both threatened and thrilled. Stunning dark eyes raked over her defensive face. 'For there is one weakness we do not share…unlike you, I will never be passion's slave. When it is time for us to part, what will you do if you find yourself possessed by a devastatingly strong need for our affair to continue?'

Imprisoned within inches of his lean, muscular body and painfully, newly aware of his erotic masculine power in a way that lacerated her pride and filled her with foreboding, Frankie stared up at him, appalled to feel a deep inner trembling begin and spread a terrifying woolly weakness through her lower limbs. 'I think I'd cut my throat!' she countered with fiery disdain.

Santino's mesmeric eyes glittered, his shapely, sensual mouth slashing into a reluctant smile of appreciation. 'Kill or cure, all or nothing…how little you have changed, *cara*. But unfortunately life rarely makes one's choices so simple.'

'It's always simple if you want it to be,' Frankie told him between gritted teeth as she fought the onslaught of that shattering sexual awareness. Her pulses were racing so fast she felt dizzy and her hands were balled into fists inside her pockets for fear that she might reach for him. Like a mindless addict she wanted to move closer and drink in the hot, achingly seductive scent of him, seek contact, actual *physical* contact to satisfy the treacherous craving that made her breath catch in her throat and her sensitive breasts tingle and swell.

A long forefinger stroked down the side of her face and her green eyes darkened and centred with compulsive intensity on the lean dark features above hers. 'Sexual hunger is never simple because we are not animals, mating without thought or feeling at nature's behest…how innocent you are in spite of your avarice. You can't even admit your own ignorance. But the higher you climb on that ladder of self-deception, the harder you will fall.'

His thumb grazed the corner of her full, tremulous lips and then almost lazily slid to probe within. Involuntarily her languorous eyes slid shut, her lips converging hungrily on that intrusive digit, the lancing bitter-sweet pain of that hunger shrilling through her slender frame, making every muscle fiercely taut with anticipation.

'And with the smallest encouragement…such a natural-born temptress,' Santino completed, his accent thickening as he closed one impatient hand over her hip to yank her closer.

The knocker on the front door sounded with thunderous urgency. Frankie almost leapt out of her skin. As her shaken eyes slowly opened, Santino was already striding out to the hall to answer the door. A powerfully built man in a dark suit, whom Santino addressed as Nardo, swept up the cases at the foot of the stairs. Of course, Frankie registered, like someone surfacing from a heavily drugged slumber, the helicopter had landed and it was time for them to leave.

She pressed moist palms to her hot cheeks. She had not meant to give Santino such power over her, had never dreamt that her surrender might weaken her defences even more. And he was wrong when he still called her innocent because she was no longer the optimistic fool who had fondly imagined that going to bed with Santino would magically exorcise her emotional turmoil.

'You'll visit again soon?' Maddalena pressed anxiously, as her great-aunts and grandfather stood waiting to see them off.

'Francesca's place is with her husband and Santino is a very busy man,' Teresa scolded her sister. 'Who else do you know who has to call for a helicopter because he can't spare the time to drive down the mountain?'

Her grandfather took her aside and treated her to a troubled and questioning look. 'Santino usually says his goodbyes personally.'

And the cruel weight of reality almost crushed Frankie then. Santino would not be returning to the village again. And the next time she visited she would come alone, bearing news which would hit her far from liberal-minded family hard. A broken marriage and a divorce in the offing. That would shame and distress her great-aunts and outrage and disappoint her grandfather, who had grown infinitely more fond and proud of Santino than he had ever been of his own unreliable and selfish son. And they would all blame her because she simply could not imagine them blaming Santino for anything...

Frankie fell asleep during the flight. When Santino woke her up, she glanced out through the window beside her and was thoroughly disorientated by the view, for they were certainly not at Rome's Fiumicino airport; the helicopter appeared to be surrounded by a boundless expanse of lush green grass.

'You look as messy as a child returning from a day on the beach,' Santino censured as he lifted her down onto solid ground again. He looked unusually tense. As he scanned the drowsy blankness of her face, his beautiful mouth tightened even more. He paused to brush straying strands of bright hair off her brow and make a somewhat pointless attempt to smooth down her badly creased cotton dress.

Smothering a yawn, Frankie let herself be walked at a smart pace across the lawn. Yes, it was a lawn, definitely a lawn—well, possibly more of a stretch of parkland really, she finally decided an instant before she fell to an abrupt halt to gape at the quite spectacular building basking in the late-afternoon heat about a hundred yards ahead of them.

'My home,' Santino advanced, a firm hand on her elbow urging her on.

'Your home? Where on earth are we?' she mumbled in a daze.

'About thirty miles from Rome. The paparazzi will not disturb us here. The estate boundaries are constantly patrolled and the surveillance technology which supports the security presence is of the highest calibre. A leaf doesn't drop from a tree at the Villa Fontana without someone knowing about it.'

Fascinated, Frankie absorbed the breathtaking beauty of the centuries-old country mansion before her. A two-storey central block with an elaborate but very pretty façade was flanked on either side by curved wings creating an inviting sunlit piazza to the front. At the great domed and arched entrance beyond, the longest limousine Frankie had ever seen sat with blacked-out windows.

'You're about to meet my parents,' Santino imparted without a flicker of expression, but his strong profile was taut. 'You should feel honoured. Evidently they have dragged themselves all the way from Switzerland to make their shock, horror and disapproval known.'

Catapulted with a vengeance back into full awareness, Frankie gulped. 'Your...*parents*?'

'Once you dreamt of meeting them,' Santino reminded her lethally. 'You imagined how you would exchange recipes and knitting patterns with my mother. You wondered if you should write to them to reassure them that I was being wonderfully well looked after. And how heartbroken you assumed my poor mother must be because she lived too far away to even attend her own son's wedding—'

'Don't remind me!' Frankie exclaimed, her lovely face burning with chagrin as they mounted the steps to pass under the entrance arch.

Through the open doors beyond they entered a magnificent long hallway adorned with marble pillars and statues in alcoves. Thoroughly intimidated by the grandeur, Frankie dropped her volume to that of a frantic whisper. 'All right, so I had about as much idea of your background then as a little green man landing from Mars, but I can't meet your parents now, looking like this!' She glanced down at herself to wonder in fierce frustration why she hadn't long since binned a dress that resembled a crumpled dishcloth after a few hours of wear.

'Francesca...it really wouldn't matter if you were a saint of stunning perfection and poise. They would find your very existence no more palatable,' Santino admitted with a wry twist of his mouth.

'Why didn't you warn me that your parents might be here waiting?'

'They rarely visit me. But scurrilous publicity involving the family name would appear to have a very enlivening effect upon them.'

'Look, you should deal with your parents on your own,' Frankie muttered. 'Not much point in getting them all worked up when I'm not staying around, is there?'

'That's my business, *not* theirs,' Santino decreed with harsh emphasis, and he curved an imprisoning arm against her spine.

An anxious-looking little woman in a smart black dress was stationed outside the last door to the left at the end of the hall. She burst into frantic, low-pitched Italian. Santino made smooth, soothing responses.

'My housekeeper, Lina. I'll introduce you later. Visitors who refuse all refreshment unnerve her, and my mother can be rather intimidating,' Santino confided in exasperation as he spread open the door on a very grand drawing room.

Her mouth dry as a bone, Frankie focused on the small, dark, exquisitely dressed older woman seated in a stiff-backed chair. 'Intimidating' was the word. The ice-blue of her suit matched her eyes, and Frankie finally saw the source of Santino's superb bone structure. A tall distinguished man with white hair turned from the windows. He held himself with the same unbending reserve and formality as his wife.

'Francesca…' Santino murmured flatly. 'Allow me to introduce you to my parents…Sonia and Alvaro.'

'I will accept no introduction,' Sonia Vitale asserted glacially. 'Explain yourself, Santino! How *could* you disgrace us by allowing your outrageous association with this woman to be exposed by the press?'

'We understood that this unfortunate affair had been buried some years ago,' Alvaro Vitale advanced.

'I made no such promise,' Santino countered levelly. 'Francesca is my wife and I expect you to treat her with all due respect and civility.'

Sonia Vitale ran coldly outraged eyes over Frankie. Her lip curling, she turned her imperious head away again in a gesture of lofty dismissal. 'I will never receive that woman into my home as my daughter-in-law.'

'Then you will not receive me either,' Santino responded harshly. 'And I shouldn't think that would be too great a sacrifice. After all, you only see me once a year at Christmas as it is.'

Frankie sent Santino an astonished glance and then focused on his mother again, shocked by the bitter hostility the older woman could not conceal when she looked at her son.

'You must see that this is an inappropriate marriage,' Alvaro Vitale intervened afresh. 'I intend no disrespect towards your wife, but on one count your mother must surely be excused her frank speech. Francesca's background scarcely equips her to take her place in our family—'

'We are not royalty, Papà,' Santino incised grimly.

'It is a waste of time to try to reason with you, Santino. You could never be anything other than a disappointment to me,' his mother condemned cruelly. 'But you betray your brother's memory with this insult of a marriage—'

Beside her, Frankie felt Santino's big, powerful frame tense like a cat about to spring, but a split second earlier she had felt him recoil from his mother's attack. She stiffened, fighting the most extraordinary urge to speak up in his defence.

His mother continued to survey him with cold condemnation. 'I would remind you that you will always walk in Rico's shadow, Santino. All that was once his has come to you. Honour should demand that you make sacrifices in his memory. And Rico would never have married a social inferior. Rico never once brought shame on the Vitale name. He was too proud of our ancestry.'

'I am not and I can never be Rico, Mamma,' Santino countered wearily, the long fingers resting on Frankie's slim hip biting painfully into her flesh.

Sonia Vitale rose from her chair. 'How you do love to state the obvious,' she responded cuttingly. 'You knew it was our dearest wish that you should marry Melina. Instead you have made a mockery of us all. When you can bring Melina to me as your bride, I will see you again…not before.'

Her husband moved forward, his strain now palpable in spite of his efforts to retain his impassivity. 'Santino…may I have a word with you in private?' he enquired. 'You will excuse us, Francesca?'

'I will wait in the car, Alvaro,' Sonia announced, and she swept past them all with her regal head held high.

Without even considering what she was about to do, her sole driving purpose one of furious incomprehension, Frankie pulled free of Santino's loosened grip and sped in his mother's wake, pausing only to jerk shut the drawing-room door behind her.

'Why don't you *love* him?' Frankie demanded fiercely of the older woman in the echoing hallway.

Sonia Vitale came to a startled halt and gazed back at Frankie over her shoulder in complete shock. 'I beg your p-pardon?' she murmured with an incredulous shake in her well-modulated voice as she turned. 'Santino is my son. *Of course* I love my—'

'No, you don't!' Frankie contradicted her, her eyes bright with condemnation. 'You look at him like you hate and resent him…you deliberately try to hurt him… All I want to know is why. *Why?* Santino is pretty damned wonderful in an awful lot of ways. He's clever and caring and honest. Most mothers would be really proud to have a son like that…'

Every scrap of colour draining from her still beautiful features, the older woman backed slowly away from her. A stunned and appalled look of confusion had blossomed in her eyes. 'How dare you attack me…how dare you say such things?'

Suddenly equally shattered by her own behaviour, Frankie froze and flushed a hot self-conscious pink. She could not even understand what had driven her into forcing such a confrontation. Out of nowhere had come this ferocious sense of angry protectiveness and it had sent her hurtling into pursuit like a guided missile, for certainly she hadn't stopped and thought about what she was about to do…no, not even for a sensible second. And what had she done now but pointlessly enrage Santino's mother more and make an already bad situation worse?

'So my son has married a real little fishwife who fights for him…like a vixen protecting her cub. But Santino wouldn't thank you for abusing me.' Sonia drew on her gloves in a series of jerky little movements that betrayed her distress and her eyes never once met Frankie's again. 'In fact he would devour you alive because naturally he *loves* and reveres his mother. And I see, not without some surprise after reading your mother's highly unladylike revelations in print, that you genuinely *do* love my son…but you are only a brief aberration in Santino's life and will fortunately soon be gone.'

Frankie flinched as if the smaller woman had slyly slid a knife between her ribs, but Sonia had already spun away from her again.

'You should have been his mistress, not his wife. Melina would have accepted that. We would *all* have accepted that,' Sonia imparted curtly. 'But it is too late for that resolution now. You have lost the anonymity so necessary to that position. When Santino tires of you, as he inevitably will, and turns back to Melina, you will see then that I am right, for you will lose him altogether.'

As the older woman walked away, Frankie reeled clumsily round behind one of the pillars and pressed her hot, damp forehead to the cold marble. She felt as if she had gone ten rounds with a champion boxer and her very flesh had been pummelled from her bones. No, she did not love Santino…no, *no*, she did not! She was a whole lot brighter than the teenager she had once been. Yes, maybe she was—maybe she was more worldly-wise, an inner voice conceded, but there was no denying that at the age of sixteen sheer gut instinct had prompted her to fix her affections on one hell of a guy.

Because Santino *was* one hell of a guy, although not in the mood he had been in since she had successfully convinced him that she was the lowest, greediest and most ungrateful female in existence. But as he *could* be, as he had once been, and as he had promised to be that very first day they met again in La Rocca, before everything had gone wrong, he was still so incredibly special and important to her.

Dear heaven, I *do* still love Santino, Frankie registered in horror. I have no hope of getting him out of my system. He's just *in* there…inside my heart…inside my head, as much a part of me as my own flesh.

In the midst of that unwelcome flood of self-revelation, Alvaro Vitale emerged from the drawing room and strode past, mercifully without seeing her lurking behind the pillar.

Looking very pale and feeling unusually uncertain of herself, indeed almost crushingly shy, Frankie finally moved back into the room the older man had vacated. Santino didn't notice her hesitant entry and hovering stance about twenty feet from him. He was pouring himself what looked like a pretty stiff drink. Cradling the whisky tumbler in one lean brown hand, he strode restlessly over to the windows and stood there, wide shoulders rigid with livewire tension, long legs braced slightly apart.

Her dazed eyes roamed over his arrogant dark head and that bold, strong profile silhouetted against the light. How could she love a male capable of ruthlessly using her body to satisfy lust alone? How could she love a man who could separate all emotion from sex and without conscience play on her inexperience, susceptibility and, cruellest of all, her deep fear of being out of control?

Oh, so easily, she answered for herself. For this was the dark side of Santino's powerful personality and forceful temperament, a side he had never shown her before but which she should always have known existed. He could not have borne to let her go unpunished and he could not forgive greed or deception. Strong men had strong principles. And without those principles she would have found Santino infinitely less attractive.

She cleared her throat gruffly and asked the first question which came to mind. 'Who is Melina?'

Santino glanced almost unseeingly at her and then away again, his preoccupation patent. 'A friend...as dear as a daughter to my mother.'

The worst of Frankie's tension evaporated. Not an explanation couched in terms likely to drive her mad with jealousy, she thought with a sensation of powerful relief. 'And Rico...? He was your brother?' she prompted tautly as Santino's dark head whipped instantaneously back to her, his beautiful dark eyes filled with a deep, tormented sadness and defensive bitterness.

'You know, you never, ever mentioned having had a brother,' Frankie remarked, choosing her words very carefully but wholly focused on a need to know what could bring such an expression to Santino's face.

'Rico died the year before I met you. He was ten years older than me,' Santino admitted grudgingly.

'What happened?'

For several thunderously tense seconds Santino fixed his attention on the window again. Then he shrugged with something less than his usual fluidity. 'Rico took me climbing in the Alps. The climb should have been abandoned on the second day. Conditions were poor and the weather was changing. But Rico—' He breathed stiltedly. 'Rico was a daredevil determined not to be beaten by the elements. An avalanche hit us. He saved my life at the cost of his own.'

'Oh, God…' Frankie framed sickly, out of her depth with words. What she most needed was the freedom to rush across the room and wrap comforting arms around him, but she was utterly terrified of the rejection she was convinced she would receive. 'That…that must have devastated your family—'

'*Sì*…the wrong son came back down the mountain—'

'Don't say things like that,' Frankie begged with a superstitious shiver. 'If your parents somehow left you with the idea that you were more expendable than your older brother, that could only have been an accidental result of their grief and—'

Santino dealt her a winging look of contempt. 'Tell me, were you or were you not present when Sonia was delivering her opinion of my worth in comparison to my late brother's?'

Frankie couldn't meet his gaze. She shifted awkwardly.

'And Rico *was* a wonderful man. My mother worshipped the ground he walked on. Hell, so did I!' Santino gritted. 'He was an unparalleled success at being all things to all people. When he died he left a great yawning hole in our lives and family unity vanished. I found myself being treated like the living dead. My mother could not forgive me for surviving at Rico's expense.'

Since that was more or less Frankie's estimate of Sonia Vitale's feelings as well, she averted guilty eyes from his. Santino would naturally scorn empty protests.

And for the first time she understood what might have drawn him so frequently to his great-uncle's isolated village in Sardinia. Father Vassari had been a kind and practical man. Santino had been treated like a pariah by his parents while he was still only a teenager. He must've been comforted by the old man's continuing affection, and no doubt his reassurance that Rico's death had been in no way his fault.

She was warmed by that image but troubled and hurt by it too, for once *she* had eagerly shared her every anxiety and fear with Santino. Yet he had never told her about his brother, never once risked burdening her with anything she might not have been able to handle. More than everything else that underlined how unequal their relationship had been then. He had put her needs and concerns ahead of his own. Always. He had been the giver, she the taker...and the long-overdue acknowledgement shook Frankie to her very depths.

'All of a sudden you're very quiet,' Santino remarked softly.

Squirming with discomfiture, Frankie lifted her bright head again. Santino was already crossing the room to her. Unsettled by his sudden proximity, threatened by her new awareness of how much she loved him, she collided involuntarily with fiercely intent dark golden eyes.

'But the act of confession must indeed be good for the soul,' Santino informed her with husky conviction as he stretched out confident hands to ease her into intimate connection with his hard, muscular frame. 'Or perhaps it is the wealth of compassion you contrive to suggest with those wonderfully eloquent green eyes. Whatever... *Dio*... I have an overwhelming need to lose myself now in sexual oblivion!'

CHAPTER NINE

'SANTINO...?' Frankie gasped breathlessly, taken aback by the volatile charge of sexual hunger in his brilliant gaze.

'You want me too,' Santino groaned, backing her up against the door without hesitation and dropping his dark head to press his mouth with burning eroticism to the sensitive skin of her throat. He sent a shiver of such electrified heat through her slender length that her legs shook and threatened to crumple beneath her.

'Don't you, *cara*?' he prompted with blatant assurance.

'Yes...' she muttered unsteadily, painfully conscious of her inability to resist him. 'Yes...'

Santino muttered something raw and husky in Italian and closed his hands over the swelling curve of her hips, spreading his muscular thighs to bring her into contact with the rampant thrust of his erection. As he trembled against her, answering fire sprang up low in her belly. Her entire body burned, infused with a surging, desperate need she could not fight.

He skimmed sure hands down her quivering thighs to part them and raised her dress with summary masculine impatience. Expert fingers teased the heated core of her through the thin barrier of her briefs and he vented a husky sigh of satisfaction as he discovered the dampness she could neither control nor conceal. Frankie shivered and shook with excitement and moaned deep in her throat, clutching helplessly at him for support. And then her dark lashes lifted and over his bent shoulder she focused on a tiny ice-blue handbag sitting like an unexploded bomb on a nearby table.

'Your mother's left her handbag behind!' she gasped strickenly.

Santino abandoned his erotic assault on the molten responsive heat he was engaged in exploring and slowly, very slowly lifted his dark head again. His eyes were as blank and uncomprehending as the blacked-out windows of his parents' limousine.

'Her bag...over there!' Frankie raised a shaking hand to point at the offending article. 'She could walk back in here again at any minute!'

Santino's lush black lashes swept down and then up again. He focused on her and his fingers slowly, reluctantly loosened their grip on her dress to let the hem fall again. He snatched in a shuddering breath, dark colour igniting over the taut slant of his superb cheekbones.

Frankie trembled, embarrassed by what she had almost allowed to happen between them. 'Maybe we should go upstairs,' she muttered unevenly.

Santino stepped reluctantly back. The silence hummed. She opened the door with a fumbling hand and finally worked up the courage to turn her head and look at him again. In a driven motion he looped a punitive hand into her tumbled hair and took her mouth with speaking passionate brevity. As he drew away from her again, eyes ablaze with hunger, his breathing audibly fractured, she very nearly snatched him back into her arms.

All of a quiver, she started walking across the hall and up the spectacular staircase. A masculine hand closed possessively, impatiently over her clenched fingers. On the semi-circular landing, she stole a glance at him. It was a mistake...or *was* it? For it was a mistake that made Santino reveal the strength of his own desire all over again. He succumbed to the apparent temptation and encouragement of that one little glance by closing his arms round her so tightly she could barely breathe, crushing her to him and kissing her until her head swam. The merest persistence might well have persuaded her that there was nothing remotely wrong with making love in a corridor.

But he jerked back from her then with a growling sound of frustration. 'Only this morning you were a virgin. I should be making allowances for that…I'm not.'

She met burning golden eyes and knew she was utterly enslaved.

'I want you so much I am in agony,' Santino gritted unevenly.

Incapable of speech, she nodded like a submissive marionette.

In silence, he snatched her up into his powerful arms and strode at speed down the corridor. He set her down in a bedroom but she had no time to absorb the newness of her surroundings. Santino was unzipping her dress, tugging it down her arms, releasing the front catch on her bra, and, without even waiting for either garment to drop away, he brought up his hands to hungrily enclose the pouting swell of her bare breasts.

She caught their reflection in a tall cheval-glass as she strained helplessly back into the hard, virile heat of his powerful physique. As he massaged her achingly responsive flesh and played with the throbbing pink buds desperate for his attention, she looked wanton, abandoned. And even as she writhed in tormented pleasure she stared, watching his dark, passionately intent face above hers, learning for the first time that she had power too, the power to make Santino crave her like a drug—the power to make him *need* her…?

Intoxicated by that knowledge, she twisted round in his arms and blindly sought his sensual mouth again for herself. His tongue stabbed between her lips, flicked over her tender palate and drove her wild. As her knees sagged she clung to him, and he tumbled her down on the bed behind her, following her there without once freeing her swollen mouth.

'*Per amor di Dio*…you're a witch…this isn't how it was supposed to be!' As Santino wrenched her from the folds of the dress still crumpled round her waist, Frankie flinched from that snarling intonation. Stunning dark eyes alight with splintering hostility clashed with hers. And then, insane even as it seemed to her in that split second of stark confusion, he kissed her again with the kind of drowning erotic thoroughness that plunged her back into sensual oblivion.

Impatiently dispensing with the silky panties which still clung to her slender hips, Santino wasted no time in rediscovering the unbearably hot, moist welcome awaiting him. With an exultant growl, he pushed back her thighs and came over her like a conqueror to thrust with urgent, forceful hunger into the heart of her yielding body.

Frankie cried out, her spine arching on a relentless surge of excitement. He was wild for her and she was hopelessly out of control. For tormenting minutes of terrifyingly intense pleasure, he drove her ruthlessly to satisfaction. The explosive, blinding shock waves of climax hurtled through every fibre of her being and totally wiped her out.

The first thing she noticed after that was the speed with which Santino jerked away from her. A sudden chill cooled her bare damp skin and she was filled with a devastating sense of disorientation and loss, because what she craved at that instant was for him to hold her tight. Then the screaming silence registered. Slowly she opened her eyes on an unfamiliar ceiling. Her gaze crept almost fearfully down the walls and found Santino. Disturbingly, he was still fully dressed.

He moved back to the foot of the bed, where she was spread out like a recently plundered human sacrifice. She was in shock, ravaged by the primal hunger of his possession. Santino was strikingly pale beneath his naturally golden skin. In that awful silence he stared down at her as if he wasn't quite sure how she had got there, or indeed who had brought her to such a state. And then those beautiful dark eyes filled with a mortifying mix of stark regret and compassion.

In an impatient movement, he snatched up a silk-fringed throw from a nearby chair and covered her shivering body with it. But out of sight was very obviously not out of mind. Dense black lashes screening his gaze, Santino breathed raggedly, 'I'll run a bath for you.'

He got about twelve feet away before Frankie unglued her tongue from the roof of her mouth to mutter chokily, 'Why don't you try drowning yourself in it?'

Rolling onto her side, she curled up into a tight ball. All of a sudden she felt like a whore he had picked up and now wanted to throw out. He was ashamed of himself, so therefore she had to be ashamed of herself too. Where had she ever got the stupid idea that his physical desire for her body could be a cause for celebration?

'I'm starting to feel like a split personality,' Santino confessed in an abrupt and charged undertone. 'I have never before fallen on a woman like a ravening beast...'

Nor had his ego rejoiced in the force of his own rapacious sexual hunger for her, she recalled numbly.

'I know you enjoyed it, but—'

At that undiplomatic reminder, Frankie reared up to face him again. 'Get out of here!' she screamed at him full blast.

Santino surveyed her in frustration and fanned out his long fingers in eloquent emphasis. 'That won't solve anything...and it would make me feel worse.'

'Good!' Frankie shot back, tears erupting without warning to pour down her cheeks.

On familiar ground with that development, Santino dropped down beside her and framed her distraught face between inexpressibly gentle hands. His vibrantly handsome features were stamped with remorse. 'I wanted to punish you...I really did want to punish you. But when I looked at you a minute ago I saw the teenager who once loved me, and you really don't look very much older now. No matter what you have done, it *was* only money and I *am* an excessively wealthy man,' he conceded grimly. 'But I wish I could go back to that day in the café at La Rocca and freeze time—'

'Y-yes,' Frankie stammered, shaken that the exact same thought which had occurred to her should now be occurring to him.

Santino's eloquent mouth quirked. 'Although, to be honest, I'm not sure it would've helped. It was your lies which enraged me most. I have a terrible temper. I'm not a very forgiving person...yet somehow all that anger has suddenly drained out of me. So I was disappointed in you, *deeply* disappointed...' He still felt the need to stress that, but a broad shoulder shifted in a fatalistic shrug of acceptance.

'But what if I wasn't really guilty of having taken all that money?' Frankie muttered in an impulsive rush. Having been hanging off his every word, she was on the very brink of confessing the truth, because it really hurt that he should still think of her as a liar, a cheat and a thief. Indeed all she needed to prompt her into telling all was a little sympathetic encouragement. 'S-suppose...I mean, suppose I was just trying to protect Mum?'

As he listened, Santino's lean face hardened and darkened again like a threatening thundercloud. 'Don't be childish, Francesca. You can't magically remake my image of you by taking refuge behind *more* lies,' he warned her with harsh impatience, misreading her motivation in having asked such loaded questions.

'I know, but I—'

'Listen to me,' Santino cut in with warning gravity. 'If it wasn't for your involvement in that financial deception, I'd have had your precious mother charged with fraud and banged up in custody by now! Believe me, it goes very much against the grain to let her escape that punishment, but I can't put her in the dock without putting *you* right up there beside her.'

Registering that her lie—her false confession of having deliberately conspired with Della to defraud him—was the only thing that appeared to stand between her mother and a probable prison sentence, Frankie dropped her eyes fearfully again and pinned her tremulous mouth shut, grateful she hadn't said enough to arouse any real suspicion that she might not be guilty as charged. It was dauntingly obvious to her that Santino, assured of her own lack of complicity in the crime, would without hesitation go ahead and prosecute her dishonest parent.

'Wise decision.' Santino complimented her on her silence. 'You have to face up to what you did…but that doesn't mean that you can't change.'

Ducking free of his hold and rubbing at her swollen eyes, she sighed heavily. 'I guess not…'

'You're still my wife and I am responsible for your well-being,' Santino continued more gently. 'That definitely shouldn't encompass reducing you to a sobbing heap on my bed. I should've controlled my desire for you.'

'Yes… I mean, *no*… I—' Meeting the questioning look in Santino's clear, frighteningly intelligent gaze, Frankie shrank and lowered her eyes again, terrified of revealing too much. What had provoked her distress was his apparent rejection of her in the aftermath of that shatteringly intense bout of intimacy.

'I imagine you're rather sore,' Santino murmured ruefully. 'And sex should always be equally pleasurable for both partners. I should never have put my need ahead of your capacity for enjoyment.'

'Stop talking down to me,' Frankie urged in growing embarrassment. 'I knew what I was doing too.'

'But you don't…that's the trouble—that's the problem,' Santino contradicted her almost fiercely, slapping down her challenge before it could even get off the ground. 'You just do what you feel like doing at any given moment. I swear that in all your life you've never looked more than thirty seconds forward into the future! And that recklessness is like a contagious disease that has spread to afflict me as well…but with me it stops, here and now!'

Having delivered that character assessment with the speaking incredulity and censure of a male who regarded her impulsive spontaneity as a highly dangerous weakness likely to lead to dire consequences, he sprang fluidly upright and strode away from her with determination. 'I'll run you a bath and have an evening meal sent up. You must be hungry…I know I am.'

Frankie scrambled off the bed, secured the vibrant blue throw with a knot above her breasts and hurried across the room to lodge herself in the doorway of the breathtakingly luxurious bathroom. She watched him turning on the gold taps above a big oval-shaped tub and his every measured graceful movement enthralled her. Indeed every facet of Santino enthralled her quite unashamedly now that she had admitted to herself that she was still head over heels in love with him.

Had that gorgeous black hair always flopped over his brow like silk when he bent down? Did any other male possess such wondrously shapely and erotically assured hands? She felt the deep, intimate ache of his possession with instinctive pride. Whether he had liked it or not, Santino *had* needed her, and similiarly, it seemed, Santino *could* be passion's slave.

So he wasn't exactly happy about that reality just at this moment, but that wild bout of lovemaking had acted like some sort of catharsis on him. That chilling anger and detachment had gone. She had the Santino she remembered back and, dear heaven, he was so perfect it was all she could do to restrain herself from hurling herself ecstatically into his arms. He could be so tender, so caring. There he was, running a bath for her. He had even admitted himself to have been in the wrong. So many men found that impossible.

She really had picked a winner at sixteen. If only she could make him feel the same way *this* time…if only she could make him fall in love with her within the space of three weeks. Please, God, she prayed, fervently promising that if she got to hang onto Santino she would try never to ask for divine intervention again.

Santino straightened to find himself the sole focus of her utterly mesmerised attention. Slight colour burnished his superb cheekbones, stunning dark eyes veiling fast. 'Don't look at me like that,' he breathed very, very quietly.

'Like what?' Frankie was dizzy with the overpowering strength of her emotions and the amount of restraint it took to keep her distance from him.

Santino expelled his breath in a stark hiss. 'Having a good time in bed doesn't naturally mean that I love you or that you love me, *piccola mia*…'

Even softly voiced, and couched with that old endearment, the message still went home with the force of an axe attack on a vulnerable target. Frankie went white. Her gaze slewed to the water shimmering in the depths of the tub. 'I know that,' she tried to say with a light, dismissive laugh, but somewhere between her throat and her lips the laugh got horribly strangled and emerged like a discordant squeak.

'Right now, you don't know what you're feeling,' Santino informed her arrogantly. 'A long time ago you were infatuated with me…and now I've become your very first lover—'

'There was no stopping you!' Frankie reminded him helplessly.

'But if I had known you were a virgin, if you had

been honest with me, Francesca…I would never have touched you,' Santino countered with that brand of deadly sincerity that struck like a cobra when it was least welcome. 'When I believed that you were experienced, demanding the wedding night I had never had did not seem such a big deal.'

Frankie crossed her arms in a jagged motion, tucking shaking hands out of sight. 'No big deal…oh?' Even to her own ears, her voice sounded unnaturally shrill, which wasn't surprising when she felt as if she was dying by inches with every word he spoke.

'Possibly that wasn't the best choice of words,' Santino conceded, his hard jawline clenching. 'But you did go out of your way to convince me that you had had other lovers… Francesca, this really isn't a conversation I want to have with you right now. I think what we both need is a little breathing space from each other.'

That news could only devastate her. She could feel her brittle control over her tumultous emotions breaking up. 'I see…yes, I really *do* see—in spite of my lack of sexual sophistication. You're the kind of creep who has one-night stands and vanishes like Scotch mist before dawn!'

'How would you know? *Dio mio*…you've never had anyone else to compare me with!' Santino launched at her rawly.

Frankie's spine was planted so hard up against the tiled wall, she was convinced she would bear the impressions of the lines of grouting for the rest of her life, but she couldn't have stayed upright without that support.

Santino slowly shook his darkly handsome head and rested steady dark eyes on her. 'And possibly I'm not sorry to know that… But what I'm trying to say is that—'

'You've come to your senses now…and you've had what you wanted, so get lost?' Frankie slotted in with distaste and pain. 'There, I've said it for you and saved you the trouble of saying anything!'

At that assurance, Santino's facial muscles tensed with fierce anger. He raised his arms high in a movement that fully illustrated his wrathful impatience and dropped them again. Scorching dark golden eyes struck hers. 'You're so bloody melodramatic! Listen to yourself,' he grated. 'How the hell could I say such things or even *think* them? Not only are you my wife, you might even be pregnant with my child!'

'Oh, not *that* again.' Frankie studied her bare pink toes as they tried to curl like strained claws into the immaculate tiled floor. It stopped her whole body from drooping. It stopped her lashing out at him in an agony of pain for telling her yet more that she didn't want to hear.

'Can you tell me it isn't an even greater possibility now? *Santo cielo*...I couldn't even wait long enough to get my clothes off; do you think I had the presence of mind to protect you?' Santino demanded rawly.

'I want my bath,' Frankie announced, staring at the tub as if it might yet provide an escape hatch to another world, because it was devastatingly clear that Santino just could not wait to escape from her. 'And then I'm going home to London where I intend to go for the fastest divorce on record.'

Temper in check again, Santino dealt her a fulminating look. 'You will go nowhere. I'll use my city apartment for a couple of days. As I pointed out, neither of us is sufficiently grounded in calm or reality at this moment to be rational.'

Frankie had already turned away. 'Just go, then!' she urged him feverishly.

'Look at me...'

'I don't want to...I just want to be alone now—'

Santino strode forward and curved strong hands over

her rigid shoulders. 'I can't leave you feeling like this, *cara*.'

Frankie yanked herself free of his hold and stalked away from him. 'Stop treating me like some overgrown helpless child. I may be much more emotional than you are but I *am* an adult!'

'You don't always behave like one.'

Frankie spun in outrage and found Santino still far too close for comfort. Planting her hands on his broad chest, she gave him an aggressive shove away from her. As the backs of his legs collided with the low rim of the tub, he uttered a startled growl and overbalanced. He fell backwards into the water with a huge splash.

Stunned, Frankie simply stared, and then hysterical giggles clogged up her throat. Santino flung her a look of seething black fury, planted two powerful hands on the ceramic edge and launched himself back onto the tiled floor. 'If you were a man, I would knock you through that wall for that!' he roared at her full blast.

Frankie covered her convulsing mouth. His suit was plastered to him like a second skin and the floor was flooded. In hauling himself out with such force he appeared to have brought half the bathwater with him. 'It was an accident,' she breathed shakily. 'It really was. I didn't mean for you to fall in—'

'I am *out* of here!' Santino raked with the slashing emphasis of one forceful brown hand. 'And I will not be back until you convince me that you can behave like a grown-up!'

The grown-up without the sense of humour stalked dripping from the bathroom, slammed the door on her, slammed the door on the bedroom… And Frankie? Frankie soaked all the towels mopping up the water and dully appreciated that Santino wasn't perfect after all. He hadn't been joking about that temper. And, sitting there on the floor in lonely silence, she was too shell-shocked by that old, horribly familiar sense of agonised rejection to even begin to move beyond that stage.

CHAPTER TEN

FRANKIE reached several conclusions within the following thirty-six hours. She paced the floor and cried and slept in frenetic bouts without once leaving Santino's spacious bedroom suite.

Infuriatingly, she was constantly interrupted by the almost continuous proffering of healthy meals, regular snacks and drinks brought by the household staff. Acquainted with her habit of holing up to brood, and doubtless cruelly aware that it might be difficult to grieve with proper passion when one had to keep on opening the door to face other people, Santino had evidently left instructions that she was to be fed and watered on the hour, every hour. She was wholly unappreciative of being physically deserted but having her 'well-being' controlled from a convenient distance.

She had found Hamish, her childhood teddy, seated on an open shelf in Santino's dressing room. He was sadly tatty but he still wore his tartan scarf. She hugged the old toy to her as if he was her best friend. She acquainted herself with every single item of clothing Santino kept at the Villa Fontana and was not once tempted to slash anything to shreds.

Santino was gone. She was miserable, bereft, tormented by loss and loneliness. The light had gone out of her life. She knew it was melodramatic to feel like that, but that was how she felt and there wasn't much she could do about it. In the grip of her emotional high she was wretchedly aware that she had made some very foolish assumptions. Santino had offered her three weeks and it looked as if one shattering day had been more than enough to satisfy him. Her swansong, she thought painfully, and an insultingly brief one.

His sole reason for wanting her to remain here in Italy for the present appeared to relate to his fear that he might have fathered a child on her. Presumably, when she was able to reassure him on that point, he would be happy for her to leave. She refused to think of the possibility that she might not be able to give him that reassurance. She was wretched enough without subjecting herself to the imagined horrors of finding herself pregnant by a male who didn't want to be her husband and who certainly didn't want to be saddled with the burden of an inconveniently fertile wife he was keen to divorce.

No, Santino didn't love her and obviously he never, ever would, because, heaven knew, if he'd been even slightly susceptible he should've fallen in love with her a long time ago. Clearly he saw her as obsessive and excessive. He was her opposite in every way. Intellectual, self-disciplined, coldly logical when challenged and emotionally reserved...at least in the love department...but he could just about cope with 'fond', she conceded grudgingly.

When Santino did marry again, it would probably be to someone like that blonde she had seen him with in Cagliari five years ago. A classically lovely woman, elegant and poised, around his age and therefore well past the stage of immature urges and inappropriate behaviour.

Someone who would smile sweetly when he got patronising, controlling or domineering. Someone who would let him have the last word. Someone who would never dream of laughing when he fell in the bath in the middle of an argument. Someone equipped with the blue-blooded background necessary to become an acceptable member of the Vitale family. Santino might have told his father that the Vitales were not royalty, but for all that he lived like a king.

The first package arrived with her breakfast tray on

the second day. She pulled off the giftwrap and found herself looking at a framed cartoon of a man who had fallen into a bath. He was the very picture of injured dignity. And along the bottom, in Santino's forceful black scrawl, it said, 'As well as the temper, I confess to a tendency to take myself rather too seriously…'

For a stunned moment Frankie gaped at it. It had been a very long time since Santino had used his artistic talent to amuse her. Then she started to laugh and she got out of bed to have a shower and wash her hair.

The second package arrived mid-morning. Another cartoon featuring a bath scene, but this time with a figure that was recognisably herself starring as the victim of an accidental drenching, and she was screeching blue murder about getting her hair and her clothes soaked. Frankie wasn't quite so quick to laugh at that scenario because it forced her to admit that, had their roles been reversed, she would've been every bit as furious as he had been.

Typical Santino; he gave with one hand and slapped you down with the other. She groaned but then she smiled. After that she got dressed in a light green shift dress that she usually wore only for dressy occasions. When she heard the helicopter, she was already expecting it and planning to greet him with her brightest smile. Santino, ever the polished diplomatist, had smoothed over raw feelings with innate charm. Even at a distance he manipulated her, but possibly on this occasion, when she did feel out of her depth, it was for the best. All she had left now was her pride and the inner prayer that she could now be as casual and cool as he would be.

She was waiting in the hall when Santino strode into the villa. Clad in a lightweight beige suit of sensational cut, complemented by a white shirt and a burgundy silk tie, he stole the very breath from her lungs. It was as if thirty-six hours without Santino had dimmed her memory and, seeing him again in the flesh, she was simply bowled over by his dramatic dark good looks, his commanding height and fantastic build. She just stared, utterly appalled by the huge, unstoppable wave of love and lust that washed over her.

'I missed you,' Santino admitted, running brilliant dark-shadowed eyes over her stiff, defensive face. 'I *really* missed you.'

Even though it was a little late for the greeting speech she had planned, because he had got in first, Frankie's mind was now so blank she still seized on that speech in desperation. 'I bet your heart sank when you saw me standing here waiting like some pantomime wife hovering eagerly for hubby's return,' she reeled off at accelerated speed and with a frantically wide smile. 'But I thought, in the circumstances, it would be kind of funny—'

'Funny?' Santino's initial smile was beginning to freeze slightly round the edges.

'Like black joke funny?' Frankie pressed brightly. 'Because I don't know about you but I'm so relieved we're back to being just friends again. You have to admit that we really couldn't connect on any other level because we've got nothing in common...except the bed thing—and that was really only mutual curiosity that sparked a couple of fun encounters. You know...not something anybody adult would take seriously.'

Santino strolled round behind her and her brows pleated as she began to turn to see what he was doing. 'What are you—?'

'I was just looking to see if there was a key in your back,' Santino confided drily. 'And then possibly I could switch you off because you are thumping with great tactless hobnailed boots over some very sensitive areas and I've only been home for thirty seconds.'

Frankie swallowed convulsively.

'Maybe if I walk outside again and we run this scene

afresh you could do the pantomime wife thing,' Santino suggested flatly.

'What do you want from me?' Frankie wailed then.

'I just want you to be you.'

'I don't understand…' she muttered.

Santino closed a long arm round her painfully taut shoulders and slowly walked her through the double doors that opened out into the loggia which ran along the rear of the villa. 'It's not important, *cara*. The fault is entirely mine. I shouldn't have left you alone for so long.'

Every treacherously susceptible sense urged Frankie to snuggle into that arm like a purring cat, but she wouldn't even let the back of her head brush against his shoulder. 'Actually, I appreciated the time alone…and your cartoons made me laugh…but I really just want to get back to my own life now…OK?'

'No, that's out of the question,' Santino said instantaneously.

'Why on earth should it be?' Withdrawing hurriedly from the shelter of his arm, Frankie glanced up at him, but she learnt nothing from the nonchalant calm stamped on that lean, strong face. She walked from the shaded loggia with its comfortable seating areas into the beautiful secluded gardens. There she came to a halt in front of a softly playing fountain.

'You're thinking about the pregnancy thing again, aren't you?' she muttered finally.

Santino dealt her a rueful smile. 'As opposed to the bed thing?'

'Be serious…' She was struggling to barricade her heart from the stunning effect of a casual smile which could send threatening shock waves of response through her. 'It's highly unlikely that we'll be unlucky.'

'That depends on your interpretation of lucky. When will you know?' Santino enquired lazily.

She tensed and shrugged. Teresa's prudish attitude to

all bodily functions had left its mark during Frankie's adolescence. 'Sooner or later...but don't ask me how soon or how late because I'm not sure.'

As that particular brief monthly event had never interfered in the slightest with Frankie's routine, she didn't bother to keep a note of dates and could only dimly recall that the last one had been two or three weeks earlier.

'We're not short of time,' Santino responded with staggering cool. 'And it's pointless to worry about something we have no influence over.'

'You've certainly changed your tune.'

'Maybe I've warmed up to the idea of being a father...maybe I might even be disappointed if you aren't pregnant,' Santino murmured rather tautly.

That amazing suggestion left Frankie with a dropped jaw. She spun away, feverishly striving to work out what good reason he could have to say such a thing. And then the proverbial penny dropped. 'You don't believe in abortion, do you?'

Right there in front of her, Santino froze. 'Surely you weren't thinking along those lines?'

She shook her head, fascinated by his inability to conceal his relief. Then her own face fell. Now she knew *why* he was being so sincere and pleasant. He was intent on improving relations between them in advance of them finding out. Very practical and sensible, she thought, loathing him for his foresight. Whatever happened, they would still get a divorce. He had made that clear from the outset, hadn't he? But gaining access to any child might be problematic if he was on bad terms with his ex-wife.

Santino smiled and she wasn't surprised. Nudged in the right direction, she seemed to have obediently served up the responses he wanted. 'I suggest we seal our new understanding by having lunch.'

And fifteen minutes later they did exactly that. A light

and delicious meal was served informally in the shade of the loggia. They had only just sat down when a marmalade cat, tail held high, strolled towards them. 'Topsy…' Frankie whispered, and instantly thrust her chair back to get down on her knees to welcome her former pet. 'Gosh, she's looking well!'

'Pudding's probably asleep on the window seat in my study. He doesn't hunt much now…he's getting too old,' Santino reminded her gently as he absorbed her uninhibited delight in the reunion.

'You didn't use to approve of pets indoors.'

'The staff pamper the pair of them. They are extremely spoilt cats. I didn't have much choice,' Santino told her, modestly downplaying his role while Topsy wrapped herself sinuously round his ankles, purring like an engine and clearly demonstrating her affection.

Smiling, Frankie returned to the table.

'By the way…I've signed those villas over for rental to your business partner,' Santino advanced, startling her. 'However, I suspect that you would still find it difficult to work with Matt Finlay again.'

'But why?'

'He's a bad loser. He'll hold a grudge because you dented his ego—'

'Matt and I are good friends…'

'Good friends don't tell crude lies about each other,' Santino responded drily.

The reminder made Frankie redden. 'A couple of months ago, he started trying to change our relationship,' she confided ruefully. 'Suddenly he was acting as if he was attracted to me when he never had been before. And then at the farmhouse he said that marrying me would've made good business sense…'

'A wife with money of her own would appeal to an ambitious man, particularly when the agency's income had dropped and he was having to tighten his belt.'

She almost opened her mouth to tell him that Matt

had never been under the impression that she had further funds to dip into after she had bought into the business, but then she remembered that Matt had commented more than once on her mother's wealthy lifestyle. He might easily have assumed that marrying Della's daughter would ultimately prove to be well worth his while.

'How *could* Matt be that calculating?' Frankie whispered sickly.

Santino was now studying her intently, hooded dark eyes not missing a single expression that crossed her shaken and hurt face.

'It's so upsetting to think of someone I liked and trusted looking on me as a potential piggybank. And it's so horribly two-faced when all the time Matt was behaving as if it was me he wanted…to think I even worried about hurting his feelings!' Grimacing, Frankie looked at Santino, wondering when and why he had gone so unusually quiet.

Spiky black lashes fanned low on lustrous dark eyes and his shapely mouth slanted into a sudden wolfish smile. 'Horribly two-faced,' Santino agreed obediently.

Frankie belatedly registered that she had completely forgotten that she herself had confessed to having spent five years ripping off Santino for every penny she could get. Her fair skin burned and she didn't know where to put herself or where to look.

Santino stretched a casual hand across the table and briefly enclosed her rigidly knotted fingers. 'Let's talk about something more entertaining,' he suggested lightly. 'How would you like to spend the next few weeks?'

She was intensely relieved by the change of subject. Extraordinary as it seemed to her, Santino didn't appear to have twinned her apparent dishonesty with Matt's.

'*How?*' A look of dreamy abstraction slowly covered her face. 'I'd love to do Rome…ancient Rome, I mean… The Forum, the Colosseum, the Basilica, the

Pantheon…all the places I read about when I took ancient history classes.' Then she frowned, thinking about all the publicity the news of their marriage had received. 'Will we be able to go out and about freely?'

'The paparazzi still think we're in Sardinia, and there are many other ways of avoiding them,' Santino informed her with wry amusement. 'In this instance, I think the wisest move would be to simply release a photograph of us together. That's really what they all want. Once that is released, it won't be worth their while to chase after us with the same fervour.'

That afternoon, Santino showed her round the estate. Since it was very large, and Santino demonstrated a surprising eagerness to introduce her to every member of staff and every tenant who crossed their path, they didn't actually get back to the villa until dinnertime. After their evening meal, he treated her to a tour of the house. Starting at the present day and working backwards in history, he entertained her with fascinating stories about the lives and loves of the previous occupants.

The Villa Fontana had been built to house the flamboyant but much loved mistress of a rich aristocrat.

'They had seven children together…those soulful little cherubs have their faces.' Santino indicated the beautiful frescos on the walls. 'He married her after the birth of their first child. He was an aristocrat and she was a peasant's daughter—'

'That sounds like the opening to a sleazy joke,' Frankie could not resist saying. After exposure to his mother's snobbery, she was supersensitive to any reference either to the existence of a class divide or that word 'mistress'.

Santino's dark eyes stabbed into her with unexpected force. 'Whatever they didn't appear to have in common kept them together for well over thirty years!'

'If that voluptuous blonde is a faithful representation of the lady, we know very well what kept her lover hooked. She looks like a raving sexpot,' Frankie opined thinly, blondes being a no more welcome subject. 'And she paid for it, didn't she? *Seven* kids in the days when women often died giving birth and there was no pain relief…he was a selfish pig!'

'I don't believe I have ever regarded their lifelong love in that light before,' Santino confessed with sudden intense amusement.

'Probably not…but then you're a man, aren't you? She traded sex for security. If a woman was poor she didn't have much else to trade in those days, and I bet her family practically sold her to him…although I have to admit that he's not bad-looking,' Frankie conceded, studying the gentleman in question. 'He was a good bit older, though, wasn't he?'

'About ten years older,' Santino supplied, his amusement ebbing.

'So she had the generation gap to deal with as well.'

Santino tensed. 'Is that how you feel with me?'

Taken aback by his personal reaction to her facetious comment, Frankie wriggled like a guppy being reeled in. 'You're only twenty-nine, Santino—'

'Take your foot out of your mouth and tell me truthfully,' Santino gritted, suddenly demonstrating his recent extreme volatility for a usually even-tempered male by backing her up against a pillar. '*Do* you feel a generation gap with me?'

Shaken and confused, she sighed, 'Santino…to me, you're just you.'

A surprisingly understanding smile drove the tension from his lean face. 'Not like anyone else?'

Urgently she nodded in agreement. 'Unique,' she added, and then, feeling inexplicably exposed beneath the onslaught of those shrewd golden eyes, she lowered her head. 'I'm really tired,' she muttered. 'I think it's time I went to bed.'

There was a stark little silence and then Santino withdrew a step.

Naturally they wouldn't be sharing a bed any more, and she wanted to clear her stuff out of his room before he went up to bed later. The less she reminded him of their brief intimacy, the more he would relax with her, wouldn't he? And she wanted him to relax; she really did. If this next couple of weeks was all the time they were ever to spend together, she wanted to make the most of it.

Frankie had just got into bed in a room across the landing when Santino strode in. With a start, she sat up again. Santino wore only a bathtowel, anchored precariously round his lean brown hips, and he looked really mad. Without a word, he plucked her out of bed and carried her back to his room.

'What are you doing?' she gasped. 'Now that we're being friends again, we *can't* sleep together!'

'I don't want another friend. I've got plenty of friends. I want you in my bed, where you belong.' Santino punctuated that announcement by settling her between the sheets, casting aside his towel and sliding in beside her. 'For the moment, that will suffice. *Buona notte, cara.*'

Shellshocked, Frankie lay there in the darkness. 'But we're on the brink of a divorce; *why*?'

'If you're really lucky these old bones of mine might give out first and you'll find yourself a very merry and extremely rich widow instead,' Santino countered sardonically from the far side of the bed. '*Madre di Dio*…is it wise for me to put ideas of that nature into your head?'

'Don't you dare say things like that even as a joke!' It was an appalled and superstitious wail of censure. 'I'd *die* if anything happened to you!'

And as soon as those words escaped Frankie she clamped a horrified hand to her open mouth.

'That sounds just a little extreme to me,' Santino countered with an incredulous derision that was hugely painful for her to hear. 'And completely unbelievable coming from a woman who lies, cheats and steals from me for five long years without once succumbing to an attack of conscience—'

'But I *didn't*...it was—'

'*Della*, the mother-in-law from hell,' Santino slotted in, his deep, dark drawl ringing with sizzling self-satisfaction.

Sitting up, he turned the bedside lamps back on and surveyed her with wry amusement. 'Don't you feel better having got that off your chest? I'm sorry I had to get nasty...well, so theatrical, but I know the right imaginative buttons to push with you, *cara*. Death and disloyalty, an unbeatable combination.'

'Oh, no...' Frankie moaned in horror at what she had let slip on her mother's behalf.

'You told me yourself over lunch,' Santino informed her gently. 'While you were wittering on with such enormous hurt about Finlay's dishonest intentions, it finally sunk in on me that there was no way in this lifetime that you would behave in a similiar fashion. And when were you ever able to keep secrets from me? You look so shifty and guilty when you're lying, a child could find you out. If I hadn't been in such a rage that day, I'd have seen that for myself.'

'Mum?' Frankie muttered shakily, barely able to absorb what he was telling her because he sounded so disorientatingly light-hearted.

'You should've known that there wasn't the slightest chance that I would prosecute her. Put Della in an open court to star in a sensational trial?' Santino chided incredulously. 'I would not expose you or my family to that experience merely to punish her.'

Still welded to the mattress by shock, Frankie whispered weakly, 'You mean, you *never* planned to—'

'Never.'

'But I *believed* you...you scared me out of my wits!'

Santino shot her a languorous smile, rather like a big predatory cat receiving a very welcome stroking of the ego. 'Didn't I just?'

Frankie shot across the big bed like an electric eel. 'How could you *do* that to me?' she raked at him furiously.

'At the time, with pleasure,' Santino admitted. 'After all, while you were industriously protecting a woman who could single-handedly gut a shoal of piranha fish and emerge unscathed from the bloodbath, it never once occurred to you to consider me—'

'You?' Frankie echoed in a tone that shook with rage after that highly offensive reference to her mother.

Santino snaked out his arms and entrapped her as she leant over him. 'Think hard,' he advised with mocking dark eyes that flared gold as they roamed over her lovely face. 'It would help me along tremendously. Poor, unfortunate Santino, evidently saddled with a wife who is an unashamed criminal…and who is also potentially pregnant. Nightmare street.'

'But I'm not an unashamed criminal,' she mumbled rather unsteadily as he drew her down, crushing her breasts intimately into the hard wall of his hair-roughened chest.

'Hmm…' Santino sighed throatily, angling his powerful hips up into thrusting contact with her slight, trembling length and introducing her to the hungry, aroused thrust of his manhood.

'No, Santino…the divorce,' Frankie reminded him breathlessly.

Santino rested his arrogant dark head back on the pillows and studied her with deceptively sleepy golden eyes. 'This intense preoccupation with divorce is beginning to worry me. I am only three days into the three weeks you signed up for. What's an extra fun encounter here and there…between friends?' he enquired with husky persuasion.

'No…' Hot in places she was too ashamed to acknowledge, Frankie gave him a look of pleading reproach even as her slender thighs somehow drifted slightly apart and she found herself inexplicably rubbing her quivering body with helpless enticement against his.

'Once again…louder and with real commitment,' Santino encouraged raggedly.

'Santino…*please*…' Frankie moaned.

'No, I'm completely impartial on this,' Santino insisted stubbornly, his palms pressing her hips down on him in the most tormentingly exciting way and lingering to ease up the nightdress inch by suggestive inch and then stop dead. 'Friendship means that you have to ask to be ravished within an inch of your life. I wouldn't want to risk overstepping my boundaries. Only a husband would be confident enough of his reception to proceed without a clear invitation.'

'Santino…you *are* my husband!' Frankie practically sobbed in her frustration.

Instantaneously Santino arched up and let the tip of his tongue sensually trace the tremulous line of her generous mouth. 'You are such a fast learner, *signora*…you take my breath away…'

'Just think…' Frankie breathed headily two weeks later. 'This was *the* place to be buried in 28 BC.'

'Just think.' Santino surveyed the Mausoleum of Augustus, a rather undistinguished mound covered with weeds. He wore the look of a male striving against all the odds to rise above prosaic first impressions.

'You've got to use your imagination,' Frankie scolded.

'You've got enough for both of us, *piccola mia*.' Santino sent her a winging smile full of megawatt charm and appreciation. 'You have taught me to view this city of mine through new eyes.'

Frankie swiftly looked away from him, heart banging

fit to burst with suppressed excitement, but as he moved fluidly closer she wandered away, pretending to be absorbed in her guidebook. By being elusive during daylight she protected herself. Everything that went on at night in bed she kept in a separate compartment. Wonderful entertaining days, endless erotic nights. It was almost like a honeymoon, she reflected with a stark pang of pain, but in her heart of hearts she knew that Santino was merely engaged in hedging all his bets.

What else could he be up to? He had been so certain she would be pregnant. Admittedly, he hadn't once mentioned that subject again, but his behaviour had helped her to work out for herself that if she did turn out to be carrying his baby there would be no divorce. Now that he knew she hadn't stolen from him, if she did prove to be pregnant, Santino would make the best of things. After all, he was *fond* of her. But suppose she wasn't pregnant? It was ironic that what she had once feared she now badly wanted to happen.

A top society photographer, who was a personal friend of Santino's, had come to the Villa Fontana to record their togetherness for posterity, and one picture had been released to a very gushy glossy international magazine without any accompanying interview. In advance of that event, Frankie had been surprised to find herself presented with a new wedding ring and a gorgeous emerald engagement ring.

'I guess I need those or we wouldn't look convincing,' she had sighed.

'I am giving you these because you are my wife,' Santino had countered levelly.

Sinking back to the present, Frankie was deeply conscious of Santino's scrutiny while she continued to finger frantically through her guidebook in search of a fresh ruin to visit.

'I think we've run out of sites,' Santino commented without a shade of irony, indeed contriving to sound deeply regretful. 'I didn't think that could be done in Rome but we have done it. Deprived of the need to tramp about like tourists from dawn to dusk, what will we do with ourselves?'

'If you've been bored, you only had to say so.'

'I don't get bored with you.'

'You've got so flattering recently...'

'But you're not listening,' Santino breathed with a slightly raw edge to his intonation.

During the drive back to the villa, Frankie tensed in dismay. A tiny little twinge had cramped low in her stomach. Instantly she knew what that sensation meant. She turned away from Santino, eyes anguished, face draining of colour. Well, now she had her answer. She *wasn't* pregnant. She ought to tell him right now, let him off the hook, but right then she hated him for hanging himself on that hook.

But she was no better, was she? Hoping to hang onto him and their marriage on the strength of a baby? That wouldn't have been right either, and she had the lesson of her own parents' marriage behind her, so she didn't even have the excuse of optimistic ignorance. Physical attraction had brought her parents together but it hadn't been enough to keep them together.

A muffled choking sound escaped her as she clambered out of the car.

'What's wrong?' Santino demanded.

'Nothing!' she cried, and ran into the villa and didn't stop running until she reached the bathroom off their bedroom and locked the door behind her.

'Francesca!' Santino rapped impatiently on the door.

'I'll be out in a minute!' she promised, struggling to face courageously up to the destruction of all her hopes.

She finally shuffled out, tear-stained and looking tragic. As yet there was no actual proof that her period had arrived, but she just *knew* there very soon would be.

In her view that one tiny twinge was utterly foolproof confirmation.

'You're not feeling well, are you? Do you think we should do a pregnancy test?' Santino asked, with an award-winning lack of tact and what she interpreted as a vastly unconvincing look of excitement and anticipation.

Reacting to that unfortunate question as if it had been a cruel and deliberate taunt, Frankie burst into great gulping sobs. 'I hate you…go away!'

Disobliging to the last in his innate belief that he always knew what was best for her, Santino lifted her up as if she were a very fragile glass ornament and laid her carefully down on the bed, slipping off her shoes. She rolled over and bawled her eyes out. 'Leave me alone!' she sobbed in between times, because he kept on trying to put his arms round her and smooth her hair and do sympathetic things that only made her feel more wretchedly guilty than ever.

Never had Frankie been more deeply ashamed of herself. She couldn't even meet his eyes now. That she had been prepared to use a baby to keep Santino made her feel like a shockingly selfish and wicked woman. It would've been so desperately unfair to him when he didn't love her. And all the love she could give him could never compensate him for being denied the opportunity to find a woman he could love.

'You really…seriously…genuinely…want me to leave you alone?' Santino prompted with astonishing persistence, crouching athletically down by the side of the bed in an effort to get a look at her tear-swollen face. 'You usually don't mean it…in fact, if I *do* go, I'm the worst in the world. You taught me that a long time ago.'

Tell him, her conscience urged, and the very words of admission formed on her lips, but unfortunately another great wail of misery forced an exit and somehow took over and she thrust her face weakly into the pillows.

'I n-need a breathing space,' she gasped in stricken defeat, borrowing heavily from his terminology.

Vaulting upright again, Santino made no response. He seemed to take a terribly long time walking to the door, but Frankie kept her head down until the door thudded softly shut on his departure.

She *had* to pull herself together before she could face discussing the end of their marriage. And what was Santino likely to think after she had treated him to such a hysterical display? Could she plead an episode of howling premenstrual tension? Dear heaven, she would tell any lie sooner than let him suspect the true source of her distress. She had worked so hard at being bright, breezy and casual. She had behaved as if they were engaged in a brief affair. Pride demanded that when she left Santino this time she would leave with her chin up high and her shoulders square.

She had known why he continued to sleep with her. He could hardly have suggested that they live in suspended animation while they waited to learn whether or not she was pregnant. Indeed every tender, caring thing Santino had done recently had simply been part of his pretence that their marriage was and could be normal. He had been fatalistically convinced that she would conceive…and he had been wrong.

Exhausted by her emotions, she decided to skip dinner. Falling into an uneasy doze, she was awakened by the phone beside the bed ringing. Still half-asleep, she snatched it up. 'I'm in Milan,' Santino's dark drawl informed her coldly.

'What are you doing there?' Frankie demanded at full incredulous volume. She had asked him for a breathing space. She had expected him to go downstairs, not transport himself to the far end of the country!

'I sense a certain contrariness in that question. What you are really saying is…how *could* you leave me?' Santino translated huskily.

'No, I just wondered...that's all,' Frankie breathed shakily, waking up enough to recall that there wasn't much point in missing him when soon she was going to be missing him every day for the rest of her life.

'I'm attending an EC banking conference.'

'That must be exciting.'

'I'll be here for two days,' Santino informed her punitively.

'*Two d*—?' Frankie bit her tongue and swallowed hard. 'Oh, how lovely for you,' she completed limply.

'I'm getting very mixed signals here. I was about to suggest that you *join*—'

'Have a really good time,' Frankie cut in chokily, before he could voice that invitation and tempt her into what would be an insane act. She snatched in a shuddering breath, despising herself for stalling on giving him the good news. Santino had every right to know that she wasn't carrying his child just as soon as it was within her power to tell him. 'Oh, y-yes, by the way,' she added flatly, 'I'm *not* pregnant.'

The answering silence pounded as noisily as her heartbeat in her eardrums.

'Isn't that just wonderful news?' Frankie gushed with tears running down her cheeks. 'I know you must be as relieved as I am. Look, we'll talk when you get back.'

She set down the cordless phone. There, it was done and she felt better for it. And telling Santino on the phone had been the best way. It had allowed them both the privacy to conceal their personal reactions. She could not have borne to see Santino's relief, not when she herself still felt so gutted by disappointment.

She now had two days to sort herself out. And it would probably take two days for her swollen face to shrink back to normal proportions. She would find out exactly when he was returning and meet him at the airport. She would be cheerful, friendly and calm. There would be no drama and no tears when they returned to the villa to discuss their divorce and the next morning she would fly back to London.

By dawn the following day, Frankie was becoming increasingly perplexed about what was going on inside her own confusing body. Her period had still not arrived. In addition, she had not experienced a single further twinge but, most unusually, her breasts were now feeling the tiniest bit tender. *What if...?* What if she had been premature in giving Santino that reassurance?

By noon of the same day, having still received no confirmation of her condition, Frankie was panicking. Santino's chauffeur, Mario, drove her into the pretty medieval town of Anguillara. Too enervated even to appreciate her lovely surroundings, Frankie purchased a pregnancy test. When the kit provided her with incontrovertible proof that she *had* conceived, she went into shock. Joy and dismay then tore at her simultaneously as she appreciated how very foolish she had been to rush into disabusing Santino of the idea that she might be pregnant. How on earth was she supposed to tell him now that she had made a mistake?

The following morning, the very day of Santino's return, Frankie began worrying that that one little cramp she had felt might be the warning of an approaching miscarriage. Appalled by the idea, already having developed powerful feelings of protectiveness towards her unborn child, she visited a busy medical practice in Bracciano. A brief examination confirmed the test results.

Then she sat feeling rather like a toddler being taught the basics while the woman doctor gently explained to her that her experience had not been unusual, nor indeed was it anything to worry about. During the earliest stages of pregnancy it was apparently quite common for a woman to misinterpret the signs that her body was giving her because it was a time of tremendous hormonal upheaval. Leaving the surgery, Frankie went shopping in a very expensive shop. She bought an elegant daffodil-yellow dress and toning shoes, her version of armour.

At three in the afternoon, Frankie arrived in the limousine at Fiumicino to meet Santino off his private jet. Of course, she could have waited until he came home, but the truth was that she just couldn't wait to see him again and gauge his reaction to the mistaken news she had given him on the phone. If he was happier than a sandboy, it would be a challenge to disenchant him.

But one thing she did know: she could not keep such news from Santino, nor could she even consider any suggestion that they should remain married for the baby's sake. It wouldn't be fair. It just would not be fair to either of them.

As Frankie watched from the VIP lounge, the jet taxied in and the steps were run up. A slim blonde woman clad in an eye-catching fuchsia-pink suit appeared first. The stewardess? No, the stewardess was still at the exit door. Santino emerged next, luxuriant black hair ruffling in the slight breeze, vibrantly handsome dark features unreadable at that distance. In odd visual conflict with his stunning, elegant appearance, he had something large and awkwardly shaped stuffed under one powerful arm.

The blonde waited at the foot of the steps for him. A bank executive? His secretary? But as Santino and the woman crossed the tarmac, drawing ever closer, their heads bent in animated conversation, Frankie began to stiffen and stare fixedly because she could not immediately accept the powerful stirrings of recognition firing danger signals from her memory banks. Her stomach gave a sick, fearful lurch, perspiration breaking out on her brow.

'Who is that woman?' she asked the chauffeur, who was standing several feet away.

The older man looked surprised by her need to ask that question. 'Melina Bucelli, *signora*.'

Frankie froze in disbelief. Simultaneously three men, seemingly springing up out of nowhere, ran across the tarmac to target Santino with their cameras. Instantly Santino's security men went into action, holding back the shouting paparazzi. Their steps quickening, Santino and his companion lifted their heads.

Frankie recognised the blonde at the same instant as Santino saw Frankie standing by the window waiting. A brilliant smile began forming on his lips and then, with the speed of light, he appeared to register what a deep, dark hole he was in and, ditching the smile for an appalled look, dropped his briefcase and the funny furry thing he was carrying and broke into a most uncool sprint, his startled security men charging in his wake.

But Santino was already too late. Breaking free of her paralysis, Frankie had raced across the VIP lounge and headed like a homing pigeon out into the mercifully crowded anonymity of the main airport building.

CHAPTER ELEVEN

FRANKIE sat staring down into her untouched cappuccino. After being forced to cope with a debilitating bout of physical sickness in a cloakroom at Fiumicino, she had finally got into a taxi and directed the driver to the city centre. She had walked the streets for what felt like miles before her trembling lower limbs had forced her to sit down at a pavement café.

Now, registering her familiar surroundings, she was ashamed to find herself in the Piazza Navona. Only last week she had been here with Santino, and undoubtedly the memory of that happy day had unerringly brought her back. Insisting that ancient sites alone were too restricting, Santino had suggested that on alternate days he would choose their destinations.

In the church of Santa Maria della Pace, he had shown her the wonderful frescos by Raphael and had linked his fingers lightly with hers. Hand in hand, like lovers, they had strolled down the Via del Governo Vecchio to admire the superb Renaissance buildings and they had lunched in a trattoria overlooking three spectacular Baroque fountains. By that stage Santino had been flirtatiously kissing her fingers one by one, mowing down her daytime defences with burnished, dark, knowing eyes that made her heart race dizzily with longing and love and need.

Frankie blinked, her mind going blank, unable to hold onto images which now filled her with such unbearable pain. She was still in deep shock. Nothing could have prepared her for the devastating discovery that the blonde kissing Santino in Cagliari five years ago and

Melina Bucelli, reputedly dear as a daughter to Sonia Vitale, were in fact one and the same woman.

Frankie had never asked Santino about the woman he had betrayed her with. She had never really wanted to know any more. In those days their marriage had been a charade. She had left that episode in the past, where it seemed to belong, never dreaming that Santino might have some ongoing relationship with the woman. Indeed she had preferred to think of that gorgeous blonde as some casual pick-up, some immoral trollop…

Yet paradoxically she could not imagine Santino choosing to become intimate with that kind of woman. And he hadn't, had he? Possessed of his aristocratic mother's stamp of approval, Melina Bucelli had to be from the same rich and privileged background. That Melina should also be exquisitely beautiful was almost too much to bear. But what continually drew Frankie to a halt in her shellshocked ruminations was a complete inability to understand the sort of relationship Santino had with the other woman.

Five years ago Santino had been Melina's lover, but he hadn't had his marriage to Frankie annulled so that he could marry the other woman. That threw up another question that Frankie could barely credit that she had never yet asked him. Why *had* Santino allowed their marriage to continue in existence for so long? Challenged, she could not come up with a single adequate explanation of why Santino had been content to remain a married man.

But then what did that matter now? Frankie asked herself dully. The night before last she had told Santino that she wasn't pregnant. She had let him off the hook and he had fairly leapt off that hook of responsibility into celebration. From that moment he had evidently considered himself free of all obligation towards Frankie. Knowing that he was now free to go ahead with a divorce, he had probably invited Melina to join him in

Milan. Naturally he wouldn't have expected Frankie to turn up to meet him at the airport. After all, in the circumstances, why should she have done such a very wifely thing?

Having stranded herself in Rome with little cash left in her purse and not the slightest idea of how to get back to the Villa Fontana by public transport, Frankie finally surrendered to hard necessity. However she felt, she had to go back to the villa to pack and she had to face Santino. After purchasing a phone card in a newspaper kiosk, she queued up to use a public phone.

She wasn't expecting Santino to answer the phone personally, and the instant he heard her hesitant voice he burst into explosive Italian, speaking too fast for her to follow. It *was* Santino and yet he didn't sound like himself. He sounded frantic, distressed, out of control.

'I want you to send a car for me…but I don't want you to be in that car,' Frankie told him in a deadened voice of exhaustion.

'Where *are* you?' Santino demanded raggedly. '*Per amor di Dio*…I've been out of my mind with worry!'

'You're really not very good at adultery, Santino…I think your life will be easier after we're divorced,' Frankie murmured flatly.

'Please tell me where you are,' Santino pressed fiercely.

She told him and added, 'If you're in the car, I won't get in,' because she couldn't face the prospect of their confrontation taking place in a confined space.

A limousine drew up in front of her less than ten minutes later. Santino's chief security man, Nardo, got out, looking very grave, and was relieved to usher her into the rear seat.

'We searched the airport over and over again,' he sighed. 'Signor Vitale was distraught at your disappearance. I was only able to persuade him to return to the villa an hour ago.'

As the door closed on her and she slumped, Frankie was surprised to find herself sharing the seat with a very large teddy bear, wearing a frilly tartan dress and, horror of horrors, carrying a miniature teddy in its arms. The teddy looked as forlorn as she felt. Her goodbye present from Milan, fully advertising Santino's apparent belief that she had no taste whatsoever and hadn't matured in the slightest. And why did the teddy have a distinctly mother-and-baby look about it? Was that supposed to be a joke he expected her to appreciate?

Obviously she was a complete fool where men were concerned. She just could not comprehend how Santino could have made passionate love to her only three nights earlier and then turned to Melina. He hadn't even paused for breath. And now she could not imagine telling him that she carried his child either...

She dozed in the car but it was like a waking dream, full of haunting slices of memory. She surfaced to find herself inside the Villa Fontana, being carried upstairs in Santino's arms. 'Put me down—'

'I thought I had lost you...I have never been so scared in my life,' Santino groaned, powerful arms tightening round her. 'Don't you ever, ever do this to me again.'

'I won't be here to do it,' she reminded him dully.

Santino settled her down in a comfortable armchair in their bedroom. Frankie studied him. He looked devastated. She had never seen a few hours make such a difference to anybody. His tie was at half-mast, half the buttons on his silk shirt were undone to reveal a brown slice of hair-roughened chest and he badly needed a shave. Beneath the stubble he was pale as death, and his eyes were haunted and dark with strain.

'You lied to me...I never thought you would do that,' Frankie confided with a jerky little laugh.

Santino frowned. 'When did I lie?'

'When I asked you who Melina was, you didn't tell me the truth.'

Santino drove long fingers roughly through his already tousled hair. 'I was thinking about Rico that day…it slipped my mind that Melina was the woman you saw me with in Cagliari five years ago—'

'*Slipped your mind?*' Frankie repeated in helpless disbelief.

'I didn't expect you to remember her… All right, I wasn't breaking my neck to raise that subject too soon. Which of us is eager to recall our more embarrassing mistakes?' Santino demanded in charged appeal. 'What you saw happen between Melina and me that day was the consequence of a moment of temptation, of weakness…and when you surprised us that was it. Nothing more happened between us, either then or since.'

'Do you seriously expect me to believe that?' Frankie whispered in despair.

'Perhaps I should have begun at the beginning. When she was eighteen, Melina was my brother's girlfriend…or his cover story, if you like,' Santino shared ruefully. 'Because Rico was gay.'

'*Gay?*' Taken by surprise, Frankie stared back at him.

'My parents could not accept him as he was. They were desperate for him to marry. They adored Melina and she adored Rico. But he never had the slightest intention of marrying her. When he died, she joined my mother in making a shrine of his memory,' Santino explained grimly. 'After a while, my mother decided that Melina would make *me* the perfect wife, but I wasn't interested. She *was*…perhaps because I look very like my late brother.'

'And that day I saw you with her in Cagliari?'

Santino tautened. 'Melina flew over to Sardinia, ostensibly to visit friends. She came to see me at the bank and I decided to take her back to my apartment for lunch. It was quite innocent until she threw herself at me in the lift…but I was not unresponsive to that invitation,' he admitted bluntly, shooting Frankie a driven look of fierce emotion. 'Had you not interrupted us, I *would* have gone to bed with her…after six months of our marriage, I was so tortured by my unsated desire for you, I would have done anything to try to kill that craving!'

Frankie was sharply disconcerted by that admission. She had never really understood, even when he had told her at the farmhouse, how hard it must have been for him to withstand the temptation to consummate their marriage. Heaven knew, she had been willing, but he had been wise to keep his distance. Then she could never have been his equal and he would swiftly have grown bored with her immature adoration.

'I would've used Melina and she deserved better. I chased after you and left her standing in the lobby that day without any explanation. It was a long time before she could forgive me for that. These days we meet solely as distant and very polite friends—'

'"Friends"…that's such an elastic term with you—'

'Melina and I met at the conference,' Santino interrupted drily. 'She has just become engaged to another banker. She flew back to Rome with me to make arrangements for a family party to announce her engagement.'

Frankie was shaken. His explanation made better sense than any other. Her suspicions vanquished, she was left feeling rather foolish and uncomfortable. 'That's going to break your mother's heart,' was all she could think to say.

'Few men marry women chosen by their mothers, *cara*.' Santino's mouth quirked. 'I should also mention that I received a rather astonishing phone call from mine this morning.'

'Oh?' Frankie had tensed.

'Surprisingly, my mother wanted to tell me how much she loved me.' Santino rested keen eyes on Frankie's betraying flush. 'She may not have shown that affection in ten years, but she was not telling me anything I didn't already know.'

'Wasn't she?' Frankie was disconcerted by that assurance.

'She has never come to terms with my brother's death, but today all of a sudden she experienced a need to contact me and say that she appreciated how very fortunate she was to have a surviving son.'

'Gosh!' Frankie exclaimed, glancing away, not wanting him to suspect her interference.

'Mamma also received the news of Melina's engagement with nothing more than a regretful sigh, and she implied that she might have been slightly hasty in saying that she would *never* accept you as a daughter-in-law. It was an amazing rapprochement.'

Silence lingered. Frankie collided tensely with clear dark golden eyes. Melina wasn't his lover, never had been his lover, or his intended wife or indeed anything else, but he hadn't even considered it important to tell her those facts. 'Why didn't you explain about Melina five years ago...why did you allow me to go on believing that you'd been unfaithful?'

'We *had* to part. You had to grow up and you couldn't do that with me,' Santino informed her tautly, watching her spin her head defensively away from him. 'To the best of my ability, I put you and our marriage to the back of my mind and got on with my life.'

'Yet you made no attempt to have our marriage annulled...'

'I didn't meet anyone else I wanted to marry. And you were a sweet memory...the woman I believed you might become figured in my mind as an ideal.'

Frankie's head swivelled instantly back to him. 'An ideal?'

Santino smiled. 'You look just like an enquiring sparrow when you do that, *cara mia*. Don't ask me to explain to you how or why I love you. I only know that I *do*...'

Her stunned eyes clung to his, her breath catching in her throat as she struggled to accept and believe in the sentiments he'd expressed with such deep and un-ashamed sincerity.

Santino strolled forward and reached down to grasp her hands and draw her slowly upright. Brilliant dark eyes scanned her face with immense and tender appre-ciation. 'We have ties that go back so many years. And you had such courage, such tremendous warmth and faith. No other woman has ever reached my heart as you did, and yet I realise now that I probably hurt you more than all the rest put together by not discouraging your attachment to me...'

Frankie leant forward into the welcoming shelter of his big, powerful body. Trembling, she rested her brow against his shoulder, eyes prickling with tears of intense happiness. 'No, I needed you then. I had nothing else,' she told him honestly. 'And being in your arms is still like coming home.'

'Today I was afraid that you weren't planning to come home again,' Santino confided unevenly, his arms clos-ing round her slowly, as if he was still afraid to credit that the worst was over and the best was all to come. 'You switched off me so fast five years ago. Then I told myself that it was for the best, but I was scared that it could happen again...'

'I just love you more with every day,' Frankie mut-tered in a wobbly voice choked with tears. 'I'm really not that easy to get rid of.'

'But you are. Five years ago you severed every con-nection between us. You had no second thoughts. You didn't go home to face me; you just climbed on a plane. And you didn't write. I was tempted so many times to seek you out, but I knew that that wouldn't be fair. You had to be free to become an adult, and yet letting go so completely was the hardest thing I ever did.'

'I never once thought you could've felt like that.'

'I couldn't end our marriage without giving us one more chance. I had such incredibly high hopes, and the instant I saw you in La Rocca the same fierce attraction leapt into being—'

'And then Della's dishonesty got in the way.'

'But I still couldn't bear to let go of you,' Santino confided. 'I promised myself that at the end of three weeks I would be cured of you.'

'Initially I had the same objective.' Frankie carefully unknotted his tie and slipped it off. 'But it didn't work.'

'No, I just got in deeper…and deeper…and deeper…'

'You said that having a good time in bed didn't mean that you loved—'

Santino clasped a strong hand over the uncertain fingers braced against his chest. Intense dark golden eyes held hers fiercely. 'And neither it does. Even if I could never make love to you again, I would still love you.'

'But you hurt me so much saying that.'

'I didn't want you to mistake your feelings for me…I wanted you to take the time to get to know me again and be sure that what you were feeling was real and lasting. I couldn't risk you waking up some day and deciding that you were too young to be tied down and that possibly it was a mistake to have stayed married to your first lover…'

Frankie was deeply touched that Santino had suffered from his own insecurities. 'I'm sorry, but you are really the only man I have ever wanted.'

Santino coloured. 'I liked that—'

'I know…you're possessive. So am I.'

'Before I went to Milan—' Santino tensed, throwing her an anxious look '—I didn't know whether you were upset because you might be pregnant or upset because you might not be.'

'You should've told me up front that you didn't want a divorce any more,' Frankie censured.

'I needed you to make your own decision about what

you wanted…but I tried to show you in every way possible how much I cared…'

'I was afraid that was just because you thought I might be pregnant.'

'Now you know differently…' Santino curved his mouth with hungry fervour over hers and kissed her long and deeply until she shivered with need against him. 'But, having got so used to the idea that I was going to be a father, I was a little disappointed… But perhaps it was for the best. You're still only twenty-one. We've got plenty of time.'

'You'll be a father in time for Christmas,' Frankie confided breathlessly.

Santino was stunned. 'Say that again…'

Frankie explained the error of jumping to premature conclusions.

A slow smile of delighted satisfaction slashed Santino's darkly handsome features. 'So my reproductive cells won that battle on hostile territory…not so hostile after all, it seems.'

Frankie blushed as he drew her down on the bed with a strong look of intent in his lustrous dark eyes. 'I found the teddy in the limo,' she told him.

'We'll call her Flora…she can hen-peck Hamish. I was planning to gauge your mood with her and suggest that if you really wanted a baby we try again.'

'What would you have done if I *had* taken all that money?' Frankie asked reflectively.

'I would've concentrated on rehabilitating you. I couldn't possibly have let you go at the end of the three weeks. I love you too much, *piccola mia*.' Shrewdly assessing the faintly troubled look still tensing her face, Santino added, 'I can afford to look after your mother, but this time I'll ensure she is kept within reasonable bounds—'

'No…it wouldn't be right for you to support her again,' Frankie protested, strongly convinced that Della was young and able enough to support herself through her own efforts, and that any other arrangement would be akin to rewarding her for her dishonesty.

'Allow me to know what is right just this once,' Santino murmured, strongly amused by the steely glint in Frankie's gaze. 'I promise you that I will wreak the revenge of a lifetime when I see Della's reaction to the news that we are about to make her a grandmother!'

Since he chose that exact same moment to extract another feverishly hungry kiss, Frankie's ability to argue was severely diminished. Her quivering body strained up into the hard heat of his virile frame and she caught fire, driven by a primal need to seal their love in the most physical way possible.

'Hal is very fond of children,' Della confided rather unnecessarily as her third husband, a rock-solid middle-aged Texan rancher, cradled her grandchild with deft hands and made chortling sounds to amuse him. 'In fact…he would like us to try for one.'

At that unexpected news, Frankie's eyes opened very wide.

Her attractive mother reddened and gave her an uncertain glance. 'I know I was pretty hopeless with you, but Hal thinks that I'd cope much better now because I'd have his support and I'm more mature.'

Nothing came so readily to Della's lips these days as 'Hal thinks…' Hal Billings, burly, blunt-spoken and bossy, had rescued Della from her job on a department store beauty counter. While she was trying to sell him perfume Hal had fallen in love, and Della, who hadn't had the slightest intention of ever falling in love again, had fallen hardest of all.

Hal was comfortably off, but he considered idleness a vice and was fond of what he called 'plain living'. Della had had to make sacrifices to meet Hal's high standards, but she had done so with surprising eagerness.

Frankie had finally appreciated that her mother had been a deeply unhappy woman, who had tried to use material things to fill the emptiness inside her. Now a new love and a challenging lifestyle with a man she could rely on had given her the chance to make a fresh start.

Having reclaimed their son, Marco, Santino strode across the room with him, his lean, strong face concerned. 'I think Marco should bow out of his big day now…what do you think?'

Frankie stretched out her arms to receive her baby, gazing down at his sleepy little face, the dark silk fans of his lashes sinking over eyes as green as her own. 'Yes…he deserves some peace and quiet.'

But it still took another half-hour for them to work through the crush of their combined relatives and make an escape. Gino Caparelli and Alvaro Vitale were in close conversation in a corner. Frankie's great-aunts, initially as nervous as they were excited about leaving the village to come all the way to the *castello*, where Santino and Frankie had decided to hold the christening, were now happily chatting with two elderly ladies from Santino's side of the family.

'He is a little darling…a precious child,' Sonia Vitale sighed, her face softening as she delicately smoothed the soft black hair lying on her sleeping grandson's brow.

Frankie smiled. Her mother-in-law's unconcealed delight in her grandchild had done much to bring down the barriers between the two women. After a decade of living in near seclusion, nourishing her grief for the son she had lost, Sonia was returning to the business of living again.

With amusement, Santino was watching Della rush to fetch a cold drink for Hal. 'When you insisted that your mother give up the house and find a job, it was you I was worried about, *cara*. I thought she would never forgive you for being so tough, but you did her a favour. She's a changed woman.'

'She's even considering motherhood again,' Frankie confided.

After an arrested pause, Santino burst out laughing. 'There's method in her madness,' he pointed out. 'If she has a baby, Hal might let her off some of the chores round the ranch!'

Together, Santino and Frankie put their son down for a nap in his cosy crib. In perfect concert, they moved into each other's arms.

Frankie thought back on the first blissful year of their marriage. Matt had found another partner for the travel agency. She had had an easy pregnancy and Marco had been born with very little fuss. The joy of becoming parents had brought her and Santino even closer together. Santino adored his son. They spent quite a lot of weekends in Sardinia. Some day Marco was destined to hear about his family's humble beginnings on that hillside above La Rocca, just as Santino had learned his from his late grandfather.

'Have I made you happy?' Santino murmured huskily as they walked down the corridor.

Frankie gazed up into those lethally dark and sexy eyes and went weak at the knees, and gloried in the sensation. 'Head-over-heels happy. When I picked you out at sixteen, I knew what I was doing.'

'And I didn't know what had hit me,' Santino confided, dark head bending with the suggestion of a male yielding to an irresistible force. 'But I'm incredibly glad I was picked.' With that ragged confession, their lips met in hungry rediscovery, and it took the couple a suspiciously long time to make it back to the family celebration.

Michelle Reid grew up on the southern edges of Manchester, the youngest in a family of five lively children. But now she lives in the beautiful county of Cheshire with her busy executive husband and two grown-up daughters. She loves reading, the ballet, and playing tennis when she gets the chance. She hates cooking, cleaning, and despises ironing! Sleep she can do without and produces some of her best written work during the early hours of the morning.

Don't miss Michelle's fantastic new book:
A PASSIONATE MARRIAGE
Out this month in Modern Romance™!

THE MARRIAGE SURRENDER

by

Michelle Reid

CHAPTER ONE

'COULD I s-speak to Alessandro Bonetti, please?'

The public call box smelled of stale cigarettes. Pale-faced, the full length of her slender body muscle-locked by the mettle she needed to make this telephone call, Joanna barely noticed the smell or the unsavoury mess littering the floor beneath her black-booted feet as she stood there clutching the telephone receiver to her ear.

'Who is calling, please?' a coolly concise female voice enquired.

'I'm…' she began—then stopped, white teeth pressing into her full bottom lip as the answer to that question stuck firmly in her throat.

She couldn't say it. She just could not bring herself to reveal her true identity to anyone but Alessandro himself when there was a very good chance that he might refuse to speak to her, and in the present state that she was in, she didn't need some cold-voiced telephonist listening to that little humiliation.

She had been there before…

'It—it's a personal call,' she temporised, closing her eyes on a faint prayer that the reply was enough to get her access to the great man himself.

It wasn't. 'I'm afraid I will have to have your name,' the voice insisted, 'before I can enquire if Mr Bonetti is available to speak to you.'

Well, at least that stone-walling response placed Sandro in the country. Joanna made a grim note. She had half expected him to have gone back to live and work in Rome by now.

'Then put me through to his secretary,' she demanded, 'and I'll discuss this further with her.'

There was a pause, one of those taut ones, packed with silent pique at Joanna's rigidly determined tone. Then, 'Please hold,' the voice clipped at her, and the line went quiet.

The seconds began to tick slowly by, taking with them the desperation that had managed to bring her this far. A desperation that had kept her awake last night, trying to come up with some other way to get herself out of this mess without having to involve Sandro. But every which way she'd tried to look at it, it had always come down to two straight choices.

Arthur Bates or Sandro.

A shudder ripped through her, the mere thought of Arthur Bates' name enough to keep her hanging onto that telephone line, when every self-preserving instinct she possessed was telling her to cut loose and make a bolt into hiding somewhere rather than resort to this.

But she was tired of hiding. Tired of—being this person who stood on her own, isolated by her own inability to reach out to another human being and simply ask for help.

So, here she was, she reminded herself bracingly, ready to ask for that help. Ready to reach out to the only human being she felt she could reach out to. If Sandro said No, get lost, then she would. But she had to give him one last chance—give *herself* this chance to put her life back together again.

After all, she consoled herself, against the fretful doubts rattling around inside her head, she wasn't intending dumping permanently on him, was she? She was simply going to put a proposition to him, get his answer, then get the hell out of his life again.

For good. That would be part of her proposition. Help me this one time and I promise never to bother you again.

Easy. Nothing to it. Sandro wasn't a monster. He was, in actual fact, quite a decent human being. He couldn't still be feeling bitter towards her, surely? Not after all this time.

Then the telephone suddenly began demanding more money and her self-consolation died a death as a much more familiar panic soared abruptly into life, gushing through her system like a raging flood.

What am I doing? she asked herself frantically. *Why* am I doing this?

You're doing this because you've got no damned choice! her mind snapped back, so angrily that it jerked her into urgent movement. Her trembling fingers reached out towards the small stack of coins she had piled up in front of her ready to feed into the pay box. She made a grab for the top coin in the stack—and stupidly sent the rest of them scattering so they fell in a chinking shower to the ground.

'Oh, damn it,' she muttered, starting to bend to pick up the scattered coins as a voice suddenly sounded down the earpiece.

'Good morning, Mr Bonetti's secretary speaking,' it announced. 'How may I help you?'

The voice made her shoot upright again. 'Just a minute,' she muttered, struggling to feed the only coin she had stopped from falling into the required slot with fingers that decidedly shook. The line cleared and Joanna took another few moments to pull her ragged nerves together. 'I w-would like to speak to Mr—to Alessandro, please.' She quickly changed tack, hoping the personal touch might get her past this next obstruction.

It didn't. 'I'm afraid I must insist on your name,' Sandro's secretary maintained.

Her name. Her teeth gritted together, eyes closing on a fresh bout of indecision. Now what did she do? she asked herself pensively. Tell the truth? Let this woman bear witness to the full depth of Sandro's refusal, instead of the other cool voice she had spoken to before?

'This is—M-Mrs Bonetti,' she heard herself mumble, the name sounding as strange leaving her own lips as it must have sounded to the woman on the other end of the telephone line.

There was a short sharp pause. Then, '*Mrs* Bonetti?' the voice repeated. 'Mrs *Alessandro* Bonetti?'

'Yes,' Joanna confirmed, not blaming the woman for sounding so astonished. Joanna herself had never managed to come to terms with being that particular person. 'Will you ask Alessandro if he has a few minutes he could spare for me, please?'

'Of course,' his secretary instantly agreed.

The line went quiet again. Joanna breathed an unsteady sigh into the mouthpiece, wondering how many cats she was setting loose amongst Sandro's little pigeons by daring to make an announcement like that.

Again she waited, so tense now she could barely unclench her jaw-bone, the thrumming silence setting her foot tapping on the debris-littered concrete base of the call box, fingernails doing the same against the metal casing of the telephone. And there was a man standing just outside the kiosk, obviously waiting to use the telephone after her. He kept on sending her impatient glances and her palms felt sweaty; she tried running them one at a time down her denim-clad thighs but it didn't make any difference, they still felt sweaty.

'Mrs Bonetti?'

'Yes?' The single word shot like a bullet from her tension-locked throat.

'Mr Bonetti is in conference at the moment.' The voice sounded incredibly guarded all of a sudden. 'But he said for you to leave your number and he will call you back as soon as he is free.'

'I can't do that,' Joanna said, feeling a dragging sense

of relief and a contrary wave of despair go sweeping through her. 'I mean—I'm in a public call box and...'

Shaky fingers came up to push agitatedly through the long silken fall of her red-gold hair while she tried to think quickly with a brain that didn't want to think at all. Sandro couldn't speak to her and she didn't think she could accumulate enough courage to do this again.

'I'll h-have to call him back,' she stammered out finally, grasping at straws that really weren't straws at all, but simply excuses to stop this before it soared out of all control. 'Tell him I'll call him back s-some time w-when I—' Her excuses dried up. 'Goodbye,' she abruptly concluded, and went to replace the telephone.

But, 'No! Mrs Bonetti!' The secretary's voice whipped down the line at her. 'Please wait!' she said urgently. 'Mr Bonetti wants to know your reply before you... Just hold the line a moment longer—please...'

It was a plea—an anxious plea, which was the only thing that stopped Joanna from slamming down the receiver and getting out of there.

That and the fact that she had just had a revolting vision of Arthur Bates smiling at her like a very fat cat who was about to taste the cream. She shuddered again, feeling sick, feeling dizzy, feeling so uptight and confused now that she really didn't know what she wanted to do.

Oh God. She closed her eyes, tried to get a hold on her swiftly decaying reason. Sandro or Arthur Bates? her mind kept on prodding at her. Arthur Bates or Sandro? The choice that was no choice.

Sandro...

Sandro, the man she had not allowed herself to make any contact with for two long wretched years.

Except when she'd told him about Molly, she then remembered, feeling what was left of the colour drain from her cheeks as poor Molly's face swam painfully

into her mind. She had tried to contact Sandro once—
about Molly.

He had ignored her call for help then, she grimly reminded herself. So there was every chance that he was
going to do the same now.

And why not? she derided. There was nothing left
between them any more, hadn't been for a long, long—

The phone began demanding more money again. She
jumped like a startled deer, eyes flicking open to search
a little wildly for another coin. It was only then that she
remembered that she had knocked them all flying to the
ground a few minutes earlier, and she bent down, func-
tioning on pure instinct now because intelligence seemed
to have completely deserted her.

But then, it always did when it came to Sandro, she
acknowledged ruefully as her fingers scrambled amongst
the dirt, cigarette ends and God alone knew what else
that was littering the call box floor.

'Mrs Bonetti?'

'Yes,' she gasped.

'I'm putting you through to Mr Bonetti now…'

There was a crackling sound in her ear that made her
wince. Her scrambling fingers discovered one of her
missing coins. Grabbing at it, she straightened, face
flushed now, breathing gone haywire, fingers fumbling
as she attempted to push home the coin, the stupid panic
turning her into a quivering, useless mess because she
was about to hear Sandro's dark velvet voice again and
she didn't know if she could bear it!

The man outside the call box got fed up with waiting
and banged angrily on the glass. Joanna turned on him
like a mad woman, her blue eyes flashing him a blinding
glare of protest.

'Joanna?'

And that was all it took for everything to come crashing down around her—the agitation, the panic—all

crowding in and congealing into one seething ball of chest-tightening anguish.

He sounded gruff, he sounded terse, but oh, so familiar that her own voice locked itself into her throat. The man outside banged again; she closed her eyes and set her teeth and felt Sandro's tension sizzle down the telephone line towards her, felt his impatience, his reluctance to accept this call.

'Joanna?' he repeated tersely. Then, 'Damn it!' she heard him curse. 'Are you still there?'

'Yes,' she answered breathlessly, and knew she had just taken one of the biggest, bravest steps of her life with that one tiny word of confirmation. 'S-sorry.' She apologised for the tense delay in taking it, and tried to relax her jaw in an effort to find some semblance of calm. 'I dropped my m-money on the call box f-floor and couldn't find it,' she explained. 'And there's a m-man standing outside w-waiting to use the telephone. He keeps banging on the glass and I—'

The rest was cut off—by herself, because she realised on a wave of despair that she was babbling like an idiot.

Sandro must have been thinking the exact same thing because his tone was tight when he muttered, 'What the hell are you talking about?'

'Sorry,' she whispered again, which seemed to infuriate him.

'I am in the middle of an important meeting here,' he snapped. 'So do you think you could get to the point of this—unexpected—honour?'

Sarcasm, hard and tight. Her eyes closed again, her chest so cramped she could barely drag air into her lungs as each angry word hit her exactly where it was aimed to hit.

'I n-need…'

What did she need? she then stopped to wonder. She had become so addled by now that her reason for calling him at all had suddenly got lost in the ferment of her panic.

'I n-need…' Moistening her dry lips, she tried again. 'Your—advice about something,' she hedged, knowing she couldn't just tell him outright that the only reason she was phoning him after all this time was to ask for money! 'Do you think you could possibly m-meet me somewhere, s-so we can talk?'

No reply. Her nerve-ends reached snapping point. A tight, prickling feeling began to scramble its way up from her tingling toes to her hairline. She couldn't breathe, she couldn't swallow, and, worse than all of that, she felt like weeping.

And if Sandro knew that he would fall off his chair in shock, she mocked herself.

'I am flying to Rome this evening,' he informed her brusquely. 'And my day is fully taken up with meetings until I leave for the airport. It will have to wait until I get back next week.'

'No!' That wouldn't do! 'I can't wait that long. I…' Her voice trailed away, her mind flying off in another direction as she bit into her bottom lip on a fresh wave of desperation. Then, defeatedly, she whispered, 'It doesn't m-matter. I'm s-sorry to have—'

'Don't you damn well dare put that phone down on me!' Sandro warned on an angry growl that told her that, even after all this time, he could still read her intentions like an open book.

And she could hear him muttering something to himself—cursing most likely—in Italian, because Sandro always did revert to his native tongue when he was really angry. She could even see him in full detail while he did it. Tall and lean, an unbearably handsome Latin dark figure, with brown velvet eyes that turned black when angry and a beautifully shaped intensely sensual mouth that could kiss like no mouth she had ever experienced, but could also spit all sorts at her without her knowing what the words were—but, hell, did she get their drift!

Then, emerging from the middle of all that Latin temperament, came a warning beep that the phone needed feeding yet again.

'I haven't any more money!' she gasped into the mouthpiece while her eyes flickered anxiously across the dirty floor at her feet. 'I'll have to—'

'Give me your number!' Sandro snapped.

'But there's a man waiting to use the telephone. I have to—'

'*Maledizione!*' he cursed. 'The number, Joanna!'

She gave it. Her time ran out and the line went dead. She dropped the receiver back onto its rest, then just stood there staring at it, unsure if Sandro had managed to get down every digit before they were cut off, scared that he had done, and terrified that he had not!

Almost faint with stress and wretched confusion, she bent again to search the grubby ground for her other lost coins, found them, then stepped out of the call box to let the man waiting outside take his turn on the telephone.

He sidled past her as though she was some kind of freak. She didn't blame him; if he had been watching her enact her nervous breakdown inside that telephone box, then she knew she must have *looked* like a freak!

Sandro's fault; it was always Sandro's fault when she went to pieces like this. No one else could make her lose all her usually ice-cold self-possession as completely he could. And he had been doing it since the first time she ever set eyes on him. A few short minutes of his undivided company, and he had always been able to turn her into a shivering, quivering wreck of a useless creature.

Sex.

That single telling word hit her with a hard, cruel honesty. The difference between Sandro and every other man she had ever met was the fact that he was the only one who could stir her up sexually.

And that was why she was standing here, a shivering, quivering wreck. Because in stirring her up sexually he also stirred up all the phobias that sent her into this kind of panic.

Fear was the main thing: a stark, staring fear that if she ever gave in to the sex then her life would be over.

Because he would know then, wouldn't he? Know what she was and despise her for it.

The man came out of the phone box. He hadn't been much more than a couple of minutes, which made her feel even guiltier for keeping him waiting as long as she had.

'I'm so sorry I was so long,' she felt compelled to say. 'Only I had difficulty—'

The phone inside the kiosk began to ring and she made a sudden desperate lurch for it, forgetting about the man, forgetting everything as she snatched the receiver to her ear again.

'What the hell happened?' Sandro's voice shot down the line at her. 'I have been trying that number for the last five minutes and kept getting an engaged signal! Were you stupid enough to hold onto the receiver instead of hanging up and waiting for me to call you back?'

Well, Joanna thought ruefully, that just about said it. Stupid. He thought her *that* stupid, and Sandro suffered fools as most people suffered raging toothache.

'I let the man I told you was waiting use the phone,' she explained.

Another of those Italian curses hit her burning eardrums, then she heard him take in a deep breath of air and his voice, when it came again, was more as it should be, grim but controlled.

'What is it you want from me, Joanna,' he demanded. 'Since when have you *ever* wanted anything from me?'

Which only showed that even when he was under control he still couldn't resist another dig at her.

'It isn't something I can discuss over the telephone,' she told him. Then as her own temper suddenly flared, 'And if this is a taste of how your attitude is going to be, then it probably isn't worth me taking it any further!'

'OK—OK,' he conceded on a heavy sigh. 'So I am reacting badly. But I am up to my neck in work at the moment, and the last thing I expected, on top of it all, was for my long-lost *wife* to give me a call!'

'Try for sarcasm,' she snapped. 'Pleasantries just don't become you somehow.'

Their simultaneous sighs were acknowledgements that they both recognised they were reacting to each other now as they had always used to do: biting and scratching.

'How can I help you?' he asked, with more heaviness than hostility.

And Joanna relented too, saying with an equal heaviness. 'If you can't find time to see me today, Sandro, then I'm afraid I *have* been wasting your valuable time. I did try to tell you that,' she couldn't resist adding, 'before you went off at half-cock.'

'Five o'clock,' he said. 'At the house.'

'No!' she instantly protested. 'I don't want to go there!' Then she bit her lip, knowing exactly how he was going to take that horrified reaction.

But his lovely house in Belgravia held only bad memories for her. She couldn't meet him there, would probably die of mortification before she'd even stepped over the threshold!

'Here, then,' he clipped. And now he really was angry: not hot, Italian angry but frozen, arctic angry. 'In an hour. It is all I can offer you. And don't be late,' he warned. 'I am working on a very tight schedule and as it is I will have to fit you in between two important meetings.'

'OK,' she agreed, wondering sinkingly if meeting him at his office was any better than meeting him at the house they had once used to share? In all honesty she had no idea, because she had never been to his place of work before. 'How—w-what do I do? When I arrive there, I m-mean?' she asked, her bottom lip beginning to feel as if it had been completely mutilated by her own anxious teeth. 'W-will I have to tell someone who I...? Only I don't like...'

'Coming out of hiding?' he suggested acidly. 'Or don't you like admitting your legal association to me?'

'Sandro...' she whispered huskily. 'Can't you appreciate how difficult I'm finding this to do?'

'And how difficult do you think I am finding it?' he threw back gruffly. 'You walked out of my life two years ago and have never bothered to so much as show your lovely face since!'

'You told me not to,' she reminded him. 'When I left, you said—'

'I know what I said!' he bit out. Then he sighed, and sighed again. 'Just be here, Joanna,' he concluded wearily. 'After all of this, just make sure you don't chicken out at the last minute and stand me up, or so help me, I'll— Oh, damn it,' he muttered, and the line went dead.

And suddenly Joanna *felt* dead: dead from the neck up, dead from the neck down. Dealing with Sandro had always ended up with her feeling like this. Drained, so sucked clean to the dregs of her reserves that it was all she could do to slump against the phone booth wall while she wondered wearily why she had set herself up for all of it in the first place!

Then a sudden vision of Arthur Bates sitting behind his cluttered desk as he issued his ultimatum flashed in front of her eyes, and, with the usual shudder, she remembered exactly why.

'Payment, Joanna, comes in cash or in kind,' he had

declared in that soft and silken voice of his. 'You know the score here.'

Payment in cash or in kind...

The very words had made her feel sick.

'How long have I got to pay?' she'd demanded with an icy composure that completely ignored the second option.

But the man himself had refused to ignore it. He had waited a long time to bring her down to this low point and he meant to savour every second of it. So he'd sat back in the creaky leather desk chair, inserted a heavily ringed finger into the gap between two gaping buttons on his overstretched shirt, then taken his time sliding his eyes over her slender figure, so perfectly defined beneath the tiny white waiter's jacket and black satin skirt she had to wear for work.

'Now would be good,' he'd suggested huskily. 'Now would be very good for me...'

Which had had the effect of freezing her up like a polar ice cap. 'I meant to pay the money.' She'd made it clear. 'How long?'

'A debt is a debt, sweetheart.' He'd smoothly dismissed the question. 'And you are already two weeks late with your payments.'

'Because I was off work with the 'flu,' she'd reminded him. 'Now I'm back at work I can pay you as soon as I—'

'You know the rules,' he'd cut in. 'You pay on time or else. I don't make them for fun, you know. You people come to me to help you out of your financial difficulties and I say, Yeah—good old Arthur will lend you the cash—so long as you understand that I don't take it nicely if you don't pay me back on time. It's for your own sake,' he contended. 'If I were to let you get behind, then you'd only end up in a worse mess trying to play catch-up again.'

He'd meant she'd have to borrow more from him to

keep up the extortionate repayments on his high interest loan and thereby sink further in his debt. It was a clever little ploy. One which kept him, the loan shark, firmly in control.

But for her it was different, and she'd always known it. Arthur Bates didn't want her money, he wanted her body, and by getting behind with her repayments she had played right into his hands. What made it worse was that she worked for him, which meant he knew exactly how much she earned; he knew he was in control of that part of her life. She waited on tables or worked behind the bar of his seedy little nightclub—the same club where she had got herself into debt by stupidly playing at its gaming tables.

Which actually meant that Arthur Bates believed he was in control of Joanna's life every which way he wanted to look at it.

But then, Arthur Bates didn't know about her marriage. He didn't know about her connection to the powerful Bonetti family. He didn't know she had a way out of the whole wretched mess—if she could find the will to use it.

Even with that will, she'd realized she was going to need time—time Arthur Bates was not predisposed to give her. So, there she had been, standing in front of him, feeling her skin crawl as his eyes roamed expressively over her, and she had done the only thing she could think of doing to gain herself time. She had lowered her lashes over the revulsion gleaming in her eyes, and offered him the sweet, sweet scent of her defeat.

'OK,' she'd muttered huskily. 'When?'

'You've finished for the night,' he'd said. 'We could be at my apartment in fifteen minutes…'

'I can't,' she'd replied. 'Not tonight, anyway…' And she had given an awkward little shrug of one slender white shoulder. 'Hormones,' she'd explained, and had hoped he was quick enough to get her meaning because she was loath to go into a deeper explanation.

He'd understood. The way his expression flashed with irritation told her as much. 'Women,' he'd muttered. Then, suspiciously, 'You could be lying,' he'd suggested. 'Using that excuse as a delaying tactic.'

Her chin had come up at that, blue, blue eyes fixing clearly on his. 'I don't lie,' she'd lied. 'It's the truth.'

'How long?' he'd asked.

'Three days,' she'd replied, deciding she could just about get away with that without causing more suspicion.

'Friday it is, then,' he'd agreed.

And she'd felt too sick to do more than nod her head in agreement before she'd turned and walked stiffly out of his office, only to slump weakly against the wall beside his closed door, in much the same way she was now slumping in reaction to Sandro.

Only there was a difference, a marked difference between having reacted as she had through sickened revulsion at what Arthur Bates *wanted* to do to her, and reacting like this through helpless despair at what Sandro *could* do to her.

Sighing heavily, she forced herself to move at last, pushing out of the telephone kiosk and hunching deeply into her thick leather bomber jacket as she walked the few hundred yards back down the street to her tenement flat in icy March winds—weather that grimly threatened rain later.

Letting herself into the tiny flat, she stood for a moment, heart and hands clenched, while she absorbed the empty silence that always greeted her now when she stepped inside. Then, after a small flexing of her narrow shoulders, she relaxed her hands, and her heart, and began removing her heavy jacket.

Time was getting on, making deep inroads into Sandro's one-hour deadline, yet, instead of hurrying to get herself ready for the dreaded interview, she found herself walking across the room to the old-fashioned sideboard where she stood, looking down at it as if it had the power to actually inflict pain on her.

Which it did, she acknowledged. Or one particular drawer did.

Taking a deep breath, she reached out and opened the drawer—that particular drawer.

And instantly all the memories came flying out; like Pandora's box, they escaped and began circling around her, cruel and taunting.

So cruel, it took every ounce of self-control she possessed to reach inside, search for and come out with what she had opened the drawer to find. Then she was sliding it shut again with a gasped whoosh of air from aching lungs, while clasped in her trembling hand was a tiny high-domed box that instantly spoke for itself.

Stamped on its base in fine gold lettering was the name of a world-famous jeweller—its provenance in a way, or a big hint, at least, that what nestled inside the box was likely to be very valuable.

But the contents meant far more than just money to Joanna. So much more, in fact, that she had never dared let herself lift the lid of the box in two long years.

Not since she'd glanced down one bleak miserable day and noticed her wedding and engagement rings still circling her finger and been horrified—appalled that she had walked out on her marriage still wearing them! So she'd scrambled around in her things until she'd found the box and had put the rings away, vowing to herself to send them back to Sandro one day.

But she had never quite been able to bring herself to do it. In fact, each time she'd let herself so much as think about Sandro, the old panic had erupted, a wild, helpless, anguished kind of panic that would threaten to tear her apart inside.

It had erupted in that telephone kiosk only a few

minutes ago. And it was doing it again now as she stood here with the small ring box resting in her palm. Teeth clenched, mouth set, grimly ignoring all the warnings, she flicked open the box's delicately sprung lid—and felt her heart drop like a stone to the clawing base of her stomach.

For there they lay, nestling on a bed of purple satin. One, a slender band of the finest gold, the other, so lovely, so exquisite in its tasteful simplicity, that even as she swallowed on the thickness of tears growing in her throat her eyes could still appreciate beauty when they gazed on the single white diamond set into platinum.

A token of love from Sandro.

'I love you,' he had declared as he'd given the engagement ring to her. It was that simple, that neat, that special; like the simple, neat, special ring which, for all of that, must have cost him a small fortune.

He'd given it to her with love and she'd accepted it with love, she recalled, as the tears blurred out her vision and a dark cloud of aching emptiness began to descend all around her. For now their love was gone, and really, so should the rings have gone with it.

She could sell them, she knew that, and easily pay off her debt to Arthur Bates with the proceeds: just another of the ways-out she had spent her sleepless night struggling with.

But she knew she couldn't do it. For selling these rings would be tantamount to stealing from the one person in this world she had taken more than enough from already.

She'd stolen his pride, his self-respect, and, perhaps worst of all, his belief in himself as an acceptable member of the human race.

'You are tearing me apart—can you not see that? We must resolve this, Joanna, for I cannot take much more!'

Those hard, tight words came lashing back at her after

two long miserable years and she winced, feeling his pain whip at her as harshly now as it had done then.

And it had been because of that pain that she had eventually done the only thing she could think to do. She had left him, walked out on their marriage to move in with her sister Molly, and had refused contact with Sandro on any level, in the hope that he would manage to put behind him the failure of their marriage and learn to be happy again.

Maybe he had found happiness, because after those first few months, when he had tried very hard to get her to change her mind and come back to him, there had been no more contact—not even when she'd phoned him up to tell him about Molly.

Molly…

A sigh broke from her, and, lifting her gaze from the box of rings, she glanced across the room to where a small framed photograph stood beneath the lamp on her bedside table and her sister Molly's pretty face smiled out at her.

Her heart gave a tug of aching grief as she went to drop down on the edge of her narrow bed. Gently laying the ring box aside, she picked up Molly's photograph instead.

'Oh, Molly,' she whispered. 'Am I doing the right thing by going to Sandro for help?'

There was no answer—how could there be? Molly was no longer here.

But Sandro was very much alive. Sandro, the man she had loved so spectacularly that she had been prepared to do anything to hang on to that love.

Anything.

But then, what woman wouldn't? Alessandro Bonetti had to be the most beautiful man Joanna had ever set eyes upon. The evening he had walked into the small Italian restaurant where she had been working waiting on tables had quite literally changed her whole life.

'Alessandro!' her boss Vito had called out in elated surprise.

She had glanced up from what she had been doing. Joanna could still remember smiling at the sight of the short and rotund Vito being engulfed in a typically Latin back-slapping embrace by a man of almost twice his own height.

Over the top of Vito's balding head, Sandro had caught her smile and had returned it as if he knew exactly what she was finding so amusing—which in turn had taken her laughing blue eyes flicking upwards to clash with the liquid brown richness of his.

And that had been it. Just like that. Their eyes had locked and an instant and very mutual magic had begun to spark in the current of air between them. His beautiful eyes had darkened, his smile had died, the full length of his long, lean fabulously clothed body had tensed up and his expression had changed to one of complete shock, as if he'd just been hit full in the face by something totally spellbinding. As she'd stood there, caught— trapped by the same heart-stopping sensations herself— she'd watched his hand move in a oddly sensual gesture across the back of Vito's shoulders, and, to her shock, had felt the flesh across her own shoulders tingle as if he had stroked her, not Vito.

'Who is this?' he'd demanded of the little restaurant owner.

Vito had turned towards Joanna and grinned, instantly aware of what was captivating his visitor. 'Ah,' he'd said, 'I see you have already spotted the speciality of the house. This is Joanna,' he'd announced, 'the fire outside my kitchen!' And both men's eyes had wandered over her bright hair, sparkling blue eyes and softly blushing face in pure Latin communion. 'Joanna—this is Alessandro Bonetti,' Vito had completed the introductions. 'My cousin's nephew and a man to beware of,' he'd warned. 'For he will be a dangerous match to your flame!'

A match to her flame… All three of them had laughed at the joke. But in reality it had been the truth. The absolute truth. Sandro lit her up like no other man had ever done. Inside, outside, she caught fire like dry tinder for him. And what was wonderful was the way that Sandro had caught fire with her.

It had been like a dream come true.

So what had happened to the dream? she asked herself as she sat there staring into space.

Life had happened, she answered her own grim question. Life had jumped out when she was least expecting it to steal the dream right away from her.

And overnight she had gone from being the lively, loving creature who had so thoroughly captivated the man she loved, into this—this—hollow wreck of a person who was sitting here right now.

A hollow wreck who was seriously about to place herself in Sandro's dynamic vicinity again?

Could she do it to herself?

Could she do it to him? That was the far more appropriate question.

Cash or kind.

Suddenly and without warning she began to shake— shake all over, shake badly. It had happened like this quite often since she'd had the 'flu.

But really she knew she was shaking like this because she had come full circle and back to making choices.

To making the choice that was no choice.

So she got up, put Molly's photograph back on the bedside table, walked over to the sideboard to replace the ring box in the drawer, then went grimly about the business of getting herself ready to meet with Sandro…

CHAPTER TWO

PRESENTING herself at Sandro's office premises at the appointed hour took every last ounce of courage Joanna had left in her—though at least she knew she looked OK. She had, in fact, taken great pains to make sure she looked her best—for his sake more than her own.

For Sandro was Italian; a sense of good taste, flair and style came as naturally to him as breathing. Joanna had witnessed him stroll around his home in nothing more than a pair of unironed white boxer shorts and a shrunken white tee shirt that showed more taut brown midriff than was actually decent—and still he'd managed to look breathtakingly stylish.

Then she grimaced, acknowledging that she had only seen him dressed like that once in their short but disastrous attempt at living together. Where most women would have found it a pleasurable experience to watch their men parade in front of them like that, she, on the other hand, had metamorphosed into a stone-cold pillar of paralysed horror.

Sexy? Oh, yes, he had looked sexy, with all of that dark, hair-sprinkled dusky brown skin on show, from long bare feet to strong muscular thighs, and his short, straight black hair looking slightly mussed, eyes sleepy because he had been dozing on the sofa, trying to combat the effects of jet lag because he had just flown back from a whistle-stop visit to his American interests. Even the signs that he needed a shave had not deflected from the fact that the man was, and always would be, sexy—to any woman.

Even this woman, whose only response had been to completely close down or go totally crazy.

Not that he had ever understood why she'd responded like that.

Not that she'd ever wanted him to understand why she'd reacted to his sexuality like that.

Yet, when she'd first met him, she had fallen in love with him on sight and had desired him so badly that sometimes she hadn't known how she was going to cope without them making love. But in those early days of their relationship he had been busy and she had been busy, and she'd also had Molly to think about.

They would wait, they'd decided. Until they were married, until she had moved in with him properly, when, at last, they would have time and space to immerse themselves in what was bubbling so hotly between them.

Then the unmentionable had happened. And it had all gone sour for them.

Her fault. Her fault.

How Sandro had put up with her like that for as long as he did would always amaze her.

Pain. That was all she had ever brought to Sandro. Pain and frustration and a terrible—terrible confusion that had finally begun to make his work suffer.

He was a banker by trade, a speculator who invested heavily in the belief in others. He was young, successful, a man with boundless self-confidence who'd had to believe in his own good judgement to have become the success he was.

Marrying her had affected that judgement, had corroded his belief in himself. Two bad investments in as many months had eventually finished him off. 'This cannot go on much longer,' he'd told her. 'You are stripping me of everything I need to survive.'

'I know,' she'd whispered tragically. 'And I'm sorry. So very sorry....'

Walking out of his life had actually been easy by the time they'd reached that stage in their so-called marriage. She'd done it for him, she'd done it for herself, and had found a kind of peace in the loss of all that terrible tension that had been their constant companion. A peace she hoped—knew—Sandro had found too. He must have done, because she'd seen his name in print over the past couple of years, in articles praising his unwavering ability to latch on to a good business investment when he saw one.

So, walking back like this was going to be hard in a lot of ways, not least because she sensed that a simple phone call from her had already set the old corrosion flowing through his blood. To Sandro she was like a virus, corrupting everything he needed to function as a normal and self-confident human being.

She would make this short and sweet, she told herself firmly as she set her feet moving through those plate glass doors behind which were housed the head offices of the Bonetti empire. She would explain what she wanted, get his answer, then get right back out of his life again before the corruption could really take hold.

And she would not show him up by presenting herself in faded old jeans and a battered leather jacket! So she was wearing her one and only decent outfit, which had escaped the clear-out she'd done just a year back, when anger, and grief, and a whole tumult of wild, bitter feelings, had made her throw out everything that had once had an association with Sandro.

Except this fine black wool suit cut to Dior's famously ageless design. The suit hung on her body a bit now, because she had lost so much weight during the last year or two, but most of that was hidden beneath the smart raincoat she'd had to hurriedly pull on because the threatened rain had decided to start falling by the time she'd left her flat again.

But, despite the raincoat, she felt elegant enough to

go through those doors without feeling too out of place, and she found herself standing in a surprisingly busy foyer, where she paused to glance around her, wondering anxiously what she was supposed to do next. Sandro hadn't answered her when she'd asked him that question; instead he'd got angry and slammed down the phone.

A sigh broke from her, tension etched into every slender bone, and her mind was too busy worrying about her next move to notice the way she caught more than one very appreciative male eye as she hovered there uncertainly, a tall, very slender creature with alabaster-smooth skin, sapphire-blue eyes and long, straight red-gold hair that shimmered like living fire in the overhead lights.

Beautiful? Of course she was beautiful. A man like Alessandro Bonetti would not have given her a second glance if she had not been so exquisitely beautiful that she turned heads wherever she went.

Not that Joanna was aware of her own beauty—she had *never* been aware of it. Even now, as Alessandro Bonetti stood by the bank of lifts across the foyer and witnessed the way half his male staff came to a complete standstill to admire her, he could see she was completely oblivious to the effect she was having on those men as her blue, blue gaze darted nervously about.

Nervous.

His mouth thinned, anger simmering beneath the surface of his own coolly composed stance. She'd never used to be nervous of anything. She might have lacked self-awareness, but she'd always glowed with vibrant self-confidence, had been strong, spirited enough to take on any situation. Now he watched her hover there like some wary exotic bird ready to take flight at the slightest sign of danger.

Her biggest danger, of course, being him.

She saw him then, and the fine hairs at the back of his neck began to stand on end in response to those eyes fixing on his own for the first time in two long years…

It was electrifying, an exact repeat of the first time their eyes had clashed across a room like this. Joanna felt the same charge shoot through her system like a lightning bolt. She stopped breathing, her heart seeming to swell so suddenly in her breast—like a flower bursting open to the first ray of sunlight it had encountered in so long—it was actually painful.

Why? Because she loved him—had always loved him. And knowing it quite literally tore her apart inside.

He was so tall, she observed helplessly. So lean and dark and sleek and special, with that added touch of arrogance he always carried with him, which only managed to increase the flower-burst taking place within her hungry breast.

He was wearing an Italian-cut dove-grey suit with a pale blue shirt and dark silk tie knotted neatly at his brown throat. His black-as-night hair was cut short at the back and styled to sweep elegantly away from his high, intelligent brow.

Her skin began to tingle, her eyes drifting downwards over sleepy brown eyes fringed by impossibly long eyelashes, and a thin, slightly hooked nose that was unapologetically Roman, like his noble bone structure, like his wonderful rich brown skin that sheened like satin over cheeks absolutely spare of any extra flesh.

And then there was his mouth, she noted with a dizzying swirl of senses that kept her completely held in their thrall. His mouth was the mouth of a born sensualist; it oozed sensuality, promised it, wanted and demanded it.

The mouth of a lover. The mouth of a Roman conqueror. The mouth she had once known so intimately that something inside her flared in burning recognition. It soared up from the very roots of her sexuality to arrive in a fire-burst of craving in her breast, making her gasp, making her own mouth quiver, making her want to taste that mouth again so badly that—

I can't do this! she decided on a sudden wave of wild panic. I can't be this close to him—face him like this and pretend to be cool and collected and indifferent to all of this—this excruciating attraction!

I've got to go. I've got to…

She was going to run, Sandro realised with a sudden tensing of his tingling spine. The urge to flee was literally pulsing in every tautly held muscle she possessed, and abruptly he jerked himself into movement, making her hesitate, bringing her flustered gaze fluttering up to clash with his own.

Where he locked it—with a sheer superiority of will; he used his eyes to lock her to the spot while he strode across the foyer towards her, as graceful as any supremely proficient cat mesmerising its prey before it pounced.

His movement brought the whole reception area to a complete and utter standstill, and the silence was stunning as all those present watched their revered employer make a bee-line for the beautiful stranger who had just stepped through their doors.

He reached her, pausing a careful foot away. 'Joanna,' he greeted quietly.

'Hello, Sandro,' she huskily replied, having to tilt her head back to keep looking into that very mesmeric face.

Then neither of them moved. For a long, timeless moment they simply stood there gazing at each other, enveloped by memories that were not all bad; some of them were, in fact, quite heart-wrenchingly wonderful.

So wonderful that her breasts heaved on a small, tight intake of air as a muscle deep down inside her abdomen writhed in recollection. Predictably she stiffened that disturbed muscle in rejection of her response.

Sandro saw and accurately read every single expression that flickered across her vulnerable face. The love still burning, the pain still hurting, the desire still clutching—then the inevitable rejection. His own eyes began to darken, sending back messages of an answering pain, of a desire that still burned inside him too and, perhaps most heart-wrenching of all, of a love well remembered, though long gone now.

After all—how could he still be in love with her after everything she had done to him?

He blinked then, slowly lowering and unfurling those impossibly long lashes as if he was using them to wipe away those answering messages and put in their place a cool implacability. Slowly his hand came towards her with the intention of taking her by the arm.

But Joanna saw the tendon running along his jawline tighten perceptibly as he did so, and was dismayed to realise that he was looking so tense because he expected her to flinch away from his touch in front of all these watching people.

She didn't flinch. Sandro couldn't know it, but she would rather die than show him up here of all places, on his own territory where he ruled supreme.

So his fingers closed around her elbow, and she felt the usual jolt of heat run along her arm in a direct warning to her brain that someone had invaded her personal space. But her blue eyes held his, calm and steady, and after a few more taut, telling moments, the tension eased out of his jawline and was replaced with a twist to his beautiful mouth that grimly mocked her small show of restraint—as if it offended him that she felt she had to protect his pride in front of all of these people.

'Come,' was all he said as he tightened his grip on her elbow then turned to begin drawing her across the silenced foyer, arrogantly ignoring every set of curious eyes that followed them.

'This is awful,' Joanna whispered self-consciously. 'Couldn't you have come up with a more discreet way of meeting me?'

'Discreet as in covert?' Sandro questioned drily. 'You are my wife, not my mistress,' he pointed out. 'My wife

I meet out in the open. With my mistress I am always very discreet.'

Stung to the core by the very idea of him being intimate with any woman, her heart began to fill with enough acid venom to curdle her system and blind her eyes to exactly where Sandro was leading her—until it was too late.

Then jealousy was suddenly being replaced by a crawling sense of horror that had her stopping dead in her tracks. 'No,' she protested huskily. 'Sandro, I can't—'

'Privacy, *cara.*' He cut right across whatever she had been going to say, 'is required before we begin.'

Privacy, Joanna repeated to herself, as the power of his grip forced her into movement again, propelling her into the waiting lift where at last he let go of her so he could turn his attention to the console.

The doors slid shut. They were suddenly alone. Alone inside a tiny eight-foot-square box with grey panelled walls and nowhere to run to if she required an escape.

No.

Her heart was in her mouth. As the lift began shooting them upwards her stomach shot the other way. It was awful. She closed her eyes, gritted her teeth and clenched her hands into two tight fists at her sides as an old clamouring reaction trapped her within a world of mindless dismay.

Sandro noticed—who wouldn't have noticed when she was standing there quivering with her teeth biting hard into her tense bottom lip? 'Stop it!' he snapped. 'I am not even touching you any longer!'

'Sorry,' she whispered, trying desperately hard to get a hold on herself. 'But it's not you. It's the lift.'

'The lift?' he repeated incredulously. 'Since when have your phobias added lifts to their great number?'

Sarcasm, she recognised, and supposed she deserved

it. 'Don't ask,' she half laughed, trying to make a joke of it.

But Sandro was clearly in no mood for humour. 'Another no-go subject I am banned from mentioning, I see.'

'Go to hell,' she breathed, her eyes squeezed tightly shut while she tried to fight off the soaring panic.

'And be virtually guaranteed to meet you there?' he derided. 'No chance.'

And once again they were sniping at each other. Like their telephone conversation earlier, they were proving yet again that they couldn't be in each other's company without all of this—emotion—spilling out.

The wrong kind of emotion.

'You may relax now,' he drawled with yet more sarcasm. 'We have come to a stop.'

Her eyes fluttered open to discover that they had indeed come to a stop without her even noticing it. The doors were open and Sandro was already strolling out onto a plush grey-carpeted corridor. He walked off, obviously expecting her to follow him. After having to peel herself away from the lift wall, she stepped out on decidedly shaky legs, feeling as if she were pulling a whole load of heavy old baggage along behind her.

He was waiting for her by a closed door, stiff-backed and angry. Smothering a heavy sigh, because this was all becoming so damned fraught—and she hadn't even got to the reason she had come here!—Joanna forced herself to walk towards him.

One of his long brown hands was resting on the door handle. He didn't so much as glance at her, yet still timed the moment he threw that door open so he instantly followed her into a big airy office where a very attractive blonde-haired woman of about Joanna's own age sat behind a desk.

She glanced up as they came in and smiled expectantly at them. But to Joanna's further discomfort Sandro ignored the look, not intending, it seemed, to introduce the two women.

And why should he? Joanna asked herself as she followed him across the room to another door. I won't be here long enough for it to mean much, even if he did!

When he opened the door he stepped aside again, obviously expecting Joanna to precede him. On an inner frisson of awareness to his electric closeness, she hurriedly brushed past him.

His office was a surprise—nothing like what she would have expected of the Sandro she used to know, she observed as she came to a halt in the middle of the room. This ultra-modern example of smoked grey executive decor bore no resemblance to the rich, dark wood antiquity of his private homes.

The door closed behind her. Joanna quelled the urge to stiffen up warily.

'Take off your coat,' Sandro coolly commanded.

Coat? She spun on her heel to stare at him, a fresh frisson of alarm stinging along her spine. She didn't want to remove her coat. She wasn't intending staying here long enough for it to be necessary!

'I—'

'The coat, Joanna,' he interrupted, and when she still didn't make a move to do it herself he began walking towards her, with his intent so clear that her fingers snapped up to begin undoing the buttons. He grimaced, mocking the fact that it took only the suggestion that he might try to touch her again for her to do exactly what he had told her to do.

Angry with herself for being so damned obvious, and annoyed with him for knowing her as well as he did, she drew off the coat and draped it across a nearby chair while he, thank goodness, diverted towards the big pale polished cedar desk standing in front of a huge plate glass window.

Then he turned and did the worst thing he could do

as far as she was concerned. He leaned his spare hips against the front of the desk, crossed his ankles, folded his arms across his wide chest, then proceeded to study her slowly, from her tensely curling toes, hidden inside plain black court shoes, to the top of her shining head.

She flushed, lowering her face and gripping tightly at the strap of her shoulder bag. He always did have this knack for completely discomposing her with a look, just as he was doing now—deliberately, she guessed. And she hated it. Hated what it made her feel inside.

But she had a suspicion that he knew that, too.

'You've lost weight,' he remarked finally. 'That suit hangs on you like an old sack. If you lose any more weight you will simply fade away. Why have you lost so much weight?' he demanded.

'I'm sorry,' she snapped. But surely he could work out *why* she had got so thin! It didn't take much knowledge of the last devastating year she had just lived through to understand it.

'Sorry—again, Joanna?' he mocked. 'I remember that being your favourite word before. It used to infuriate me then. It still does now,' he added grimly.

Her chin lifted, blue eyes flashing him a glinting warning that the very short fuse to her temper was alight. 'You said you were busy,' she reminded him curtly.

He dipped his dark head in wry acknowledgment of both the short fuse and the reminder that his time was precious. This was something else Sandro could never resist—riling her too-ready temper. He had once told her that it was the only really healthy emotion she had in her. He was probably right. It was the only one she had ever shown him during their short, disastrous marriage, anyway.

There was a knock at the office door. Joanna jumped nervously. Sandro grimaced at her nervousness, then his secretary was entering the room, carrying a tray set with coffee things.

The tension in the room must have been stingingly obvious, because she glanced warily at her employer, then skittered her gaze over Joanna, before murmuring some incoherent apology as she hurried across the room to place the tray down on a glass-topped coffee table set between two low leather sofas.

No one else moved. Sandro wouldn't, Joanna couldn't, and the silence gnawed in the air surrounding them all as the poor woman did what she had to do then turned to leave again with a brief, wary smile aimed somewhere between the two of them.

Joanna watched Sandro watch the intruder leave, watched him run his eyes over the woman from the top of her sleek blonde head to the slender heels of her black patent shoes. It was born in him to study women like that, Joanna was sure he wasn't even aware that he did it, but God she hated it!

Beautiful, she seethed in jealous silence. Of course the woman had to be beautiful! Sandro would not accept anything less in a woman who worked within such close confines!

'*Grazi*, Sonia,' he murmured rather belatedly, just as 'Sonia' was about to walk through the door.

She sent him a glance and it spoke volumes. Sonia was offended that he had not introduced her to his wife. But Joanna was only relieved. She had no wish to be nice to his secretary when she was too busy trying to subdue a second bout of jealousy that was so strong it literally fizzed beneath the surface of her skin.

Did Sonia do more than his typing for him? Could she be the very discreet mistress?

The door closed them in once again, and Sandro's attention was back on her. He studied her stiff-boned, firmly blank stance for a few moments, then sighed as though her very presence here irritated the hell out of him. He waved a long-suffering hand towards the seating area.

'Sit down for goodness' sake,' he muttered. 'Before your shaking legs give out on you.'

'They're not shaking,' she denied, but went to sit down anyway, choosing one of the sofas and perching herself on the very edge, hoping he wouldn't play his old trick of sitting himself down beside her. It was just another tactic he'd used to employ to completely unsettle her. He'd used to gain some kind of morbid gratification from placing her on the defensive.

But this time, she was relieved to see, he decided not to bother with that one. Instead he turned his attention to pouring out two cups of coffee.

Joanna watched his every move, every deft flick of those long brown fingers as he poured out two black coffees, added sugar to his own but none to hers, used the small silver spoon to stir the sugar, then silently handed a delicate white china cup and saucer to her, before going to sit down on the sofa opposite with his own.

And he did it all without bothering to ask her if that was how she liked her coffee. Sandro possessed almost instant total recall. He could remember names, places, facts and figures without having to try very hard. It was a major asset in his line of business, he had once told her, to possess fast recall of any information he might have acquired concerning the subject under consideration at the time. It saved him a lot of hassle because it meant he didn't need to waste time going off to gather up the information.

On top of that, he was astute, *very* astute. Few people managed to con him. Though she was one of those few who had managed to do it. And in some ways she believed he'd found that harder to forgive than anything else she had done to him.

'OK,' he said flatly. 'Let's have it.'

She shook, rattling the delicate bone china cup in its

saucer so badly she had to lean forward and put them down before she spilled the coffee all over herself.

Sandro crossed one elegant knee over the other. That was all, no other reaction whatsoever, but the action captured her restive attention. He was wearing charcoal-coloured socks, she noticed inconsequently. His shoes were hand-made lace-ups in a shining black leather.

'I need some money,' she mumbled, hating herself for having to ask him, of all people, for it.

'How much?'

Just like that. No hint of surprise, no raised voice. She had never asked him for anything before, not even a tube of toothpaste. He knew that. The man with total recall would remember that telling little fact.

Which also meant he had already worked out that this was a dire situation for her.

'F-five…' The rest got stuck in her tension-locked throat and she had to swallow before she could say it. 'Five thousand pounds.'

Still nothing. No reaction whatsoever. She even glanced up, wary, puzzled, searching his impassive face for a hint of what he was thinking.

She saw nothing.

'That is a lot of money for you, Joanna,' was the only comment he made.

'I know,' she admitted. 'I'm s…' Sorry, she had been going to say, but she stopped herself and instead got stiffly to her feet, unable to remain still beneath that dark level stare for a single moment longer.

With a tight restlessness she moved herself away from his close proximity, aware that his eyes were following her, aware that his brain was working faster than any other brain she had ever known.

Aware that he was waiting for her to tell him what she wanted the money for but was determined not to ask her himself.

Reaching his desk, she rested the flat of her hips

against its edge and crossed her arms over her body so her icy fingers could curl tensely around her slender arms.

The silence between them began to stretch; she could feel it vibrating like a tautened wire between them. But, in a way, it made her want to do something to stop it, so she turned abruptly to face him, lifted her chin and forced herself to look directly into his carefully neutral eyes.

'I have a proposition to put to you,' she announced. 'I need some m-money and, since you are the only person I know who has any, I thought you could give it me in the f-form of a settlement.'

'A settlement to what?'

Her heart suddenly decided to stammer. 'A divorce.'

No response, not even a flicker of those long, lush, lazy lashes, the super-controlled bastard!

'I know you can't possibly want to hang onto this so-called marriage of ours,' she raced on quickly. 'So I thought it might be best to make a clean break of it.'

'For five thousand pounds?'

Her cheeks warmed with guilty colour. 'Yes.'

'So, let me get this straight,' he recounted, 'You want to divorce a multi-millionaire for the princely sum of five thousand pounds. Now that, Joanna, insults my ego,' he informed her, moving at last to get rid of his own cup and saucer, then relaxing back again. 'Why not go for the jackpot and demand half of everything I own?' he suggested. 'After all, you are entitled to it.'

No, she wasn't. She wasn't entitled to anything from Sandro, not even the five thousand she was asking him for. 'I just want f-five thousand pounds,' she reiterated, staring down at some unremarkable spot on the smooth grey carpet, because the next bit was going to be even harder to say, and she couldn't look at him while she said it. 'And I need it today, if you can lay your hands on that much.'

'Cash?'

She swallowed, then nodded. 'Please…'

No reply. Again she was forced to look up so she could search his face for a hint of what he was thinking—and she saw nothing but a sudden terrible gravity that almost cut her in two.

Face flushing, she dropped her gaze once more, agitated fingers picking at the fine woollen sleeves of her suit jacket.

'Perhaps you had better tell me why you need it,' Sandro suggested very quietly.

'I've got myself into debt,' she admitted, so softly that Sandro was lucky to hear it. 'And the people I borrowed the m-money from are riding my back for payment.'

He heard. 'Who?' he demanded. 'Who exactly is riding you?'

She didn't answer, her small chin lowering to her chest in an act of sinking shame, and another tense silence followed because she found that now she had come this far she just didn't have it in her to tell him the full truth. He was bound to be so disappointed in her!

She had never done anything a man like Sandro would consider worthy. It had used to annoy him that she worked at two different jobs as a waitress, six days and nights out of seven each week. He could never understand why she had no ambition to do something better with her life. He'd disliked the tiny flat she used to share with Molly, and had even offered to put them both up in something more fitting.

But more fitting for whom? She'd always suspected he'd meant fitting for a man like him to visit; that, in his own way, Sandro was ashamed of his little waitress girlfriend, even if he was too besotted at the time to walk away from her.

And, on top of all of that, he hated gamblers. Said they were weak-willed losers in life who wanted everything the easy way. How did you tell a man who thought like that that you'd spent the last year working in a casino for miserable peanuts, only to gamble those peanuts away at the tables yourself!

She couldn't. It was as simple as that. She could not do it. And she was just wondering if he would detect a lie if she came up with one that would cover a five-thousand-pound debt, when he pulled one of his other little tricks and confused her by suddenly changing the subject.

'Where have you been living recently?' he asked.

'Here in London.' She shrugged.

'Still waiting hand and foot on other people?'

'Yes.'

He sighed, his disappointment in her clear this time. 'You did not have to go back to doing that kind of job, Joanna,' he said grimly. 'When we parted, I had no intention of leaving you so destitute that you had to return to that.'

'You owed me nothing.' And both of them knew there was more truth in that than really bore thinking about.

'You are my wife!' he bit out raspingly. 'Of course I owed you something!'

Which led them neatly back to the money, Joanna wryly supposed.

'What I find difficult to believe,' he continued, 'is that you, of all people, have got yourself into that kind of debt entirely on your own! In fact,' he extended frowningly, 'you always shied right away from the risk of getting yourself into debt for even the smallest amount.'

She grimaced, shamed and contrarily mollified by those few words of praise from this, her biggest critic. He was right, money had never been one of her gods—not in the shape of cold, hard cash in the pocket, that was.

'So, who is it for, Joanna?' Sandro demanded grimly. 'Who really needs this five thousand pounds you are asking me for?'

Her chin came up, the frown puckering her smooth brow telling him that she did not follow his meaning. 'It's for me,' she stated. 'I got into this mess all by myself.'

But he was already shaking his head, expression grave again, saddened almost. 'It's for Molly,' he decided. 'It has to be. Has your sister managed to get herself into financial difficulties, Joanna?' he demanded. 'Is that what this is really about?'

Whatever Sandro had expected her to do or say at this very critical point, he certainly had not expected her to draw the air into her body in the short, sharp way she did—or for her face to drain of every last vestige of colour.

'My God, that was cruel,' she breathed out eventually, staring at him as if he had just thrust a ten-inch blade into her chest. 'How could Molly be in trouble,' she choked out thickly, 'when you already know she is dead?'

CHAPTER THREE

SANDRO'S reaction was to shoot to his feet. 'What did you say?' he raked out hoarsely. Then, 'Please say again,' he commanded, sounding as though he had suddenly lost his grasp of the English language. 'For I think I must have misheard you.'

'But you knew!' Joanna cried. 'M-Molly was knocked down and killed in a traffic accident twelve months ago!'

'No!' The angry denial literally exploded from him. 'I do not believe you!'

But Joanna wasn't impressed. 'I rang you—right here, at this office!' she contended. 'You wouldn't speak to me, s-so I left a message with your secretary!'

That secretary? she wondered suddenly. Had she spoken with the lovely Sonia that day her whole world fell apart?

'You rang here?' What she was saying was finally beginning to sink in. He sounded punch drunk, suddenly looked it too—utterly punch drunk. 'Molly is dead?'

'Do you honestly think I would lie about something like that?'

Of course she wouldn't, and acknowledgement of that fact actually rocked him right back on his heels, shock ripping down the full length of his lean, tight body as he stood there and stared at her—stared while his richly tanned face went pale.

Then, quite without warning, the famous Bonetti self-control completely deserted him and, on an act of savage impulse, he spun jerkily on his heel and brought his clenched fist crashing down on the glass-topped table!

Joanna gasped, eyes widening in numb disbelief as delicate china rattled on impact, then began to bounce upwards, tumbling through the air to land with a splintering crash just about everywhere! The glass table-top broke, not splintering like the china, but folding in on itself and shattering into big lethal pieces.

The ensuing silence was appalling. Broken china and glass, spilled sugar, cream and coffee lay spread across everything—the two grey leather sofas and the carpet!

And there was Sandro. Sandro slowly straightening from the utter carnage he had just wreaked, teeth bared, lips tightly drawn back, face ashen, blood oozing from the knuckles of his still clenched fist.

'Oh, no,' she whispered, coming out of her horrified daze to push a trembling hand up to mouth. 'You didn't know…'

'Astute,' he clipped, driving his uninjured hand into his pocket to come out with a clean handkerchief.

He began wrapping the handkerchief around his bloody knuckles while, shaken to her very roots, all Joanna could do was stand there and watch him. She tried to breathe but found that she couldn't. Her lungs seemed to have seized up while her heart was thundering against a steel casing of shock that had wrapped itself tightly around her chest.

The door suddenly flew open, Sonia almost falling into the room with it. 'Oh, good grief!' she gasped, her eyes going wide in horror as they took in the carnage.

'Get out!' Sandro barked at her, swinging a look of such unholy savagery on her that she whimpered with a muffled choke and quickly stepped out of the room again, shutting the door behind her.

'Th-there was no need to take your anger out on your secretary,' Joanna murmured in tremulous reproach.

Sandro disregarded the rebuke. 'I never got your message,' he bit out. 'Did you think I would have ignored it if I had? You did,' he realised, seeing the answer etched into her unguarded face.

She had insulted him. Simply allowing herself to believe that he didn't care about Molly's death was probably the biggest insult she had ever given him.

And she had given him a few, Joanna acknowledged. 'I'm...'

'Don't dare say it,' he warned her gratingly.

Her mouth snapped shut, then on a shaky little sigh it opened again. 'At first I refused to believe you would just ignore her death like that,' she allowed. 'But when I heard nothing from you, f-for days and days, I decided you...' An awkward shrug finished what really no longer needed to be said. 'And I was in shock,' she continued huskily. 'I could barely think straight. It was only after the f-funeral, w-when I'd moved from the flat and found somewhere else to live because I couldn't bear to stay there without—without...' She couldn't say Molly's name either, 'It was only then that it really began to sink in that you hadn't—hadn't...'

At last she stumbled into silence. Sandro didn't say a word, not a single word, but just ran his uninjured hand across the top of his sleek dark head, dropped it stiffly to his side again, then turned away from her as if looking at her at all offended him.

'I'm sorry' hovered on the tip of her tongue again but managed to stay there while she simply stared at him, feeling helpless, feeling guilty, feeling hopelessly inadequate to deal with the fractured emotions clamouring around the two of them.

'When?' he asked suddenly. 'When did this happen?'

She told him the date, her low-pitched voice unsteady.

'*Madre di dio,*' Sandro breathed.

Molly had been killed a year ago to the very day.

Then he was moving, making her eyes instantly wary as he strode towards her, right past her, to angrily round his desk. His hand snaked out, catching up the telephone, while his other hand remained tensely at his side, the handkerchief bandage slowly staining red.

'I want a print-out of all calls to this office on this date a year ago,' he snapped at whoever was on the other end of the line. 'And while you are about it you will bring in last year's appointments diary.' Slam. The telephone landed back on its rest.

Joanna blinked, still staring, still stunned by the incredible display of emotional fury from this man who was usually so controlled. It was awful, she *felt* awful for being the one to cause it. And it only got worse because, quite suddenly, he dropped into the chair behind his desk then slumped forward, both hands going up to cover his face.

Once again the desire to say sorry was hovering precariously close to the edge of being spoken. She had truly believed that he was no longer interested in anything that happened to her. It had caused her so much hurt at the time—oh, not only because of her own wretched feelings of desertion, but also for Molly. Molly, who had thought the world of Sandro.

Joanna had hurt him with her bitter and twisted view of everything life had to throw at her. Now she wanted to go to that desk and put her arms around him, hold him—offer him some kind of consolation for the shock she had just dealt him.

But she couldn't because her own maimed senses wouldn't let her. So she turned and moved away a step or two, then just stood with her arms tightly folded across her body and her eyes grimly lowered from the temptation of Sandro, who looked still so in need of comfort.

The tentative knock which came on the office door before it hesitantly opened was actually a relief.

Sandro straightened in his seat, face still pale, features drawn, eyes so black they wrenched at Joanna's useless heart strings.

He didn't look at Joanna but honed his attention directly onto his secretary. 'The print-out you asked for,' she murmured, hurrying forward to place it down on the desk in front of him. 'And last year's appointments diary…'

Sandro began scanning the print-out while Sonia hovered warily, uncertain what was expected of her—she was curious, curious enough to keep sending Joanna furtive glances that scurried away before their eyes could clash.

'I was away in Rome throughout the whole month of March,' Sandro sighed out eventually.

Sonia nodded. 'I remember,' she said, and heat bloomed into her cheeks.

Guilty heat? Knowing heat? I-remember-because-we-were-there-as-lovers kind of heat? Jealousy licked a sandpaper-rough stroke along Joanna's backbone, stiffening it, leaving it tight and tingling.

'So, who took over here?' Sandro demanded.

'Luca brought his own secretary here with him,' Sonia explained, then dared to ask the big question. 'Why? Was there some kind of oversight?'

'Oversight?' Grimly Sandro repeated the word and let loose a short huff of a laugh. 'You could say that,' he clipped out, then, heavily, 'OK, Sonia you can leave this with me now.'

A dismissal in anyone's books. If they were lovers, Sandro obviously knew how to keep the two relationships separate.

'Discretion' was the word he had used himself.

Sonia walked stiffly out of the room, leaving another fraught silence in her wake. 'Come here, Joanna,' Sandro commanded grimly.

But that awful, blinding, bitter jealousy was now licking its way around her whole body and she couldn't move a single muscle. Didn't dare even glance at him, because if she did she would be spitting out filthy accusations, like, You're sleeping with that woman while you're still married to me, you bastard!

'Joanna…'

Oh, God, why had she come here? Why had she set herself up for all this grief? Grabbing desperately at some hint of composure, she walked forward until once more the flat of her hips touched the desk.

'Read,' he commanded, stabbing a long finger at a single line of type on the paper print-out.

It was a list of some kind. Frowning, she leaned a little closer so she focused on what was written. 'Female asking for Mr Bonetti,' it said. 'No name. No message.'

'This is a computer print-out of all telephone calls that come into this suite of offices,' he explained. 'Look at the date. Look at the time. That was you calling me, wasn't it?' he suggested gently. 'On the day of Molly's accident you called here, and in your shock and confusion when you could not get through to me personally you forgot to leave your name or mark the urgency of why you were calling, didn't you?'

Had she? Was that what she had done? She frowned, trying to remember, but found that she couldn't. That dreadful day was very hazy. She could barely remember anything about it except trying to contact Sandro.

'And see this…' he continued levelly, turning the old appointments diary to face her next. The whole of the month of March was scored through with a pen. 'ROME' it had printed in big letters. 'I was not in the country. I was, in fact, away for the whole month.'

'You don't have to go to these extremes to convince me it was an oversight,' she murmured uncomfortably. 'I believe you without it.'

'Thank you,' he said.

'You're not a liar,' she tagged on with a jerky shrug of one slender shoulder. 'Your honesty and integrity have never been in question for me,' she felt constrained to add.

'Well, thank you for that, also,' he very drily replied.

Then in one of those quick-fire changes of mood he could undergo which tended to make her flounder, he suddenly stood up and rounded the desk.

'Come on,' he said, taking a grip on one of her hands.

She stiffened up like a board, but he ignored the stiffening, being so used to it from years ago. Just as he had become used to having to ignore it if he wanted to go on touching her. He began pulling her towards the door.

'But where are we going?' she demanded warily.

'My hand needs attention,' he clipped out, that was all.

The door opened, he pulled her through it, then pulled her past his wide-eyed, beautiful secretary without so much as glancing her way, out of that office, down the corridor and into a waiting lift.

Another damn lift.

He let go of her at the one time in her life when she wished he'd hang on tightly, digging his unwrapped hand into his inside jacket pocket and coming out with what looked like a plastic credit card. Sliding the card into a narrow slot in the lift console, he pressed one of the floor buttons, then slid the card out again.

But Joanna didn't see which floor number they were going to; she was too busy bracing herself for the moment when those wretched doors would close them in.

'You are quite pathetic, do you know that?' he observed deridingly.

Yes, she acknowledged, she knew it, but knowing it didn't stop the war of abominable memories she was desperately trying to suppress.

The doors closed, the lift began moving, and she pressed herself back against its panelled wall, expecting to begin sinking downwards—but didn't. The lift shot up, then came to an almost immediate stop again.

Startled, she opened her eyes to find Sandro watching her with a half-frowning, half-contemptuous expression.

She stared back, vulnerable—without knowing it, she looked vulnerable.

The doors slid apart. Sandro wrenched his gaze away from her and walked out of the lift, like the last time, obviously expecting her to follow him.

She did so reluctantly, once again having to peel herself away from the wall and walk forward on shaking legs—only to stop dead two steps on to stare bewilderedly around her.

'Where are we?' she asked sharply.

'Up one floor,' Sandro replied. 'In my private apartment, to be exact.'

Predictably, all hell broke loose inside her, blue eyes flickering around her new surroundings like a trapped animal looking for a means of escape. 'Y-your apartment?' she repeated unsteadily. 'Here?'

'Yes,' he confirmed, his tone spiked. 'Convenient, is it not?'

He knew what she was thinking. He knew what she was feeling. He knew that to her, a private apartment meant intimacy, and intimacy translated into panic.

She flicked him a very wary glance. He answered it with a mocking one, challenging her to protest, to give in to what was beginning to bubble up inside her and run screaming for the dubious safety of the lift behind her.

A choice of two evils. Like the one she'd had to make between facing Sandro again, or facing what Arthur Bates had in store for her.

Then there was no choice to be made, because the lift doors gave a soft warning whoosh. She almost jumped out of her skin, spinning jerkily around to stare as her one means of escape smoothly closed on her.

'Well, well,' Sandro drawled so silkily she winced. 'Caught like a frightened little mouse in a trap. Poor Joanna. But please,' he continued before she could retaliate against his biting sarcasm, 'make yourself at home, if you can,' He was dry and he was cutting. 'I need to attend to my injured hand.'

Then he had gone, disappearing through a door and leaving her hovering there, staring dazedly around her.

It was nice, was the first sensible thought to reach through the scramble her mind had become. The lift had opened directly into a large airy sitting-room that reflected Sandro's very classical Italian tastes much more than his ultra-modern office had done.

Pale pastel-shaded walls made a tasteful backcloth to timeless pieces of elegant antique furniture that blended easily with the more modern oatmeal sofas and easy chairs sitting comfortably on a thick-piled cappuccino-coloured carpet.

No smoked glass to pound his fist into here, she noted wryly—only to feel her breath catch in her throat when she relived the appalling sight of Sandro, of all people, losing control of himself like that. It just wasn't like him. Sandro had always been the most patient and controlled person she knew.

He had to be, around you, a small voice inside her own head grimly taunted. She sighed, the dark, weighty truth of that sitting heavily on her narrow shoulders.

Then he was back without warning, striding through the door he had disappeared through a few minutes earlier, and instantly any feelings of guilt or remorse she might have been experiencing towards him left, because she was suddenly feeling that inner sun-burst of pleasure begin to erupt all over again, holding her captive; she was mesmerised by the sheer animal sexuality of the man.

His jacket had gone, and his tie; the top button to his pale blue shirt had been yanked impatiently open at his taut brown throat, the sleeves rolled up his hair-peppered arms.

'Here,' he said. 'Do this for me.'

She blinked, trying to clear the hypnotic effect he was

having on her, her darkened eyes lowering to the snowy
white towel he now held to his injured hand.

'It needs covering until it stops bleeding,' he explained, holding out a band of sticking plaster to her.

But he was much too close, much too vibrantly, ag-
gressively, electrifyingly real. So real she could feel his
body heat, could smell the subtle tangy scent of him.
Her fingers fluttered, her nails scraping against the sides
of her skirt, lungs beginning to fill her chest as memories
swam up from the depths of nowhere, memories of how
it had felt to be held against his warm, tight, very masculine body. And she wanted him. She closed her eyes,
almost groaned out loud. How badly she wanted to feel
this man against her, around her, deep, deep inside her!

'Joanna!' His voice was tight, it was angry, and it
showed how completely he misunderstood the reason
why she was standing here white-faced and quivering
like this. 'I am asking you to place a small plaster on
my hand—not take all your damned clothes off!'
Offence shuddered through him on a wave of personal
resentment that stiffened his muscles and hardened his
face. 'I will do it myself!' he raked at her harshly.

'No!' she protested, her emotions hitting an all-time
high of helpless confusion 'No,' she repeated huskily.
'I'll do it.'

Quickly she took the dressing from him, plucking it
with a snap from his fingers and ripping away its protective paper casing.

In hot, acid silence, he let her remove the covering
towel and inspect the damage, her trembling fingertips
carefully checking for tiny shards of glass while her
teeth clamped hard into her tense bottom lip because his
eyes were boring into the top of her bent head with such
bitter antipathy.

'Can you feel anything in that?' she asked, pressing
gently either side of the open cut.

'No.'

'It isn't as bad as it could have been,' she remarked, as casually as she could. 'It was a stupid thing to do, Sandro.'

'Believing me capable of ignoring your sister's death was stupid.'

Joanna grimaced. It was true, and she had been stupid. Stupid with shock, stupid with grief, stupid in so many ways that at this precise moment she didn't dare let herself think about most of them.

'So, tell me how it happened,' he requested quietly.

Her fingers stilled in the act of smoothing the plaster across his grazed knuckle, then, almost unknowingly, they straightened, stretching out along the length of his. Only Sandro's fingers were longer than her own, stronger, but beautifully sculptured, the short nails well kept and neatly rounded, his skin warm to the touch.

'She was on her way to college,' she murmured in a voice devoid of emotion. 'Standing at the bus stop when a car ploughed into her. Its breaks had failed,' she explained. 'The driver lost control... Molly wasn't the only one to be killed outright,' she said flatly. 'Three more people died and another three were seriously injured. It was in all the newspapers at the time,' she added huskily. 'Names printed. Addresses...' Which was why she had been so sure that Sandro had to have heard what had happened. Even if he'd missed her phone call, he couldn't have possibly missed the press coverage.

And quite suddenly she began to shake with those wretched violent spasms that had been catching her out when she least needed them. Sandro muttered something in Italian and the next thing Joanna knew she was being folded against him and held there fast by determined arms.

'Weep on me if you want to,' he invited thickly. 'You never know, I may even join you!'

A joke? No, he wasn't joking; the situation was just too wretched to turn into a joke. But she didn't weep.

She hadn't wept in years, couldn't weep—wouldn't weep.

Why? Because she knew that if she so much as gave in to the smallest sob, then the floodgates would open wide and the whole lot would come pouring out.

Everything—everything.

So instead she just stood there, letting him hold her, gaining some small measure of comfort from his all-encompassing embrace. But she needed to cry—she knew that, in some deep, dark place in her; she knew she was teetering right on the very edge of a complete mental collapse if she didn't release some of the monsters lurking inside her.

'I am sorry I wasn't here for you, *cara*,' he murmured.

'It doesn't matter now,' she mumbled into his warm brown throat.

It was the wrong thing to say, obviously, because he was suddenly angry again. 'Of course it damned well matters!' he rasped, pulling away from her to leave her standing alone, feeling cold and deserted, having to fight a desperate urge to throw herself against him again. 'You make a cry to me for help for the first time ever—and I do not answer you!' His sigh was harsh as he abruptly spun his back towards her. 'Of course it bloody well matters,' he repeated gruffly.

And here I am, thought Joanna, one year later, and making another cry for help. Only this time it's money I want, not commiseration.

No comparison.

Which also brought her neatly back to the reason why she was here at all.

Money. The one commodity which Sandro had in abundance, and in which she had never shown the slightest interest before. In fact, how they'd ever got to the stage of wanting to marry each other was a real enigma to her. She'd lived in a cheap bedsit and waited on other people for a living. Sandro's homes were all in the very best places. His London townhouse was in Belgravia, for instance, and his elegant Italian apartment a mere stone's throw away from Rome's Colosseum.

Even this penthouse, this small-by-comparison apartment that she hadn't known existed until today, was something out of the ordinary to a girl like her. But a handy apartment situated above his place of business was a reflection of the man's wealthy lifestyle.

In short, Sandro came from top-drawer Italian stock and had never waited on another person in his life. He lived surrounded by luxury, he travelled in luxury, he *wore* luxury like a mantle that demonstrated his exclusivity.

Yet what had happened to this very exclusive man? He'd taken one look at the little waitress in a tiny back-street Italian restaurant, and had seemed to fall flat on his very exclusive face for her.

She'd never understood it. But had never thought to question it because she'd been so young then, so innocent and naïve and eager to fall in love and *be* loved by this man who, to her besotted eyes, had been a god among men.

And he'd treated her with such tender loving care— wooed her in the old-fashioned way, with flowers and small presents and gentle kisses that had not been allowed to get out of hand even though they'd both known it was frustrating the hell out of both of them.

'I want to marry you with respect. I want you to come to me wearing the white of a virgin and to know I am paying the correct price for the gift of that virginity.'

Oh, dear God, she thought painfully now. Beautiful words, warm and caring—enchantingly romantic words. Words that had given him idol status in her impressionable mind.

But it had been those same beautiful words that had finally ruined it all for them.

Would always ruin any hope they had of being anything but poison to each other.

Suddenly he spun back to face her. Their eyes caught, and she wondered if his own thoughts had been taking him down similar painful pathways because he looked so damned sad.

'Did she feel anything?' he asked. 'Was she in any pain before she—?'

He meant Molly. He had been thinking about her sweet-natured baby sister, not herself. She shook her head. 'It was instant, so they tell me. She would not have known much about it.'

'Good.' He nodded. Then, out of the dull, throbbing silence that powered down around both of them, a telephone began ringing somewhere in the room.

Sandro muttered something and strode off to answer it. *'Si?'* he bit into the receiver—a sure sign that he still had not got himself totally in hand yet, because he had spoken in his native tongue.

He listened, his dark eyes snapping with irritation. 'No—no,' he said. 'You must cancel. I am too involved here.'

Cancel? Cancel what? Joanna wondered, then, on a jolt of understanding, 'Oh—no, Sandro!' she protested. 'Please don't cancel your meetings on my account!'

But he was already replacing the receiver on its rest and turning back to her with an expression carved into his features that had her old friend panic skittering to life.

He looked like a man who had come to a decision, and that decision most definitely involved her. 'Sit down,' he invited, 'while I pour us both a drink.'

'But y-you told me this morning that you were very busy,' she reminded him anxiously. 'And—and I have to be leaving now anyway!' she lied as her eyes darted over to the closed lift doors, as if they could be her saviours and not the source of one of her worst nightmares.

'Leave without your five thousand pounds safely stashed away, *cara*?' he mocked. 'What a waste of all this anguish you have been putting yourself through by making yourself come to me.'

And it was absolutely amazing—Joanna made incredulous note. Today Sandro had swung himself through just about every emotion that existed. Now he had come full circle and was back to being the sharp-eyed cool headed businessman again, while she—

Well, she was back to making choices, seeing Arthur Bates' grotesque figure looming threateningly in front of her and knowing that once again she had to draw the same conclusion she had drawn each time she reached this same unpalatable point.

There was no choice.

She was caught, held fast in a trap of her own making. Her own fears, failures and wretched inadequacies the bait with which she had ensnared herself.

As if knowing all of this quite instinctively, Sandro turned away from her pale-faced defeated stance and moved over to a cupboard which, when opened, revealed a comprehensive selection of bottles and glasses.

No choice. Those two little words began to rattle with dizzying speed around her head until she had to give in to them and sit herself down—before she actually fell down. She chose one of the soft oatmeal linen-covered chairs, dropping into it and lifting a shaky hand to her aching eyes; that lingering 'flu virus, worry and lack of sleep were really beginning to get to her.

On top of all that, she mocked herself grimly, there was all the stress entailed in making herself come here; it was no wonder she was feeling drained to the very dregs of her reserves now.

The cold touch of glass against the back of her raised hand brought it jerking away from her eyes.

'Try this,' Sandro advised. He was standing over her, holding out a glass. 'Gin and tonic,' he informed her as she stared suspiciously at the contents. 'It may help give you back some courage. You seem to be flagging.'

Mock, mock, mock. She took the glass, put it to her lips and swallowed half its contents down in one go in sheer defiance.

He ignored her defiance, going to seat himself in the chair opposite to sip more slowly at his own drink, looking supremely relaxed while her body was bone-gratingly stiff, his eyes annoyingly implacable while hers were giving much too much away.

'Since when have you had this apartment up here?' she asked, cowardly, shying away from what she knew she should be talking about—the money.

'Since always,' he replied. 'It has always been here.'

She frowned. 'But I never knew about it.'

'That is because I have a perfectly acceptable house in Belgravia where I preferred to live with my *wife*,' he answered with sardonic bite. 'This place is merely a convenience for when I have to work late. Time zones being the inconvenient things they are,' he explained while her own mind leapt backwards and began wondering if all those nights when he hadn't come home to the house in Belgravia while she'd lived there he had been right here instead.

The perfect escape from the pressure of his lousy marriage.

'Where are you living now, exactly?' he asked casually, bringing her mind crashing back into sharp focus on him.

But she had to look away from him as she answered that question, not wanting to see the distasteful expression that was bound to cross his face.

It was clear in his voice, though; she could not escape that. 'Do I have to presume, from that kind of address, that the five thousand pounds is protection money?'

Inside she shuddered. Sometimes, she decided, she hated him—despised his sarcasm and his superior attitude. 'I can protect myself!' she snapped.

He made no comment—a derisory comment in itself. She took another deep slug at the gin and felt her head start to swim. She'd had no food today, couldn't remember when she'd eaten last, so the alcohol was hitting her empty stomach and instantly entering her bloodstream.

'All you have to do, Joanna, is say it,' Sandro suggested gently.

'Say what?' Her eyes flashed him a wary glance.

'Say what you need the money for and I will give it to you.'

Just like that? No strings attached? She could barely believe her luck—except for one small thing. It was confessing *why* she needed the money that was the most difficult.

'I've been working behind the bar in a casino nightclub for the last twelve months,' she said, trying to sound casual and knowing she failed dismally. 'S-since Molly died,' she added, because it was in actual fact a very important part of why she was here today. 'I...' Her glass was empty and she was suddenly wishing it wasn't.

'A refill?' Sandro offered, getting smoothly to his feet.

'Please.' She held the glass out to him. He took it and walked away, giving her a few moments to sag while he wouldn't see her doing it.

'So,' he prompted as he mixed her second gin. 'Molly died and you went to work in a casino. What happened next to make the penny-conscious Joanna get herself into debt?'

Did he know—had he guessed? She frowned at his back and couldn't decide. He was acute, he was perceptive, he always had been able to out-think her brain ten to one in any discussion. But...?

No, she decided, even Sandro wouldn't suspect her, of all people, of gambling.

Gambling. The word on its own could actually make her feel physically sick now! Or was it the gin? Or the lack of food? Or the stress she had been living under recently?

Or was it just sheer reluctance to confess the full truth that was making her feel so sick?

He came back, handed her the refilled glass. She accepted it and took a gulp at it while he returned to his own chair.

'Please go on,' he invited.

'When—when Molly died, I...' Fell apart, was the wretched truth of it. She'd felt as if she had nothing and no one left to live for. 'The job was offered to me by the same man who lent me the money to pay for Molly's funeral...'

The choking sound coming from Sandro brought her eyes up to clash with his. He wasn't quite in focus, she realised—which made it easier to keep this story moving.

'He said I could pay him off quicker if I worked for him,' she explained. 'B-because the wages were higher than restaurant work, and he could even find me a flat within walking distance of the club. S-save me travelling expenses...'

'But it turned out to be not as simple as that?' Sandro grimly suggested.

She gave a shake of her bright head. 'H-he kept on putting up the weekly repayments, and I suppose I st-started to panic in case I fell behind, which therefore m-meant borrowing more money from him. I'd seen some of the other girls get caught out like that,' she explained huskily. 'It was f-frightening...'

'So, you did what?' Sandro demanded. 'To keep up your payments?'

Joanna took another gulp at her gin as if her very life depended on it. 'I played the tables,' she confessed on a soul-crushing rush of shame. 'I took a chance on trying to win back what I owed him. It didn't work.' Well, who in this room is surprised at that? she wondered grimly. 'One—one thing led to another,' she went on. 'And now I'm in debt so deep to him that if you won't help me, then…'

She trailed to a stop, aware that she had said too much already.

But Sandro wasn't going to let her stop there. 'Then…?' he prompted.

She shrugged, refusing to answer, and lifted unfocused eyes to him. 'Will you help me?' she asked.

But even through a gin-induced haze, she could see the anger in Sandro's expression. 'I want to know what happens if you do *not* pay this man off!' he grimly insisted.

And her own temper flared, putting a bright, condemning spark into her blue eyes as she tossed at him bitterly, 'Oh, you should know the answer to that one, Sandro, since you once used very similar tactics on me yourself, in an effort to get me to do what you wanted me to do!'

'What the hell is that supposed to mean?' he demanded.

'Blackmail!' she flashed at him, and uttered a scornful little laugh. 'Which is probably the most polite way of describing the pressure you exerted to get me over the colossal hurdle of—now, what did you call it?' She pretended to ponder, angrily ignoring the slow, warning way his body was stiffening in the chair opposite. 'Ah, I remember. My "freakish aversion to sex!" That was it! Only where you used your wonderful self as a lever, this man is using my debt to get what he wants from me!'

CHAPTER FOUR

'I NEVER used force on you!' Sandro denied that.

But, 'Let me make love to you or get out of my life', had been force enough, Joanna argued silently. In the end, when she still could not let him touch her, she had saved him the bother of throwing her out and walked out on him instead!

'So let me get this straight,' he continued angrily. 'What you are trying to say here is that some man is forcing you to have sex with him in return for the five thousand pounds you owe to him?'

'Yes!' That was exactly what she was saying!

Then, quite without any prior warning, she was getting rid of her glass and lurching to her feet, turning away from Sandro and hugging herself, a hand pressed against her quivering mouth.

He was slower in rising, his anger replaced by a grim kind of recognition of what it was she was struggling with. He had been here before after all—had seen it all before.

After a few moments of watching her, he released a heavy sigh. 'OK, Joanna,' he murmured quietly. 'Take it easy. No one is going to touch you like that here.'

Her bright head nodded in acknowledgement of his grim reassurance. 'I'm sorry,' she breathed behind her straining hand, and for once Sandro did not chide her for the apology.

All he did do was move right away from her, going to stand by the window, staring out, giving her some privacy while she pulled herself together again.

Yet for some reason that small show of sensitivity hurt

her so badly it sent the wretched tears sweeping across
her eyes. She didn't understand it, couldn't explain it,
but it had something to do with the man himself and the
way he was standing there, tall, sleek, unbearably special, hands resting in the pockets of his grey silk trousers,
shoulders straight, that noble dark head held high.

And he was alone.

That was what hurt. It was the space between them,
the huge gulf, physical and emotional. A gulf she had
caused and one he maintained because he had learned
the hard way not to attempt to bridge it.

And what had she just done? Thrown into his face
one of those very few times he had attempted to cross
that wretched bridge.

Dropping her hand to her side, she clenched it into a
tight fist of bitter aching despair. It wasn't fair—none of
it. They'd had so much going for them once, and now
look at them.

Miserable, both of them. Each better off without the
other.

He turned half towards her, giving her hungry senses
a view of his long, lean shape in profile. 'If I give you
the money, what then?' he asked.

'I'll pay off the debt,' she said.

She couldn't offer to pay Sandro back because it
would take her years to save up that kind of money on
a waitress's meagre pay. Which was why she was offering him a divorce as compensation.

'And you'll stop working for him?'

'Of course,' she declared, as if that should be obvious.
'I never want to set eyes on him or his nightclub again,
if I can help it.'

'And the gambling,' he persisted, despite that statement. 'Does that stop also?'

'Of course,' she repeated, almost affrontedly this time.
She was not going to fall into the same trap again in this
lifetime; did he think she was a complete fool?

'There is no "of course" about it,' he sighed. 'Gambling is a disease, and you know it. If you can use it as an excuse to get you out of financial difficulties once, you are likely to use it again if the situation ever presents itself. Then what comes next?' He turned to fully face her, his expression so stone-cold serious that she shivered. 'Do you have to force yourself to come to me again, and will I be expected to pay up again, and keep on paying until you do what you are really trying to do to yourself, Joanna? Tip yourself head-long into the deep, dark pit you struggle so hard to stay out of?'

He knew about the pit? Her whole body jolted with horrified shock. Sandro knew about the big black hole she spent most of her waking hours staring into, watching it open wider and wider with each passing day...

'You are refusing to help me?' she breathed in a frail little voice that seemed to absolutely infuriate him.

'Damn it, Joanna! I am not refusing you!' he exploded in frustration. 'But I would be a fool if I did not insist on some assurance from you that this will not happen again!'

'It will never happen again,' she promised instantly.

But it wasn't enough. She could see it wasn't enough. The way his lips clamped together and his hand raked through his hair told her he was not content with just her verbal promise.

Fear struck a direct line down her trembling spine, the sudden thick silence that fell between them locking up her throat as she stood there staring at him in an open plea, while he frowned darkly down at his feet.

Then he gave a sigh, sounding like a man who was surrendering to something he had no wish to surrender to. 'Give me the name of the club and the name of the man,' he clipped out.

'Why?' she questioned warily. 'W-what are you going to do?'

He didn't reply, but his eyes, when they lifted up to

clash with hers, sent a fresh wave of dread running through her. He didn't trust her to deal with this problem properly, so he was going to deal with it himself! He was going to go to the nightclub, would see the kind of place she worked in, see the kind of man she had stupidly got herself embroiled with. And his opinion of her was going to hit rock bottom—if it wasn't already floundering near there already.

'Come on, Joanna,' he prompted very grimly. 'You say you have no wish to see this—person or his place of business again. So, prove it,' he challenged. 'Give me all the relevant information and I will deal with it for you.' And when she still stood there, saying nothing, he added very softly. 'Or you don't get a single penny from me.'

Her heart split open, surrender spilling out from the jagged crack—along with the hapless knowledge that she had nowhere else to turn if she refused his wretched offer. And she gave him the information in a breathless rush of words that turned his face to granite as he recognised names and places where the lowest of the low lurked.

Weak-kneed by it all, she dropped back into the nearest chair as Sandro strode grimly by her, eyes hard, mouth tight, his whole demeanour one of utter boneclenching distaste.

And why not? she asked herself miserably. She felt the exact same way about it all herself!

A shaky hand fluttered up to touch her brow. She really should not have drunk all that gin, she realised, because now, on top of everything else, her head was beginning to throb.

'Luca?' Sandro's hard voice cracked like a whip over the top of her bowed head. She looked up to find him holding the telephone to his ear again. 'Get five thousand pounds out of the safe and meet me in the foyer with it,' he commanded. 'And I want two of our security men standing by with the company limo. What?' he snapped, his frown as black as thunder. 'No, not for protection! For damned intimidation!'

Joanna winced. Tight-lipped, Sandro turned abruptly and walked over to a door which, she presumed, led through to the rest of the apartment. He disappeared through it without so much as glancing her way; that was a further condemnation, just another thing she had been judged on and found utterly wanting.

He came back looking so different from the man who had left the room five minutes before that Joanna shot to her feet, and then just stood there staring, trapped into a sense-sizzling silence by the whole incredible trans-formation.

He had changed his clothes. Gone were the dove-grey trousers and the pale blue shirt with its casually open neck and rolled up sleeves. In their place he was wearing a very dark pin-striped three-piece suit made of the kind of fine fabric that shrieked money at her from every superbly-stitched invisible seam. A pristine white shirt sat neatly around his brown throat, knotted with a slen-der red silk tie.

But none of that—devastatingly effective power-dressing as it was—caused her breath to catch and her eyes to widen in horrified appreciation of what he was out to achieve by dressing himself like this.

It was the full-length black cashmere overcoat he had slung about his elegant shoulders that made the real statement, along with the fine black wool scarf hanging negligently along his lapels and the stretch-tight black leather gloves he was tugging over his long fingers.

Sandro was a man on a mission. A man aiming to make an immediate impact before he even opened his tight-lipped mouth. Every inch of him screamed Italian, from the arrogant way he had slicked back his jet-black hair to the unblemished shine on his black leather shoes.

He also screamed power. He screamed danger.

'W-what are you going to do?' she asked breathlessly.

At first he didn't answer, his lean face closed up as tight as a drum, eyes as hard as iron, mouth like steel, so deeply sunk into his chosen persona that her heart began to quail in her trembling breast.

'Pay your debt for you,' he clipped out.

Pay the debt or kill the lender? she found herself extending nervously, and almost laughed—not with amusement, but in sheer nervous response to the strange kind of sensual arousal that was suddenly tugging at the lining in her abdomen. The whole thing—Sandro, how he looked and what she was experiencing because of that look—was disturbing her in ways she could barely cope with.

'You—you're not going there to start trouble are you, Sandro?' she questioned cautiously. 'He—he has bouncers with him all the time. Big guys who don't mind h-hitting instead of listening.'

'And you are concerned that I cannot take care of myself?' It was mockery, hard and spiked.

Her tongue ran an unsteady track around her paper-dry lips as she sent her gaze skittering over that lean tight body locked inside those beautiful clothes.

'Th-they'll eat you for breakfast,' she told him flatly.

He laughed, not in the least disturbed by her opinion. 'They will not lay a single finger on me, *cara*, be sure of it.'

Because he was taking this man Luca with him, and two of his security guards? He must be mad or just plain arrogant if he truly believed that.

'I'm coming with you.' At least she knew these people, was even on friendly terms with some of them. They would listen to her before using their fists. But with Sandro in this mood, in *this* fighteningly provoking guise… She shuddered, glancing distractedly around the room for her bag, only to remember annoyingly that she had left it with her coat downstairs in Sandro's office. 'I left my bag and coat in your...'

'You will remain right here.'

Voice soft, dripping ice; that was all he needed to say to bring her scrambling mind into full focus. Spinning back to face him, Joanna found those iron-hard eyes fixed on her for the first time since he'd entered the room, and suddenly the tension sizzling between them was enough to fill her with a spine-tingling sense of dread.

'Sandro—please don't do this!' she pleaded, wringing her hands in front of her. 'I know these people! I can deal with them. I don't want you to be hurt!' she concluded shrilly.

He didn't bother to deign to give all of that a reply, but simply strode to the lift, tapped the call button with a leather-coated finger, watched the doors slide obediently open, then stepped firmly inside.

The doors closed. Joanna stood there staring at them, feeling angry and frustrated and useless and wretched—so damned wretched that her eyes filled with hot aching tears.

He was gone for over two hours, and in that time she worried herself into a nervous frazzle. She paced the floor. She tried out each chair, only to find she couldn't sit still in any of them. She even found the will to face the horrors of a lift journey, after a sudden decision to go and collect her bag from downstairs and then go after him.

But when she pressed the lift call button nothing happened. The ruthless swine must have disabled it so it could not leave here!

By the time he reappeared she was locked into a state of brittle high anxiety, sitting in a chair, shoes off, knees tucked up beneath her chin, arms hugging them tightly.

But her knees dropped and her spine straightened as her anxious eyes quickly checked him over from the top of his slick-styled head to the tips of his shining shoes. The overcoat had gone, the gloves and scarf, but there was no sign of any physical damage, she noted with a sinking sense of relief. No cuts or bruises, except the ones on his fist he had caused to himself earlier.

'Your receipt,' he drawled, dropping a flimsy scrap of paper down on her lap.

He moved away immediately, going over to the drinks cabinet where he helped himself to what looked like a neat whisky.

Helplessly her eyes lingered on him, then slowly dropped to the piece of paper. 'Joanna Preston,' it said. '£5,000 paid in full.' And Arthur Bates' signature was scrawled beneath.

'You don't even use my surname,' Sandro remarked, his back to her.

She didn't use his name because she had never felt she'd earned the right to use it, but to say that out loud was the surest way to bring other, much more unpalatable subjects lurking out into the open. So she kept her eyes lowered, bit down into her tremulous bottom lip and said nothing.

He turned, glass in hand, then simply stood there looking at her for what seemed like an age, until she couldn't stand it any longer and glanced up warily. 'Thank you for this,' she said, fingers fluttering across the receipt.

He made no comment; there was no expression in those lean dark smoothly sculptured features. She knew he was angry, knew he felt like spitting nails at someone—preferably her, she ruefully accepted. But for some reason he was keeping it all firmly dampened down inside him.

'That place was the pits,' he said.

Not *that* dampened down, she noted, and she flushed, looking quickly away from him again.

'At least when you waited in a restaurant there was some dignity to it,' he went on grimly. 'But that place was an insult to yourself, Joanna. Why did you go there?'

She shrugged and refused to answer. What was the use? He wouldn't understand it if she tried to explain it to him. After all, what did a man like Alessandro Bonetti know about having nothing, or being nothing, either to yourself or to others.

He could stand there in his smart suit of clothes, that most probably had cost twice as much as the five-thousand-pound debt he had just discharged for her, looking down his classical Roman nose at her, as if the insult she'd given herself had also rubbed off on him. If that was the case, then he should be grateful that she had *not* used the Bonetti name!

'Well, that side of your life is now over,' he suddenly decreed. 'So we will not speak of it again.'

Subject closed. Joanna lifted her head to stare at him, refusing to believe what she was really hearing—what she had a horrible feeling she was hearing threaded between the actual spoken words.

'I'm not going to live with you again, Sandro,' she said, coming stiffly to her feet.

'No?' he challenged, and folded his elegant arms across his equally elegant chest. 'Then where are you going to live?' he enquired, so smoothly that she sensed the trap even as she walked herself right into it.

'I still have my flat,' she declared. 'I will find myself another job easily enough!'

He didn't say a damned single word, but Joanna knew, even as he then unfolded his arms and began walking towards her, that her world was about to come tumbling down right into Sandro's waiting clutches.

Dipping a hand into his jacket pocket, he slid it out again so smoothly that she almost missed the fact that he had collected something as he moved. Then she saw it, and sure enough, everything came clattering down on top of her.

She fell back into the chair, her eyes fixed and staring. 'W-where did you get that?' she gasped.

'Where do you think?' he drawled, and dropped the tiny photo frame onto her lap before moving away again, leaving her to stare down at her sister's sweetly smiling face and come to terms in her own time with what it meant for him to be in possession of it.

'I have stored most of your things at the house in Belgravia,' he continued quite casually. 'But I did bring a few essentials back here with me…'

Lifting her shock-darkened eyes, she watched him stroll into the lift, only to come out again almost instantly. He was carrying a suitcase—one of her own suitcases, she recognised—which he stood against the wall. Then he smoothly straightened.

'Y-you've been in my flat!' She gasped out the obvious.

He nodded. 'Been in it, been appalled by it. Been so damned angry as I stood there in the middle of it, seeing how my wife—*my wife*!' he repeated angrily, 'was living! Here…' Striding back to her, he calmly added her bag to the growing stack of possessions he seemed hell-bent on piling on her.

And each one sent its own message, she realised mutely. The receipt for the money, which told her she was now in his debt. Molly's picture frame taken from her bedside table, which told her he had been to her flat. Now her bag, which was telling her exactly how he had found and gained access to the flat in the first place.

And don't forget the suitcase, she told herself grimly. Your own suitcase, personally packed by this man, which is telling you clearly that he has gone through all your personal things like a robber!

'I can't believe you've actually done this!' she choked out shakily.

'Done it,' he confirmed, 'and finished it,' he added. 'There is not a loose end left to be tied as far as I can tell. Your flat has been emptied, your lease has been closed, your job terminated and your debts paid. Did I miss anything?' he enquired with an acid innocence that did not hide the burning antagonism beneath the surface of his calm demeanour. 'Ah, yes,' he drawled, bringing those elegantly clad legs in her direction while all she could do was sit there and look at him, too totally, mind-numbingly stunned to do much more than blankly watch his approach.

Coming to lean right over her, he braced his hands on the arms of her chair so she was quite effectively pinned where she sat.

'There is you,' he said, eyes hard, expression tight. In fact, he was so locked into his role of macho intimidator that he didn't even seem to care that he was seriously frightening her. 'You, *Signora Bonetti*,' he murmured, using the name like a dire threat, 'are about to begin the first day of your new life.'

'I don't know w-what you think you are talking about,' she stammered, shifting nervously back in the chair as his face came ever closer.

'No?' he quizzed. 'Then let me explain it to you. Because this is the deal, *cara*. No bartering, no haggling. I have paid your five-thousand-pound debt for you. I have sorted out your life for you. And in return you, my dear *wife*, are going to start being a *wife* to me!'

'I can't believe you're even saying this!' she spat into his determined face. 'It makes you no better than Arthur Bates—can't you see that?'

She shouldn't have said that, she accepted warily, when she saw the kind of sneer that tugged an ugly line into his beautifully moulded mouth. 'Oh, surely I am the much better option, *cara*,' he contended softly. 'Even you, with your distorted view of the whole male race in general, must be able to appreciate that!'

Appreciate it? Of course she could appreciate it! Did he think she was blind as well as stupid? But appreciating what Sandro undoubtedly was by comparison to every other man she'd known—never mind the awful Arthur Bates!—did not alter the fact that she could not let him do this to her. Could not let him do it to himself.

Not again. She shuddered. Never again.

'I hate you,' she whispered, her voice shaking on the wicked lie. 'You can't possibly want to live with a woman who can't so much as stand you touching her!'

That should have sent him into recoil—she had said it to make him do exactly that. But Sandro seemed to have some hidden agenda of his own here, because instead of recoiling, to her consternation he laughed.

'Hate?' he mocked. 'Can't stand me touching you? You have been hungrily eating me up with your eyes ever since you set foot into my building!' he accused.

'That's a lie!' she denied.

'A lie?' His hard mouth curved upwards, without actually smiling. 'Well, let us just see, shall we?'

And, with no more warning than that, he took hold of her arms and pulled her to her feet as panic came back to envelop her. She hit out at him with her closed fists, imprisoned arms struggling to break free from his grasp.

'So wild,' he muttered, fielding her blows by capturing her wrists and using them to pull her hard up against him. 'So very wild when protecting that precious virtue you hang onto so tenaciously!'

Her mind went white—a complete white wipe-out of bright, blinding pain that had her fighting all the harder to get free. Pulling, pushing, kicking, scratching. 'Let me go!' she choked, trying uselessly to twist her captured wrists free.

'Never,' he declared. 'You are back with me now. And this time I will make sure you stay!'

Then his dark head was lowering, his parted mouth angling across her own tensely held lips, his arms coming around her, imprisoning her, holding her trapped by the one thing she feared the most.

The power of his kiss.

It was like being tossed back through dark lonely chasms to a time when she'd barely existed between moments like this.

Sandro—Sandro—filling her mind, her heart, her body with a wild, wanton need that broke through every single barrier she had ever erected between them. It was wonderful, it was right, it was like touching Heaven after spending years as an outcast in Hell. It was heat after the big freeze; it was solid land after being cast adrift. It was her destiny rediscovered in the soul-healing crush of his warm, wonderful mouth.

She groaned, whimpering because she could feel herself coming alive, every emotion she possessed exploding through the constraints she exerted over them. Her lips began to cling instead of trying to break free, her heart was thundering with a power that almost completely enveloped her, breasts tightening, their tips seeming to waken from a long, long sleep that now set them pulsing and stretching, reaching out like twin sensors towards the only stimulus that ever roused them.

And deep, deep down inside her a fire began to erupt, an old fire, a fierce fire, a fire that was lit only by the match this man had the power to strike.

He felt it. His mouth lifted from hers, his parted lips moist and pulsing. '*Cara mia…*' he breathed, bringing her stunned blue gaze jerking up to meet the driven blackness of his. 'I knew it.'

'No,' she denied, trying—trying to tug it all back under wraps again.

But it was already too late. She could see it burning in the knowing glitter of his darkened eyes, see it in the flush of heat striking out from his high cheekbones, could feel it in his body that was slowly tightening with desire against her.

She could taste it in his mouth, which was suddenly

covering her own again with a passion that left her no room whatsoever to scurry back into hiding.

Sandro had kissed her before many times. He had kissed her gently, he had kissed her coaxingly, he had even kissed her teasingly—especially during those earlier, happier days of their relationship. Later had come the impassioned kisses, the ones he'd struggled to keep in check because their desires had ignited so easily then. After they were married, and frustration began to play a vital part in any kisses they used to share, he would kiss her hungrily, sometimes angrily, but mostly with a painful kind of plea that used to tear her apart inside.

But this was different. This wasn't teasing, or angry, or anything like that wretched pleading that used to tear her apart so much. This was mutual need, pure and simple, and it flooded through both of them in a hot and torrid gush of dark, dizzying pleasure.

Then, 'No,' she breathed. 'I can't do this.' And she abruptly broke free of him, taking a couple of very necessary steps backwards, haunted eyes fixed on his oddly sombre expression, considering the victory he had just won over her defences.

'Why can't you?' he asked, very, very gently.

Tears washed across her eyes, then left again. 'I can't,' she repeated shakily—then, almost tragically, '*I just can't!*

He sighed, a flicker of pain disturbing his long, lush lashes—before he was grimly blanking it out. 'None the less,' he said firmly, 'this is where we begin, *cara*, not where we end it. Now, come,' he commanded, giving her no chance to clear her brain of one trauma before he was resolutely swinging her into another by firmly taking hold of one her hands.

Ignoring the way she tried to break free from him, he pulled her towards the waiting lift. 'We are late,' he informed her as they reached it. 'We will have to hurry if we are to make it in time.'

'But—where are we going?' she demanded, trying not to react to a new wave of panic, which belonged to the lift, not to Sandro's grimly determined behaviour as he pulled her inside it.

'You will see soon enough,' he replied, holding onto her wrist as he turned to set the lift doors closing.

Then his attention was fully back on her, his grip shifting to her slender waist as he propped her up against the lift wall and held her there. They began to move. She closed her eyes and tried very hard to fight the whole gamut of horrors suddenly rocketing through her. Not least was his closeness, the shattering residue of that incredible kiss they had just shared, and his words, which had carried such a threatening thread of finality with them.

And, of course, there was the lift, that wretched lift.

'Tell me, why are you so frightened of travelling in this lift?' Sandro asked huskily.

She shook her bright head, eyes squeezed tight shut, face white, trembling lips pinned back against her clenched teeth.

'I can feel your heart fluttering like a trapped butterfly...'

And you're too close and I can't breathe, and I feel like I'm about to explode with stress! she thought hectically.

He kissed each of her pulsing temples, brushed his mouth over each quivering eyelid before doing the same thing to either corner of her quivering mouth.

'Don't...' she breathed, turning her head to one side in rejection, then, contrarily, her hands were jerking up from her sides and clutching tightly at his jacket lapels in case she drove him away.

It was awful, this dizzying tumble of confused emotions that wanted their own safe space—yet they wanted him to fill it. She wasn't even sure if she was reacting like this because of the lift or because of Sandro any more!

'You are so very beautiful—do you know that?' he murmured with an excruciating low-voiced intimacy. 'Even after all of these years, you can still take my breath away.'

'I'm poison for you,' she gritted, hating him—loving him.

'You don't taste like poison,' he said, and ran the moist tip of his tongue along her extended jawline. 'You taste of vanilla. I adore vanilla...'

Oh, dear God! 'Sandro!' she pleaded. 'I can't bear this!'

'Me or the lift?' he questioned huskily.

'Both!' she cried. 'Damn it—both!'

'Well, the lift has stopped moving,' he informed her lazily. 'Which only leaves me to wonder why you are still clinging to me as though your very life depends on my being this close to you...'

Stopped? Her eyes flicked open, struck directly into his—his smiling, mocking, teasing eyes, eyes that were challenging her even as they darkened with yet another message that had her fingers flexing on his jacket lapels.

'No,' she protested.

'Most definitely,' he insisted. Then he kissed her again, long and deep and achingly gently.

'This is it, Joanna,' he warned as he drew away again to watch her lashes flutter upwards to reveal eyes dazed by a hopeless passion. 'So keep looking at me,' he urged. 'For this is what I am now. Not the guy who crept stealthily around your problems the way I did the last time we were together—but this man. The one who means to invade your defensive space at every opportunity he gets. And do you know why?' he enquired of those dazed and shimmering pure blue eyes. 'Because each time I do it, you shudder with horror less, and quiver with pleasure more. An interesting point, don't you think?'

Was it? She didn't think so; she thought it was utterly terrifying. What was happening to her? Had the two years of never letting herself go near him made her so hungry, so desperate, that she couldn't even fight herself any more?

'I can never be a proper wife to you,' she warned him, and she meant it—knew it as a fact so solid that even this dreadful, aching clutch of need would never change that for her.

'You think so?' he pondered. Then, 'Well, we shall see.'

At last he moved away from her, gave her space to wilt, then pull herself together, gave her the chance to take in her strange new surroundings.

They seemed to have arrived in a basement car park, judging by the rows of cars she could see beyond the lift's open doors. One, in particular, stood like a shiny black statement of wealth right in front of them: a long and shining luxury limousine.

Sandro took a grip on her arm again and led the way towards it. A man dressed in a black chauffeur's uniform jumped to open the car's rear door. Sandro saw Joanna inside, then followed her, and it was only as she shuffled quickly along the soft leather seat in an effort to place as much distance between them as she possibly could that her fingers made contact with something soft and bulky. She glanced down to find Sandro's black over-coat, scarf and gloves lying tossed on the seat like yet another statement.

The war guise of a man on a mission, she recalled, and shivered. Because it was becoming very clear that Sandro was still on that mission. Arthur Bates had only been one part he had already dealt with; the rest of Sandro's mission involved herself.

'Where are we going?' she dared to ask, once the car

was in motion and sweeping smoothly out into thin March daylight.

He didn't answer immediately, so she sat there tense, waiting with her senses already prepared for him to say, The house in Belgravia.

But he didn't. Instead his hand went into his jacket pocket and came out with something else to drop casually onto her lap. 'You forgot to put these on when you came out this morning,' he drawled. 'Put them on now.'

It was her ring box. Her fingers fluttered down to touch it. Her ring box which had been safely stashed away inside her drawer of memories when she'd left her flat this morning.

Her drawer of memories, which Sandro must have sifted through. He must have seen what was hidden there. Her wedding photograph, in which she stood in her gown of flowing white silk beside this man, dressed not unlike the way in which he was dressed right now. A photograph that wasn't framed like Molly's picture because it was just too painful to be placed out on show, so it had gone in the drawer with her other painful mementos.

Wild colour ran up her throat and into her cheeks in a mottled flush of mortification. She stared at the box, just kept staring fixedly at it while Sandro stared at her bent head, knowing.

It was crucifying, knowing that he now knew how she had kept every tiny insignificant thing he had ever given to her. The simple but exquisitely made gold studs for her ears and the fine link gold bracelet with its double heart safety catch. The pretty lace-edged handkerchiefs embroidered with her name and never used because he'd had them made specially during one of his trips abroad and she treasured them too much. Or the stack of postcards, one for every journey he had taken away from her in those months leading up to their wedding day. 'Missing you' was all he had written on every one, but—her throat locked—'Missing you' had meant so very, very much.

Then there was the silly set of toy cartoon characters, one for each quickly snatched lunch they had shared between his busy working day and her lunch and evening shifts at a fast-food restaurant. But of all those none of them bruised her heart more than the knowledge that Sandro had looked into the very private and personal centre of her, and had seen the leather-bound book, inside which was lovingly pressed the head of a flower from each bouquet he had ever given her.

Hot tears stung across her eyes, then were winked away again. She couldn't speak, didn't even try to. Sandro let the knowing silence pulse between them for a while, then reached out with a long gentle set of fingers to her chin, pushing it upwards so she had no choice but to look directly at him.

'They are safe,' he assured her. 'You need not worry.'

The tears came again, and again were winked away, but not before he'd seen them, and not before she had witnessed the expression written in his.

'Sandro…' she began unsteadily.

But—no. He was not going to allow her to say anything he did not wish to hear right now.

'We are going to Heathrow.' He totally threw her by announcing this, letting go of her chin, letting go of her eyes, and returning to man-on-a-mission mode again. 'We catch the late afternoon flight for Rome, where we will begin from the very beginning again.'

From the beginning.

Joanna sat there, stunned into total paralysis as the full meaning of those coolly delivered words sank in. Rome, where they had begun their married life three years ago. Rome, where it had all gone so terribly sour for them. Rome, to his beautiful apartment overlooking the Colosseum.

Rome. They were going back to Rome, to begin at

the beginning again. Only this time Sandro intended to
make sure the outcome was nothing like the last time.
She knew that without him having to say so out loud.
Knew it because every single thing he had said and done
since he arrived back from seeing Arthur Bates had told
her as much.

'I can't do this…' she whispered.

'Put on your rings,' was all he replied.

CHAPTER FIVE

THEY flew out from London's cold grey skies into the warm blue of the Mediterranean. Joanna barely noticed. She barely spoke, barely focused on anything going on around her. She felt emotionally grid-locked, trapped, with no way to turn, nor any hope of escaping from the coils of control Sandro had smoothly bound about her.

He had done it all within a few short hours of leaving her locked away in his plush penthouse prison. Not a bad achievement, she grudgingly acknowledged. He had dealt with Arthur Bates, gone directly to her flat to clear it out, terminated her lease, made their arrangements to fly to Rome, then returned to deal with her.

Efficient? She'd always known him to be efficient. Stubborn? It went without saying that a man of his character must be stubborn or he would not be so effective. Determined? No question about it; the very foundation of his success in life was built on his own steadfast determination to succeed.

But suicidal? She could not bring herself to believe that he was crazy enough to want to set himself up for a second dose of married life with her.

But every time she opened her mouth in an attempt to reason with him he seemed to sense the words coming, and he would reach across the gap between their two seats to pick up her hand and raise it lazily to his lips, where he would keep it, his breath warm against her trembling skin, while he continued reading the business papers he had brought with him on the trip and waited patiently for her to subside again.

Only when she eventually subsided did he let her have

her hand back. The man was unassailable when he had his mind set on something, and, right now that something was his failed marriage, and his estranged wife who had been foolish enough to go to him in her hour of need.

Now she rued that decision more than she had ever rued anything else in her entire life—except marrying him in the first place, of course.

'Sandro…' She actually managed to get his name out before her took hold of her hand.

'Not now,' he said, his attention still fixed on his precious papers. 'I like privacy when I fight with you, *cara*. Try to contain yourself until we reach home.'

Home. A short sigh broke from her and she twisted her hand free from his so she could subside again, her eyes bleak, her concerns acting like spurs to her agitated nerve-ends—which were not allowed to appear agitated because Sandro did not like public scenes.

And she adhered to that because—despite every bitter and resentful thing she was feeling—she still, still could not bring herself to show him up in public.

But his Rome apartment would always be the place of her very worst memory. She felt sick to the stomach even thinking about it. The closer they got, the worse she began to feel.

So much so that by the time they had left the plane and made their way to the low black Ferrari that had been parked ready for their arrival she was paler than pale, features drawn, eyes bruised by a deep sense of foreboding that was almost eating her up inside.

Sandro ignored it—of course he ignored it! she noted angrily as she sat beside him on the final leg of this journey down memory lane. He was the man on a mission, focused, blinkered. He didn't care what it was doing to her, only that he was determined to do it!

'I hate you,' she whispered at one point as they ground to a halt in Rome's famous traffic.

He ignored that too, preferring instead to switch on the in-car stereo. Orchestral music blared out from the radio: Verdi's 'Requiem'. It seemed so utterly fitting that she was surprised, therefore, when he quickly flicked it into CD mode so the much less provocative sound of a Mozart concerto filled the car.

He parked in a side-street beside his elegant apartment block, in one of those parking spaces that always seemed to magically open up for people like Sandro. Then he was shutting down the engine and climbing out of the car. By the time he had opened Joanna's door she was in a state of near collapse. His hand came out, dealing first with her seat belt for her, then firmly anchoring itself around her wrist to pull her out of the car.

She refused to look at him but she could feel his grimness, his dark sense of resolution, as he held onto her wrist while he shut the door and locked up the car.

Then—there it was: the aged ochre walls of a seventeenth-century building that had once been a beautiful *palazzo* and was now converted into three luxury apartments, one to each floor. Sandro had the top one; his bank owned the whole building, but of course its chairman lived at the top—which meant a lift was needed to get there.

His hand moved from her wrist to curve around her waist and, even as her spine tensed in tingling response, he set them moving, touching her, as he had promised, at every opportunity now, and she felt so brittle she wondered if her bones would actually snap if he squeezed her too tightly.

'Where's the luggage?' she asked tensely. Until that moment she had been too lost within her own growing nightmare to have noticed that they had traversed the whole airport and driven away in his car without collecting bags of any kind.

'There is none,' he answered coolly, still keeping her moving with that hand at her waist, so the full weight of his arm was angled across her rigid spine. 'We won't be needing it.'

They'd reached the apartment building entrance by now, stepping inside the luxurious foyer with its original wall frescos so beautifully renovated, like the priceless furniture surrounding them and the cleverly disguised lift hidden away behind its carved solid oak doors.

Joanna pushed a hand up to her trembling mouth as her stomach began to churn with an increasing frenzy. 'I feel sick,' she breathed.

Sandro ignored that too, grimly calling down the lift, then walking her inside it. It was palatial, red and golds mingling with oak, a gilded mirror fixed to its back wall.

She turned quickly away from her own haunted reflection, found her face pressed against Sandro's broad chest and left it there, trembling and shaking like a baby while he grimly started the lift, then closed both arms around her.

'I can't do this!' she choked into his chest, where she could feel the persistent throb of his beating heart.

'Shush,' he soothed, brushing his mouth across the top of her head. 'You can do it,' he insisted. 'And you will.'

The man with the mission had spoken, so no argument. She had never known him like this before, so rock-solidly determined that nothing seemed to get through to him.

The lift stopped. He helped her out, almost carried her across the deep red carpet to double doors set in two-foot-deep reveals that marked the true beginning of her nightmare.

One of Sandro's hands snaked out, briskly unlocking then pushing those big doors inwards. He stepped inside, attempting to take her with him, but she could not step over that wretched threshold as the bad memories began circling all around her.

This place, she was thinking tragically, this beautiful place so tastefully refurbished, in keeping with the build-

ing's great age and history. This large-roomed, high-
ceilinged, exceptionally refined place where Sandro had
brought her three years ago, with his ideals riding high
on a buffeting cloud of anticipation—only to have them
all brought crashing down at his disbelieving feet.

'I don't think I can bear it,' she whispered threadily.

She was clutching at him, one set of anguished fingers
clawing at his shirt front while the other did the same
to the back of his jacket.

'Shush, *cara*,' he soothed her yet again, his arm still
curved around her, holding her securely anchored to his
side. 'You must learn to trust me…'

Trust him? It wasn't a matter of trust! It was a matter
of sheer self-preservation!

'Let me go to a hotel,' she pleaded. 'Just for tonight!
Please, Sandro! I can't go in there!'

'You must know that the only way forward is to face
the ghosts, Joanna,' he determined grimly. 'We will face
them together. Now, come,' he urged, trying to draw her
over that threshold while she dug her heels in like some
recalcitrant donkey and refused point-blank to budge.

'Joanna, stop this,' he sighed in exasperation. 'You
have no need to be afraid of this apartment!'

I do! she thought. I need to be quite this afraid of it.

'Let go of me or I shall s-start screaming,' she warned.

'But this is foolish!' he snapped, losing all patience
with her. 'You are becoming hysterical!'

Hysterical? Yes, she was becoming hysterical. She
didn't want to be here; she didn't want this—laying of
ghosts he was threatening her with. She just wanted
to—!

'I know, Joanna!' Sandro rasped out suddenly. 'You
are hiding nothing by acting like this! For I know why
you treated me the way you did the last time we were
here together!'

He knew? For a short shocked moment she just stared
at him blankly. Then—of course he didn't know! She

completely denied the claim. He couldn't know. Nobody knew except for Molly—and she'd only ever known a tiny fraction of it!

Of course Sandro couldn't know—could he? 'I don't know what you're talking about,' she murmured shakily.

If anything, his face went all the harder, more determined, frighteningly determined. 'Yes, you do,' he insisted. 'I am talking about what happened to you the week before you married me. The night you were attacked.' He spelled it out brutally. 'On your way home from working late. I know, *cara*,' he repeated with a pained kind of gentle intensity. 'I know…'

It was like having a spring uncoil inside her and she jumped violently away from him. 'No,' she said, as her surroundings began to spin. 'You can't know.' She denied it absolutely. 'No.'

'Listen to me—' he urged.

'No!' she began to back away from him, face white, eyes gone slightly wild, while Sandro watched her with a kind of distressed understanding that almost sliced her in two. 'No,' she said again when he took a step towards her. 'You don't know,' she insisted. 'I don't want you to know!'

'But, Joanna—'

'Not you, Sandro. Not you!' she cried out in such heart-rending agony that he seemed to catch it in his chest like a blow.

Her stumbling backward steps took her all the way to the wall opposite the doors to his apartment, but still she kept going, sideways now, tracking herself along the wall while Sandro stood there watching her with such grim compassion in his eyes that she wanted to die, wanted to shrivel up where she was; she wanted the floor to open up and swallow her whole.

'Don't look at me like that,' she breathed, feeling trapped and helpless and so exposed she could have been standing here naked, while her fevered mind filled with looming dark shadows, lurid bulks of silently moving flesh leering at her, laughing, sniggering.

And then there was Sandro, coming towards her, slowly, stealthily, like a man approaching a frightened animal. 'It had to come out into the open!' he uttered in a harsh, driven voice that pleaded even as it whipped her. 'You cannot—*I cannot* keep it hidden any longer! *Madre di dio!*' he sighed. 'Can you not see what it is doing to you?'

'No.' Refusing to listen, refusing to accept, she shook her head. 'You don't know,' she repeated. 'I don't want you to know.'

'But why?' he demanded in pained bemusement. 'Why can you not trust me with this? Why do you need to shut me out!'

Why was easy, but she was in no state to answer him. Her tracking fingertips made contact with wooden framework, sending her face twisting sideways to where she found herself staring through the open doors to the waiting lift. Somewhere inside her head there was a strange buzzing sound, and in the distance Sandro's voice, low and deep and oddly constricted, was saying something about them going into the apartment and talking about it.

But she didn't want to talk about *it*! She didn't want to be here in this place!

Escape.

She had to escape before it all came crashing down on her.

'Joanna—'

She made a dive for those open lift doors, almost hurling herself inside them.

And suddenly there it was, the big black hole she had spent so many months carefully skirting around. Only this time it claimed her. She tumbled headlong into it, falling—falling for what seemed like for ever, until eventually there was nothing, nothing but a strange feeling of utter weightlessness and the blackness, that terrible, all-enveloping, mind-numbing blackness...

The climb back to reality was a long and arduous one. Every time she thought she might be getting there, the rim of the dark hole would crumble beneath her grasping fingers and she would slide back down again, sobbing in anguish and in fear, her teeth gritting in frustration. Her fingers scrambled to catch hold of something, anything, to stop her falling, so she could begin the laborious climb out once again.

Sometimes she feared she would never make it, that she was destined to spend the rest of her life climbing the steep walls of this hole, only to slide down again. And sometimes ghastly familiar faces would come leering at her over the rim, laughing and taunting her wasted efforts. Sometimes it was the leering young face of a skinhead yobbo; sometimes it was Arthur Bates, his greedy eyes warning her what to expect if she did ever get out of her dark prison.

Then Molly would come, pushing those awful men out of the way and smiling reassuringly at her, urging her upwards with a hand stretched out for her to try and catch hold of. But the hand always stayed those few precious few inches out of reach. 'It isn't fair,' she whimpered fretfully. 'It just isn't fair. I can't reach you.'

'Shush,' a soothing voice murmured. 'I am here. I have hold of you.'

And she frowned, because that voice wasn't Molly's voice; it was Sandro's. She looked up, saw him leaning over the rim of the hole and reaching down for her. His arm was longer than Molly's, he managed to grab a hold on her wrist, pull her up. Up and up. He bodily yanked her over the rim of the hole, then tossed her to ground which was too far away for her to tumble back in.

It was such a relief, such a wonderful relief, that she

smiled and thanked him. He covered her up with a blanket. 'Go to sleep,' he commanded. 'You are safe here.'

And she really did feel safe at last, so safe that she drifted into a blissfully peaceful and uncluttered sleep where she felt warm and protected by the arms enfolding her.

Joanna opened her eyes to find sunlight seeping in through a silk draped floor-to-ceiling window onto a cream and pale blue colour-washed room. It was a lovely room, she decided sleepily. She liked the high ceiling and the feeling of space it seemed to offer. She liked the subtle use of the two pastel colours; they were cool and restful. She wondered who the room belonged to.

Where was she? She frowned, having a hazy recollection of something terrible happening, but as for what, she couldn't quite manage to recall at the moment.

Then a grimly protracted voice murmured flatly, 'How do you feel?' making her head turn sharply on the pillow to find Sandro reclining in an easy chair beside the bed.

His dark head was turned her way, his brown eyes fixed on her with absolutely no expression whatsoever. Gone was the electrifying power-dressing suit she had last seen him wearing, and in its place were casual linen trousers and a plain black polo shirt.

Power-dressing, she repeated to herself, and suddenly it all came back in a horrified rush. The memories, where she was, why she was lying here like this, and why Sandro was sitting there like that, looking as though he had been there for hours—hours just watching her—knowing...

'What happened?' she asked, desperately playing for time while she tried to come to terms with what had taken place earlier.

'You don't remember?'

She remembered almost everything in razor-sharp detail, but to admit to that meant facing it, and at the moment she couldn't bear to face it. 'Not much,' she lied. 'Only a vague recollection of you and I arguing. Did we have a row?'

'You could say that.' He smiled an odd twist of a smile. 'Then you—became ill.'

Became ill, she mused balefully. She had not merely become ill, she had jumped into the screaming pits of Hell rather than face up to what Sandro had claimed he knew about her.

'Where am I?'

'In Rome. In my apartment,' he said, eyeing her narrowly. 'Where you collapsed. When you showed no sign of recovering, I called in a doctor.'

A doctor? Oh, good grief! How long had she been lying here like this? 'And he said—what?' she enquired, very warily.

His eyes made a critical sweep of her too-slender shape beneath the thin layer of bedding, and for the first time she realised that she was wearing nothing more than what felt like a tee shirt.

Her eyelashes lowered, quickly covering a burst of flurried heat because she was suddenly acutely aware that someone had undressed her and put her to bed like this—and that person could only have been Sandro.

'He called it a combination of too much stress,' he answered, 'and not eating enough food to keep a mouse alive.'

Sandro—had Sandro undressed her?

'I've had the 'flu recently,' she said, pushing a decidedly shaky hand to her brow so she could hide behind it. 'Maybe it was that.'

He didn't answer, made absolutely no comment, and she didn't dare look at him to see if she could discover what he was thinking.

'I'm thirsty,' she announced, trying to moisten paper-dry lips with an equally dry tongue.

He was instantly on his feet and stepping over to a

bedside table where a crystal jug full of iced water and a glass tumbler stood glinting in the rich sunlight. While he poured the water she pulled herself into a sitting position, only to stop, pushing her hand back to her brow, when her head began swimming dizzily.

Sandro stopped what he was doing to reach out a hand towards her. She saw it coming and instinctively stiffened in readiness for its electrifying touch. It hovered there in mid-air for a long second while her teeth gritted and the silence in the room became thick with tension.

Then the hand diverted, going to pick up the pillows from behind her and resettling them so she could lean back against them. She did so out of sheer necessity, face pale, eyes closed, feeling so weak inside it was almost pathetic.

Silently Sandro waited. When she could stand it no longer she opened her eyes, and honed them onto the glass full of iced water he was holding; she simply stared at it, wondering how she was going to take it from him without letting her fingers brush against his.

'I am not a monster,' he said grimly, knowing exactly what she was thinking.

'Thank you,' she mumbled, feeling cruel and heartless, and forced herself to take the glass.

She wanted to apologise, but when she did that it tended to make him angry, so instead she said nothing and sipped at the refreshing water, wishing he would sit down again, because when he stood over her like this she felt so intimidated. Wishing he would go away because she needed some time to herself to come to terms with yesterday's catastrophic developments.

Then a frown touched her brow. *Was* it only yesterday she had walked herself right into Sandro's power again? She had no real idea what day it was, or of the time, except the sunlight was suggesting to her that this was at least one new day. Maybe there had been others.

Maybe she had been lying here for days and days, fighting to climb out of that awful dark pit.

Then, no, she told herself, as the nerve-ends throughout her whole system began to tighten. She must not let herself think about those dreadful dreams or she might start to fall apart all over again.

'How long have I been here?' she asked Sandro

He sat down again, which was marginally better than having him stand over her. Then he really brought the whole lot bursting back out in the open by informing her with super-silk sardonism, 'Today is the second day of your new life, *cara*. You spent what was left of your first day half-comatose, you see…'

See? Oh, she saw everything! And nearly dropped the glass. She hadn't fooled him in the slightest. He knew she remembered and he wasn't going to let her get away with lying about it!

'I think I hate you,' she whispered miserably.

'*Si,*' he sighed. 'So you are continually telling me.'

Then suddenly he was back on his feet again, taking the glass of water from her and setting it aside so he could come and lean over her, much in the same way he had done yesterday, when he'd meant to make a very important point.

'But don't think—' he warned, dipping his head to catch her eyes and, when she quickly lowered them, placing a hand on her chin to *make* her look at him— make her look and see the grim determination written in his own glinting dark eyes. 'Don't think that your lousy opinion of me or my own lousy guilty conscience for putting you into this damn bed the way I did is going to reverse what actually happened yesterday, because it is not! Now I have you out in the open, you are staying out,' he vowed.

Then he straightened, turned and walked out of the room, leaving her sitting there wondering balefully what he had in store for her if he could still be this angry so many hours later.

'Oh, damn it,' she sighed as her head began to swim again.

What in heaven's name had she let herself in for by setting herself up for this? She didn't need it—didn't want it! And she was as sure as anything that Sandro couldn't want to put them both through this kind of hell a second time!

It had been bad enough the first time around, she recalled heavily. Her loving him, needing him, wanting him so badly but unable to let him touch her. His hurt, his frustration, his soul-crushing bewilderment at why she was reacting to him like that!

Why should he understand it? The week before they were due to be married she had barely been able to keep her hands off him. Then he'd flown here, to Rome, to put in place the finishing touches on the wholesale transfer of his head offices to London—because Joanna needed to stay in London until Molly was old enough, and financially independent enough, to survive there on her own.

Molly…

The pretty, pale blue-washed ceiling clouded out of focus. In Joanna's view, Molly had been the absolute opposite of her more determined and fiercely independent big sister. But then, Joanna had needed to be, because, at the tender age of eighteen, she had taken over full responsibility for her fourteen-year-old sister, when their mother had died after a long, long illness which had left them with no one else to turn to; four years before that Grandpa had gone, taking with him the only period in her life when Joanna could have said with any certainty that she had felt truly cared for, instead of being the one who did the caring.

But that was another story, one not worth rehashing,

because she still missed Grandpa and his tiny small-holding in Kent as much as she still missed Molly.

They had been half-sisters really, born by different fathers to a mother who, by her own admission, had loved many men—though none of them well enough to want to tie herself down. And, in the circular way life tends to turn, both Joanna and Molly had secretly yearned for the so-called old-fashioned and conventional close family unit, with a father as well as a mother to claim as their own.

It was not to be. A small sigh shook her. Consequently, growing up had been tougher for Molly and herself than most—though not so tough as some. They'd had a home of sorts: a rented flat in the East End district of London where their mother had taken them to live after Grandpa died. Their mother had worked all hours to keep them reasonably fed, clothed and healthy, and Joanna had taken care of Molly—then of her mother and Molly, when their mother eventually became ill.

So, continuing to take care of Molly after their mother had gone had not been any real hardship. She'd been used to doing it. They'd stayed on in the flat their mother had rented, and Joanna had started working all the hours she could to keep that same roof over their heads while Molly finished her education.

Molly had been clever. She'd been quiet, shy and studious, and incredibly pretty: blonde-haired and blue eyed with sweet gentle features. Joanna had harboured a secret dream where Molly would go on to university, make something of herself, then meet a wonderful man who would treasure her baby sister for the rest of her life.

Only, it was Joanna who had met the wonderful man. It was as if Sandro had stepped right out of her dreams for Molly and had become her own dream.

It had been magical. Once again, she was transported back to that tiny back-street Italian restaurant where she'd worked at in the evenings. He'd been superbly dressed, beautifully groomed and so handsome he took her breath away. She had never in her life come face to face with a man like Alessandro.

He'd come to visit Vito and had ended up staying all evening to flirt with Joanna instead, seemingly fascinated by the pretty red-haired waitress who was so bright and cheerful, and contrarily shy when he tried turning on his charismatic Italian charm.

He'd waited for her until she'd finished work that night and walked her home. Within a month he was like a permanent fixture—at the restaurant, and at the small flat she'd shared with Molly. And Joanna had been so blindly in love with him, she hadn't really thought much about who he was or what he was. It hadn't seemed to matter that he drove a fast car and wore designer clothes. Or that he was always having to fly off somewhere on business. He wasn't standoffish, though he had been critical of the fact that she'd held down two jobs—working during the day-time in a wine bar and nights at the restaurant—but only because it hadn't left her much time to be with him.

The problems had started when he'd asked her to marry him and come to live with him, here in Rome. She couldn't leave Molly, who had only been seventeen then, and had had another full year in education before Joanna could even begin thinking of her own future.

He'd accepted it—amazing, now, as she looked back and thought about how Sandro had accepted every obstacle she'd tossed in his way: 'Molly needs me here; I won't desert her after all we've been through together.'

'Fine,' he'd said. 'Then I will have to find another way.' And he had. He'd decided to move himself to London. 'I will move heaven and earth if that is what it will take for you and I to be together,' he'd explained.

Then there was the night when she'd shyly told him that she was still a virgin. Later she'd wished she'd kept her silly mouth shut, because he had been about to make love to her then, finally and fully. For the first time in weeks they had actually managed to grab a full evening at her flat without Molly, because she was staying at a friend's house. So there they'd been, half undressed and wonderfully lost in each other, when it had suddenly occurred to her that she should warn him.

He'd been so stunned, then so damned pleased about it that she'd been almost offended. 'I can't believe it.' He'd grinned at her. 'I have a real live angel in my arms and she's going to be all mine!'

'I'm no angel!' she'd protested. 'Just a very busy girl who's not had time to get into heavy relationships!'

She should have seen the writing on the wall then, when he'd suddenly changed towards her, stopped being so passionate, stopped trying to seduce her at every opportunity he could get, and begun treating her like some rare object he had to cosset and protect from the big bad wolf lurking inside him.

'You are special,' he'd explained. 'I want our wedding night to be special. I want you to wear white when you marry me and I want to stand beside you and think, This woman is special and she is coming to me pure of body! What more could any man wish for in the woman he loves?'

And that was when she'd begun to worry that Sandro loved her virginity more than he loved her!

But she had been busy, still working two jobs because she was stubbornly insisting on paying for her own bridal gown and trousseau, and time had been racing by, so she hadn't particularly dwelt on his obsession with her virginal state because she'd had more important things to think about—like being nervous about meeting his very large family, or moving into his lovely home in Belgravia, where she'd felt like a duck in a swan's nest from the moment she'd first stepped over the threshold. Then there'd been Molly to worry about, because she was suddenly making noises about not going on to university, about getting a job instead and maybe even a flat to share with some friends. And Joanna had been worried that Molly was saying all of this because she felt she should be leaving Joanna and Sandro alone to start their marriage.

So she'd been pretty lost in worries that night she travelled on the Underground home from work a week before her wedding day. Too preoccupied to be alerted to what was brewing around her on that train.

Afterwards—well, afterwards she'd found her whole world had come tumbling down, bringing Sandro's world tumbling down with it.

Could he really be serious about thrusting them both back into that kind of living breathing hell again? she wondered heavily. Did he think anything would be different this time just because he believed he now knew why she had been like that with him?

Well, he was wrong, because no one knew the real truth about what had happened that night because she had never told the truth, not even to Molly. And nothing was going to change. It couldn't—she couldn't.

The bedroom door swung inwards, allowing Sandro to walk in carrying a tray loaded with coffee and a rack of freshly made toast.

He looked different again, dressed for business in an iron-grey suit and white shirt, a dark silk tie knotted at his throat.

'I have to go out for a short while,' he said as he placed the tray across her lap. 'If you want me for anything, then the number of my mobile phone is written on a pad by the telephone.'

'The prisoner is allowed to make telephone calls, then?' she said caustically.

He didn't answer, his mouth straightening. 'I will be about an hour,' he informed her instead. 'Try to eat, then rest. We will talk again later.'

Talk! Talk about what? she wondered apprehensively

as she watched him depart again. The past? The present? The future?

Well, she didn't want to talk about any of them. She didn't want to eat. She didn't want to rest. She just wanted to get out of here!

Without warning, the old panic hit.

She needed to get out of this apartment, where bad memories lurked in every corner! She needed time to herself, to think, go over what had already happened and how she was going to deal with what was promising to come next. But, above all, she needed to do it now while Sandro wasn't standing guard over her!

CHAPTER SIX

PUSHING the breakfast tray from her lap, Joanna scrambled quickly out of the bed, only to land swaying on her feet, feeling about as weak as a newborn kitten.

A quick shower might help, she decided, glancing around the room until she spied a door that promised to be an adjoining bathroom.

Ten minutes later she was back in the bedroom, feeling better—clean, refreshed, more alert—wrapped in a snowy white bathrobe she'd found hanging conveniently on the bathroom door. It smelled faintly of Sandro, that subtle tangy scent that was so uniquely him. But then, she grimaced to herself, her whole body now smelled like Sandro since she had just used his soap.

Which led her to another troubling concept—Sandro's soap, Sandro's bathroom, Sandro's bed!

The bed she had just been lying in had to be Sandro's bed! But, if that was the case, then it was not the same bedroom he had taken her to the last time he had brought her here. That room had been bigger than this one, more opulent, and fifty times more frightening.

She shuddered, remembering why the room had been so frightening; then grimly shoved the memory aside while she dealt with her next most pressing problem—namely, some clothes to wear.

No luggage, she remembered. No need for it, Sandro had said. Did that mean he really did intend to keep her here as a prisoner until he had managed to make this a real marriage?

Alarm shot through her, lending her limbs the required impetus to open wardrobe and cupboard doors; she was expecting to find Sandro's clothes and frowned when she didn't.

Instead they were full of the most stylish women's clothes she had ever laid eyes on—even during her one-year long marriage to Sandro she had never owned out-fits as stylish as these!

But then, she had always insisted on choosing her clothes herself, stubbornly refusing to let him spend gross amounts on her because she hadn't felt that she deserved it. So, although she had been forced to accept the odd designer outfit Sandro bought for her him-self—like the Dior suit she had worn yesterday—most of her clothes had been good but not designer-label, and nothing—nothing like the garments hanging here.

Who did they belong too? she asked herself frown-ingly, then felt her spine stiffen as the answer came to her.

Did these beautiful clothes belong to his very discreet mistress?

She felt sick again suddenly, too sick to think beyond the need to get away from here. So, with heart pounding and hands trembling, she dragged a pair of denims and a tiny white tee shirt off their hangers, and almost sank to the ground in relief when she noticed they still pos-sessed their shop tags—which meant that all these clothes were brand-new.

They also fitted her slender figure as if they had been bought for her, which led to the next uncomfortable sus-picion—that, if they did not belong to his mistress, he must have had them brought here specifically for her.

New clothes, new life.

The two fitted together so neatly that the old sense of wild panic hit all over again, and she scrambled urgently around, looking for something to wear on her feet. She found a pair of lightweight leather slip-ons and hurriedly pushed her bare feet into them. Her freshly-shampooed hair slid like a curtain around her face, drying quickly

of its own accord in the heat Rome was basking in—
while London still shivered.

At last she was ready to walk out of the room and
down the hall to the apartment's main doors. It took
mere seconds to make it as far as the lift, only then to
use up precious minutes having to talk herself into using
the damned thing.

It's either that or stay here, she told herself grimly.
Because she couldn't see any sign of a stairwell in the
vicinity.

Frustration bit hard into her lily-white cowardice,
sharp white teeth doing the same to her full bottom lip.
Oh, stop being so pathetic! she told herself angrily. One
bad experience in a lift didn't make all lifts evil places!

Still, even as she stepped forward and made herself
press the call button, she was half hoping that the lift
wouldn't come. But there was a whirring sound and a
click as it arrived at its destination. The doors slid open
and Joanna looked warily inside, memories of what had
happened the last time these doors had stood open in
front of her like this mingling with all her other wretched
lift memories.

With a deep breath, she made herself walk forward,
turn to face the console, then sent up a tense finger to
stab at the 'down' button. The doors swished shut. She
closed her eyes, felt the lift start to move and curled her
hands into tight fists at her sides as her heart began to
hammer.

Oh, why did it have to be like this? she asked herself
tragically. Why did she have to live in fear of lifts, or
have to run away from a man who had never once lifted
a single finger towards her in anger?

A man she loved, a man she cared for; a man who
had once loved her enough to move heaven and earth
just so that he could be with her! It wasn't fair—it just
wasn't fair!

The lift stopped. Her eyes flicked open, bright blue

and wretched, because she'd suddenly realised that she couldn't do it; she just couldn't run out on him like this!

The doors parted; one of her hands snaked up to press the 'up' button...

'Well, well,' a smoothly sardonic voice drawled. 'Now, why isn't this as big a surprise as it should be?'

He was leaning against the lift's outer casing, smiling at her but in an angry way—very angry; she could see the twin fires burning in his dark eyes.

'How...?'

'How did I know you were on your way down here?' he accurately interpreted. 'Because each time this lift is used an alarm sounds in the concierge's office—where I was sitting enjoying a cup of coffee and a pleasant chat,' he explained with acid bite.

'I...'

'You were on your way to look for me?' he suggested lazily. 'How nice.'

'No,' she denied, flushing slightly. 'I...'

'Because you missed me so much, you could not bear to be away from me for a single moment longer.' He nodded sagely. 'I am most flattered.'

'Will you stop finishing my sentences for me?' she snapped. 'That was not what I was going to say!'

'I also see you are feeling much better,' he drawled. 'For the shrew is back.'

'I wasn't leaving,' she retorted, wondering why she had changed her mind about running when, really, two seconds in his company was enough to make any woman run!

'Just working off your phobia about lifts.' He nodded again, clearly not believing her. 'How brave, *cara*.'

Joanna sighed and leaned a defeated shoulder against the lift wall. 'I only wanted some fresh air, Sandro,' she told him heavily.

'Fresh air? Of course. Why did I not think of that?'

And before she could react, his hand snaked out to catch her wrist and with a tug he had her out of the lift.

'W-where are we going?' she demanded as he began pulling her towards the rear of the apartment block.

'For fresh air,' he answered laconically. 'As the lady requested.'

Then he was pushing open a door that took them outside into the sensually warm dappled sunlight, and a cobbled courtyard, high-walled on three sides with the building itself forming the fourth. In its centre the requisite Italian fountain was sprinkling fine droplets of water into a rippling pond. The walls hung with colour, all brilliant shades, and the sunlight filtered down through the spread branches of a fig tree onto a stone bench seat and table set beneath it.

'Is this fresh enough for you?' Sandro enquired lightly as he pulled her over to the bench and virtually forced her to sit down on it before leaning his hips against the table behind him. He folded his arms, then proceeded to view her with enough mockery in his eyes to make her wince and blush furiously.

'I was not running away from you!' she tried a second time. 'I—I was going to,' she then reluctantly admitted, 'but then I changed my mind.'

'Why?'

Why? Oh, hell. 'I haven't got anywhere to go, have I?' she shrugged.

'And you only remembered that on the way down here?'

'Yes,' she sighed.

He nodded his dark head as though she had just confirmed every bad opinion he harboured about her. Then, in one of those complete turnabouts in manner which he could make to such devastating effect, he smiled—just smiled—and her heart turned over. The man was too charismatic for his own good!

'You're precious,' he murmured as he dipped a hand

into his jacket pocket and came out with something. 'I adore you for it. Tell me what you think of that,' he invited amiably, offering her what looked like a glossy magazine.

Bemused, confused, most definitely wary, because his tone had gone from bitingly sarcastic to tender so quickly that she just didn't trust it, she took the magazine while her eyes remained fixed on his handsome face.

His expression told her nothing.

But then again, she mused as she lowered her eyes to study what was now in her hands, that face of his was just too riveting for anyone to see past its beauty and read what was going on in his mind!

She was staring at a glossy coloured brochure, not a magazine, she realised. A brochure with a photograph of a lovely red-roofed villa set in the middle of the most delightful surroundings.

For some reason it reminded her of Grandpa. She wasn't sure why, unless it was because she had been thinking about him earlier; she could draw no comparison between Grandpa's very modest smallholding and the aerial view of very large country estate she was seeing in this picture.

The villa itself was a low, rambling place, with yellowing walls and green paint-washed wooden frames to the windows and doors. There were outbuildings, a swimming pool and several large fenced paddocks; not to mention fruit groves and long rows of grape vines spreading out over rolling countryside.

A magical place, she decided, set in magical surroundings.

Puzzled as to why Sandro wanted her to look at this, she opened the brochure's cover, expecting to gain enlightenment from its inner pages. But the print was in Italian—though there were more photographs, of the inside of what looked like a commercial wine cellar lined with huge old-fashioned oak barrels, and another one showing a beautifully cared for stable block.

'Are you thinking of investing in a vineyard?' she asked in a guess, since the brochure reminded her of those you found in the very best estate agents.

'Wine-making is not one of my family's interests,' Sandro answered reflectively. 'As you know, we are bankers by tradition. But I stayed close to this place a while back and was enchanted by it. What do you think?'

'I think it's beautiful,' she answered softly. 'All that blue sky and open space and peace and tranquillity…'

'No buses, no trains,' he wryly tagged on. 'No shops within miles of the place…'

'No people?' she asked.

'Local people, who have worked the land for as far back as their family history will take them. But, no,' he said quietly. 'No people in the way that you mean.'

'Perfect, in fact, then,' she murmured wistfully.

'You could say that,' he agreed.

The mobile phone in his pocket began to ring then, and as he turned his attention to answering whoever was calling him Joanna got to her feet and moved a couple of steps away to look over the brochure in relative privacy. As a barrage of friendly Italian began to wash over her, she heard the name of the person Sandro was speaking to.

'Ah, Guido!' he greeted. *'Ciao! Ciao…!'*

After that she was lost, but the name Guido was familiar to her—very familiar. He was just one of Sandro's many relatives—a cousin who worked as a lawyer for the Bonetti Bank. He was also the man who had stood witness for Sandro at their wedding.

Guido wasn't built in the same physical mould as Sandro, nor did he wield the same power. But he was a nice enough man. He had been keen to like her because she was marrying Sandro, all of whose family had been eager to like the woman their great chief had chosen to spend the rest of his life with.

Even Sandro's mother, she recalled, her eyes glazing over as her mind built a picture of Sandro's slender, dark-haired mother, who had been so warm in welcoming Joanna into her family. Her husband was dead, so she'd poured all of her love into her only child. Anything Sandro wanted, his mother wanted for him too. 'You are my daughter now,' she had said kindly. 'Make my son happy and I will be forever your friend.'

But Joanna had not made her son happy.

'Si—Si,' Sandro murmured, bringing her attention swinging back to him in time to watch him grin before he continued in another fast spate of Italian.

She hadn't seen him this at ease with himself since she'd come back into his life, she noted bleakly. Hadn't seen that attractive grin warm his mouth, or heard that happy lilt in the deep bass of his sensual voice.

Seeing that grin come alive now made her wish she knew what he was talking about; she wished she'd taken the time to learn his language so maybe *she* could make him smile like that occasionally.

But she didn't need a grasp of Italian to make Sandro smile, she recalled. It took her simple desire to please; that was all. Something she'd once used to have, but now was no longer allowed to have.

This beautiful country estate pleased him, she reflected as she looked back at the brochure. She had seen the pleasure in his face as he'd looked at it, seen the desire to own a place like this.

'So, shall I purchase it or not?'

She blinked, not realising he had finished his conversation and was concentrating on her again.

'You're the investment expert,' she said, passing the brochure back to him with a dismissiveness that brought the old frown back to his face.

'You don't like it?'

'I think its beautiful; I told you that,' she snapped, half hating herself for raining on his parade like this.

'Good.' Casually he put the brochure aside. 'Because I have just closed a deal on it, via Guido,' he announced, beginning to smile again. 'So, if you are feeling up to it, *cara*, we will drive up there tomorrow and look over our new home.'

Predictably, Joanna froze while Sandro remained leaning where he was, ruefully watching it happen.

'I don't understand,' she whispered finally.

'Yes, you do,' he parried in a soft-toned taunt that sent warning quivers shooting down her spine. 'For tomorrow will be the third day of your new life,' he chanted, in what was becoming his most effective barb to keep her mind fully concentrated on who was in control around here. 'It will begin with a drive out of Rome towards the *Orvieto* region, and end on the estate, with just you, me, and our marriage to work on.'

'No.' The protest was purely instinctive, as was the way she was already stiffening up, making to move right away from him—

But Sandro stopped her with a hand on her arm.

'No more running from what you don't want to face, Joanna,' he warned. 'That tightly closed door in your head is now open and I mean to keep it that way.'

'And I have no say in the matter, I suppose,' she bit back, trying to sound shrewish and only managing to sound anxious.

'Not while you still fight me, no,' he confirmed. 'You see, I know the problem now, so I intend to deal with it.'

The problem, she repeated to herself. The problem which was Joanna's aversion to sex! But he didn't know the real problem—didn't know even half of it!

'I need to go and—' Once again she tried to move away.

'No.' Once more Sandro stopped her, the hand on her

arm firmly drawing her in front of him and keeping her there with both hands spanning her narrow waist while he studied the strain written in her face through very grim eyes.

Not angry, but grim. There was a definite distinction, because his anger gave her something to spark on, but his grimness only made her want to break down and cry.

'I won't let you touch me!' she flashed, eyes snapping everywhere they could go, so long as they did not settle on him.

He didn't answer, he just kept her standing there in front of him in the dappling sunshine while he moved his eyes over her, from her freshly washed hair to the clothes she had pulled on in her haste to get away from him.

Now she almost wished she'd run naked through the streets of Rome rather than having wasted those extra minutes agonising over whose clothes she was going to have to wear.

'You know,' he remarked suddenly, 'you have the best pair of legs I have ever set eyes on. Those jeans do the most exciting things to my libido…'

So low-voiced and sensual, so evocative of a time when he'd used to say things like that to her all the time. She hadn't realised how precious those kind of words were to her until she no longer dared to listen to them.

'Please, don't,' she choked, feeling desperate, feeling flustered, feeling other senses begin to disturb her oh, so fragile equilibrium with low, droning vibrations of awareness to him.

But he only gave a small shake of his head and drew her even closer, parting his legs and wedging her between two long, strong muscular thighs. Her breath caught; her breast-tips were ready and waiting to sting into life at this mere hint that their most favourite stimulus was so close again.

His expression was so intense, so—Italian, a raw animal sexuality seeming to ooze from every silk-smooth golden pore. 'You smell of me,' he detected softly. 'I find it most alluring…'

Oh, please, she prayed. Don't let him do this to me! 'This is crazy,' she jerked out in rising panic. 'I don't know why you think it will be any different now than it was before!'

'Tell me then, why you gambled away all of that money?' he countered.

The money? What did the money have to do with this?

'I told you why,' she murmured distractedly, trying to prise away his imprisoning hands with her own. She couldn't budge him, not one bit. 'Sandro—please!' she cried out in stark desperation.

He ignored it. 'Your Mr Bates was of the opinion that you went about losing that money with a vengeance,' he informed her. 'With your eyes wide open to the eventual consequences.'

'And you believed him?' she charged, feeling sick to her stomach at the very sound of Bates' name. 'You of all people should know that had to be a damned lie!'

'You would assume so,' he agreed. 'But then—I have never met a man more likely to send any woman screaming for the nearest place of safety…'

She realised then just what he was implying, and her eyes began to flash with stunned incredulity. 'You think I got myself into that mess deliberately so I had an excuse to come begging from you?' She gasped at his absolute arrogance.

'Did you?' he challenged outright. 'Or was it more complex than that?' he then suggested, eyes narrowed, like two hot lasers trying to probe into the very darkest part of her brain. 'Did Arthur Bates or do I bear a close resemblance to the man who attacked you, *cara*?'

Joanna went white, her whole stance stone-still for the

few stunning seconds it took her to thoroughly absorb what he was actually suggesting here.

Then the words came, hot and hard and crucifyingly pungent, bursting forth from the very depths of her vilified psyche. 'Two,' she corrected. 'It was *two* men who *raped* me, *caro*!' she sliced at him with a stinging black mockery. 'In a *lift*, if you want the full truth about it!'

And while he leaned there, seemingly locked into total immobility by what she had just thrown at him, Joanna knocked his imprisoning arms aside, pushed herself right away from him and made for the door back into the building, with nausea rising in her throat, the dire need to get away from everything giving her shaken limbs the impetus to carry her quickly.

She actually made it as far as the front entrance before Sandro's hand snaked out to grab her arm and pull her to a jarring stop.

'Don't touch me!' she bit out, angrily knocking the hand away again.

Sandro said nothing, his face white and drawn. But he took hold of her arm again and led her back to the lift. The doors stood open; he drew her inside. Joanna whirled away from him to stand glaring at the panelled wall while he grimly hit the 'up' button.

The doors closed. A thick silence throbbed in the very fabric of the walls surrounding them. Joanna closed her eyes and held her breath, and this time it had nothing to do with her aversion to travelling in lifts!

They stopped and she swung around, hair flying, eyes burning with a rage beyond anything she'd ever experienced before. She completely ignored Sandro's existence as she stalked out of the lift and back into the apartment.

'Forgive me,' he murmured huskily from somewhere behind her.

'May you burn in hell,' she replied, and found herself walking as if by instinct into what her subconscious mind must have remembered was the drawing room of this super-elegant place. With the same unerring accuracy she found the drinks cabinet, snapped it open, poured herself a neat gin, then swallowed it.

'I only knew you had been attacked on your way home from work,' Sandro persisted. 'I knew none of the details. Molly refused to discuss them with me. I jumped in with both feet, and I apologise. It was both cruel and thoughtless.'

Molly, she repeated angrily to herself. It had to be Molly who had broken a confidence and told him, because no one else had ever known! And even Molly had never known any of what she had just spat at Sandro.

'She was worried about you, Joanna,' he explained, seeming to need to defend her own sister. 'She was worried that if you did not talk about it to someone you were going to make yourself ill.'

'So, because I wouldn't discuss it with her, she decided to discuss it with you.' Joanna pushed the gin to her lips, but her hand was shaking so badly that the glass chattered against her teeth so she pulled it away again.

'What did you expect her to do?' Sandro sighed, her attitude sparking his anger. 'You shut her out! You shut me out! The two people who loved you!'

'I shut myself *in*!' she responded angrily, swinging around to glare at him through eyes so hard and bright they actually looked dangerous. 'It was *my* problem— *my* choice how I dealt with it!'

'It was *our* problem!' he retaliated harshly. 'I had a right to know why the woman I'd believed loved me suddenly developed that sickening aversion to me!'

'And what was I supposed to say to you, Sandro?' she challenged him. 'Oh, by the way, I was raped on my way home from work last week, so don't worry if I can't let you touch me. It isn't personal! Would that have done?'

'You should have trusted me enough to expect love

and support from me! I could at least have given you that!'

'Are you joking?' she gasped, slamming the gin glass down with enough force to shatter it with the power of her anger. 'Sandro—you had me up on some kind of damn pedestal! You went on and on about how wonderful it was that I was still a virgin! How you wanted our wedding night to be perfect—pristine white—no shadows!'

Her voice cracked. He spun his back to her, his shoulders bunched, his body stiff. It made it easier; she could shout out all the ugliness to his back much better than she could do to his face.

'I was raped one week before our perfect wedding!' she cried. 'You were here in Rome! I was deep in shock! It was h-horrible!' She shuddered, her arms wrapping tightly around herself. 'I didn't want to remember it, never mind talk about it! I wanted to pretend it hadn't happened and keep floating through the perfect dream marriage you had mapped out for us!'

'So you thought you could marry me, come to my bed and pretend you were exactly what I was expecting?' He spun back to lance her with embittered eyes and she lowered her gaze.

'Yes,' she sighed. 'Something like that.'

'But when it came to it you could not even let me touch you, never mind make love to you. So the perfection was ruined anyway. You should have told me then,' he directed. 'Explained then. Absolved me of blame for your revulsion! But instead you let me suffer,' he rasped out thickly, 'not knowing what it was about me you could not tolerate! What you did, Joanna, was punish me for the sins of those animals who attacked you!'

He was oh, so deplorably right! So much so that she suddenly decided she couldn't take any more! 'I don't want to talk about it,' she said, spinning jerkily towards the door.

'No!' The refusal seemed to explode violently from somewhere deep down inside his angry breast, pulling her to a tense standstill. 'We will deal with this now!' he insisted. 'We will drag it all out into the open and kick each other to death with it, if we have to! But we will deal with this now, Joanna. Right here and now!'

'What more do you want from me?' she reeled back to blast at him. 'Absolution of all blame? Well, you have it!' she declared, with a wild wave of one badly shaking hand, eyes glinting, hair shimmering, slender body quivering with a furious provocation. 'I was at fault! I didn't trust you enough to confide in you! I punished you for other men's sins! I made your life a misery!'

'You broke my heart and did not even notice,' he tagged on gruffly.

That rocked Joanna on the very axis upon which she stood. She couldn't believe he had actually said it! It was such an awful, awful thing for a man like him to openly admit!

Yet there was no longer any anger in his lean, dark expression, no biting regret that he had been driven to voice such a dreadful admission. He was simply responding to his own dictum and telling it as it was.

The truth, the full truth and whole truth—even if it was a gut-wrenching truth!

'But you did more than that,' he went on in a voice suddenly devoid of all emotion. 'You despoiled me, *cara*. As surely as those men despoiled you without a qualm, you emasculated me with your revulsion. You stripped me naked of my pride in myself as a man—in my manhood! You scorned me as a lover and you revolted at my touch. You recognise these effects? They ring bells for you?'

'Oh, my God,' she whispered in shaken comprehension.

'Now we will discuss cause and effect for you, if you please.' As always, when his emotions were under pressure, his near perfect English slipped into a bone-melting Italian inflection. 'For I think I have earned the right to know exactly what happened to make you treat me like that!'

CHAPTER SEVEN

IT WAS downright amazing! Joanna decided astoundedly.
How he had somehow managed to turn everything on
its head like this! Just what did he think it was? she
wondered. A competition as to which of them had received the worst treatment? Did he think she *liked* doing
that to him? That she *liked* becoming that abominable
creature he had just described to her?

'All right!' she declared, facing up to him like a boxer
who had decided to come out of her corner and fight.
'You want the full and gory details, Sandro? OK, I'll
give them to you!'

And, leaning forward to brace her hands on the back
of one of his elegant lemon-drop sofas, she told him—
told him everything in a tight staccato voice that described in detail the whole wretched ordeal, from the
moment she'd found herself alone with those two men
to the moment when they'd walked away from her.

By the time she came to a shuddering halt she was
whiter than white, and Sandro had dropped into a nearby
chair where he had buried his face in his hands.

Then he was slowly sliding his hands away from his
face, though his dark head remained lowered, as if he
was unable to bring himself to look at her now the full
truth of it was out. It was like adding insult to injury,
considering he was the one who had insisted on all of
this.

Perhaps he was thinking something similar, because,
'I'm sorry,' he dropped with a dull thud into the drum-
ming silence. 'I should not have put you through that.
But I needed—'

116

'To know,' she finished for him when he stopped to swallow. 'If their "despoiling" of me was as brutal as my *emasculation* of you? Well, actually, it wasn't. They didn't even hurt me,' she informed him, hands rubbing up and down her ice-cold arms. 'I had no cuts,' she explained, 'no bruises. Nothing much at all to show that anything dire had ever actually happened. So I went home to Molly and said nothing,' she said. 'I went to work the next day and the next and the next...'

'Stop it now, Joanna, please,' Sandro inserted rawly.

But she couldn't stop—didn't want to stop. He had started the torrent, now it had to run its full course whether he wanted to listen or not.

'I dressed myself up in white for purity, and walked down the church aisle with you as the perfect virgin bride. I smiled for the cameras, for you, for Molly and your family. The hazy fog surrounding me only lifted when I found myself alone with you here in this apartment, and I looked at you and thought—My God! This man is expecting his bride to be a virgin! And, well...' She shrugged. 'You know the rest.'

Oh, yes, she confirmed silently, Sandro knew the rest. He had already described it with a raw and cutting honesty.

His life with a wife who had been utterly incapable of being a wife.

The day she left him she'd had visions of him going down on his knees to thank Heaven for deliverance from a marriage made in Hell; she had expected to feel the same way about the break-up herself!

But living without him had been worse than living with him—and living with him had been torment enough. She loved him and had missed him, even though the thought of going anywhere near him had brought her out in a cold sweat.

So—what now? she wondered. Where did all of this

wretched soul-baring leave them now that he knew it all?

Was he regretting his decision to begin their marriage again, now he knew exactly what he would be getting? Something was certainly troubling him because of the way he was sitting there, frowning at his own feet like that.

Panic flared—a new kind of panic, a panic that almost knocked her sideways, because it revolved around Sandro *not* wanting her now, rather than the other way round.

And this time, she told herself painfully, I really can't take any more.

'I'm sorry,' she choked, then turned and ran—out of the room, down the hallway and to the room she had been using before.

Once inside she closed the door behind her, then leaned back against it with a death grip on the door handle while she tried to snatch at a few short breaths of air in an effort to calm what was threatening to completely overwhelm her.

The fear of losing him—again.

Last time she had lost him because she couldn't tell him the truth; this time she was going to lose him because of the truth.

Her heart gave a painful lurch, her eyes deep, dark pools of utter despair. Then she glanced absently at the bed, saw the rumpled covers she had scrambled out of that morning, saw the breakfast tray lying on top of them, where she had left it untouched.

Quite suddenly it all closed right in on her, the hurt, the grief, the ugliness and misery, tunnelling down to that silly tray with its rack of cold toast and its pot of cold coffee.

Her hand snapped away from the door handle and she walked unsteadily forward. She came to a stop by the bed then bent, her eyes blurring out of focus, as trembling fingers picked up what she hadn't noticed lying on the tray that morning when Sandro had brought it to her.

It was a rose, a single red rose, with its stem cut short, its thorns removed and its bud just about ready to burst open.

He'd used to do this all the time, she recalled. An incurable romantic, who would bring her short-stemmed roses with their thorns removed so she would not prick herself. He'd used to lay them on the table at Vito's restaurant and wait until she decided to acknowledge that the rose had been placed there for her, his eyes mocking, hers wickedly teasing, because it was a game they played.

The lover waiting to be acknowledged as the lover. The loved making him wait, because it had heightened the wonderful electric tension between them until it fairly sizzled in the atmosphere as she went about her business, serving at other tables, and Sandro watched her do it with a lazy understanding of what was really going on.

Loving without touching. Knowing without words. A single short-stemmed rose that lay on a table making its own special statement, the link between the red-haired saucy waitress and the excruciatingly sophisticated, tall, dark Italian diner.

This latest rose floated across her trembling lips, its delicate scent filling her nostrils and closing her eyes, making her heart ache in bleak sad memory.

He had done the same kind of thing after they were married, too. Even in the midst of all the tension that surrounded them then, red roses would appear—by her plate at breakfast, on her pillow at night when she would crawl into her lonely bed in the room next to his.

Sandro's silent statement. Sandro's reminder that she was loved—still loved—no matter what she was doing to him.

Now here was another rose, making a statement when

statements were no longer valid, because he hadn't known it all when he'd left the bloom for her this morning.

He hadn't known.

The floodgates opened quite without warning. Only this time it wasn't bitter, ugly words that came flooding out—but tears—tears she hadn't cried for years: tears of misery, tears of anguish, tears of pain, grief, anger and bitterness that had her sinking down onto the rumpled bed and keeling sideways, where she curled herself into a tight ball beside the tray with the rose clutched to her breasts and just completely let go of it all.

Outside, down the hallway, through the half-open door to the drawing room, Sandro stood by the window, his fists rammed into his trouser pockets as he listened to the dreadful storm without moving a muscle. His eyes were fixed on some obscure point on the distant skyline, his jaw locked solid, his teeth clenched behind grimly pressed lips.

When it finally went quiet, he pulled his fists out of his pockets and continued to stand there a few moments longer, staring at the plaster still covering his grazed knuckle, shifting his gaze to the other uninjured knuckle. Then he grimaced, as if he were considering throwing that fist at some solid object but knew it would be insanity to do it.

He moved then, gave himself a mental shake and walked into the hallway. Fifteen minutes after that he was knocking on Joanna's bedroom door and pushing it open, bringing the tempting aroma of a tomato-based Italian sauce in with him.

'Lunch,' he announced. 'Five minutes, in the kitchen, *cara*.'

Lunch, Joanna repeated silently as she watched the door draw shut behind his retreating figure. The emotional holocaust was over, so it was back to normal.

The man must have emotions cased in steel, she decided bitterly.

Then she remembered the rose still clutched in her hand, and bitterness changed to a melting softness that threatened to bring the tears rushing back again.

She made herself join him for lunch, simply because she had had previous experience of what happened if she went against him; she knew what came next when Sandro used that coolly detached tone of voice.

But she refused to look at him, refused to so much as acknowledge his presence in the kitchen as she sat down at the table already laid out with steaming hot pasta topped with a delicious-smelling sauce.

'Help yourself,' he invited, sitting down opposite her.

Silently she did so, spooning a small amount from the dish onto her plate, then breaking off a chunk of warm bread while he watched her, saying nothing. Yet even his silence was critical.

He waited until she had forced the first forkful to her reluctant mouth and swallowed it before deciding to help himself, and every move he made, every perfectly normal gesture, played across her nerve-ends like static along live wire.

They sat through the whole meal like that: silent, tense—she forcing herself to eat because she did not want the sarcastic comments if she gave up on the first food she'd allowed into her stomach in more than twenty-four hours. And he, she suspected, was aware that her self-control was being held together by the merest thread which he did not want to snap.

And, to be fair, the food improved with each mouthful; Sandro was a surprisingly good cook. He enjoyed it, he'd told her once during one of those rare moments of harmony when they had been moving about his Belgravia kitchen preparing dinner together on his housekeeper's day off.

But those moments had been very few and far between. Most of the time there'd been this same tension between them. Tension, tension, tension…

'What now?' she asked huskily when the silent meal was finally over.

He glanced up, looking startled by her voice, as though he had forgotten she was even there. Their eyes clashed, then his became hooded again. She wasn't surprised; Sandro had not looked her directly in the face once since she'd made her grand confession.

'I have to go to my office here for an hour or two,' he said, with a quick glance at his watch. 'I suggest you try to rest,' he advised. 'You look—wrung out.'

Washed out, wrung out and hung out to dry was probably more truthful. 'I mean…about this—situation…' She made it clearer. 'I need to know what you intend to do now.'

He leaned back in his chair, the action so graceful it drew her eyes towards him, to his shirt-front, then to the long, lean length of his upper torso.

The man with everything, she thought to herself, and grimaced. Good looks, great body, loads of class and style and sophistication. And, of course, there was that other extra ingredient he possessed in abundance called sex appeal.

The kind of sex appeal that few women were able to resist. She'd seen it happen so many times—all he needed to do was walk into a room full of people to automatically become the centre of attention for every female present.

Old and young alike; it didn't make any difference. He possessed what Molly had used to call charisma—that special quality which turned just a chosen few into stars.

'Do?' he repeated, bringing her blue gaze fluttering up towards his face, then instantly down and away from it again. 'But I have just told you what I intend to do,' he coolly informed her. 'I will spend the rest of today attempting to clear my desk so I can keep tomorrow free for us to drive to Orvieto.'

Tomorrow—the beautiful villa in the brochure he had shown her; she had forgotten all about that! 'But I th-thought…' Her voice trailed off, her bewilderment so clear that Sandro sighed.

'Nothing has changed, *cara*,' he said. 'You are still my wife and I am still the man to whom you are married. This is still only the second day of this new life we are building, and, whatever transpires, you will remain my wife and I will remain your husband. You understand me?'

She understood only too well. She understood why relief was flooding through her right now—followed by the expected burst of alarm. But she also understood that he was reminding her of one very small but important point she seemed to have forgotten throughout all of this.

Mainly, that there was no way out for either of them. They had been married in accordance with the Roman Catholic faith, had made their vows to each other in front of God. Under Church law, that meant no going back, no matter how sour the marriage became. Therefore she was, in his eyes, his responsibility for life—for richer or poorer, for better or for worse.

Just another point of conflict for them to bite on, she concluded. Because when she'd let him marry her, knowing what she did, she had been playing him false.

'Y-you could get an annullment,' she suggested. 'I would support your claim if you wanted to go to the Church and ask for a release from your vows to me.'

'Well, thank you,' Sandro drawled, coming to his feet with a suddenness that spoke of anger. 'That is so very kind of you, *cara*, to allow me the pleasure of offering myself up for public ridicule by announcing to all and sundry that I have not been man enough to make love to my own wife!'

Joanna flushed at his sarcasm. 'I was only trying to be objective about the situation!' she snapped.

'Well, don't bother, if that is the only idea you can come up with,' he advised, then was suddenly leaning over her, one hand placed on the table, the other on the back of her chair, effectively trapping her, while his eyes made glinting contact with hers at last. 'Because you owe me, Joanna,' he informed her grimly. 'You owe me my pride, my self-respect, and my belief in myself as an acceptable member of the human race. None of that has changed simply because I now know *why* you treated me the way you did.'

'You want revenge,' she whispered in appalled understanding.

'I want—reparation,' he corrected.

'Oh, very Italian,' she mocked, turning her face away from him because looking at him hurt—hurt every which way she thought about it.

'No,' he muttered. And she wasn't sure what angered him the most, her turning away or her mockery, but suddenly he was taking hold of her chin and tugging it back round to face him. '*This* is very Italian!' he rasped.

Then his mouth was crushing her mouth with a kiss aimed to make a statement, a very angry sexual statement. It was ruthless and it was savage; he was parting her lips to deepen the kiss without any compunction.

She mumbled a protest and closed her eyes tightly shut, her body stiffening instinctively within the grip of his hands while she waited for the expected burst of panic to go rolling through her.

But it didn't come; instead she felt pleasure, a too long subdued, aching kind of pleasure that flared up from the very depths of her dark memories to rage in a pulse-singing rampage that had her lips parting and moving in hungry rhythm with his.

What's happening to me? she wondered deliriously. I should be fighting him like a lunatic. I *need* to fight him!

But she didn't fight him. Instead her hands flew up, clutching at his wide shoulders, then shifting in a hectic jerk to clasp him around the back of his neck. Her fingers tingled as they ran urgently into his hair, revelled in the muscles cording his nape as she drew him closer. She gave herself up to the intense pleasure she discovered in the warm, moist hollow of his hungry mouth.

Someone groaned, she wasn't certain who, but in another moment she was standing, her chair pushed out of the way and her body pressed against the full length of his. Sandro's hands were stroking her, moving in sensually urgent caresses from underarms to waist, then back up again, his thumbs brushing against the sides of her breasts. They responded by pulsing into tight, tingling life, ecstatic to join in with the whole wild conflagration.

She was on fire—that quickly and that violently—she was on fire for him, could hear his fractured breathing, could feel the fire burning through him, too, as he pressed himself even closer, letting her feel the strength of his desire, letting her know by the way he deepened the kiss even further that he was very aware of what was happening to her.

Then he was putting distance between them, prising his mouth from hers to hold her at arm's length while his eyes spat a bloody kind of anger at her and his kiss-swollen mouth pulsed with an undisguised passion.

'Well, that was a revelation,' he mocked with silken cruelty.

But she was much too shocked to appreciate the mockery. She just stared at him, dazed and shaken, still lost within her own stunningly passionate response to what had begun as a punishment and ended up as the most intensely erotic kiss she had ever—ever experienced.

'Keep this up, *mi amore*,' he continued in that same

taunting vein, 'and reparation is going to be well worth the years I have waited to get it!'

She flinched, his cruelty finally managing to get through the haze. 'I can't bear this,' she breathed in stark confusion.

'Correction,' he clipped. 'You are bearing it very well, if my senses are telling me the real truth of it.'

And, to punctuate the humiliating point, he kissed her again, capturing her mouth but waiting only long enough for her lips to cling helplessly to his before he brutally separated them again.

'See what I mean, *cara*?' he drawled. 'You want me so badly you cannot hide it any longer.'

Letting go of her altogether, he watched her sway dizzily, her long lashes fluttering dazedly over her darkened blue eyes.

Then, drily, he remarked, 'Tonight should be interesting.' On that strategically-placed barb he strode coolly for the door, tossing casually over his shoulder, 'And just in case you consider trying it,' he warned, 'the lift will not be operational to this floor until I return. So don't start any fires, *cara*—not while I am away at least.'

And with that he was gone, leaving her with that tasty little tit-bit to chew over.

Tonight, he had said—and said it calculatingly. Which, in turn, could only mean one thing.

Weakly she sank back into the chair. It was all getting worse by the minute.

It didn't matter one bit to him that she had just bared her very soul to him. He wanted reparation and he was determined to get it. And reparation could only come in one form as far as he was concerned.

Sandro fully intended to make their marriage a real one tonight.

Consequently she was in a state of high anxiety by the time he returned that evening. Out of sheer desperation she had kept herself busy throughout the afternoon—clearing their lunch away, tidying her bed but refusing to so much as take a step towards the other bedroom Sandro had used the last time she had been here. Then she went to search out something to cook for dinner, something mind-consuming enough to stop her driving herself into hysterics at the terrible sense of helplessness that was just too familiar to her to deal sensibly with it.

It didn't matter that she knew without a doubt Sandro would never, ever use force on her; that awful feeling of utter helplessness still ate away at her nerves as she stood rolling gnocchi—tiny bite-sized potato dumplings—and prepared her own fresh pasta—all learned during her time at Vito's restaurant. She could cook French food too, and English, of course, and she wasn't too bad with Chinese dishes—again picked up during various restaurant jobs.

But this was an Italian man's kitchen, so the ingredients in it were mainly Italian. So gnocchi it would be for starters, dropped into a rich, hot butter sauce and followed by a pasta bake, packed with mushrooms, onions and peppers in a creamy sauce and topped with mozzarella cheese.

'Mmm,' a light voice said. 'This all looks and smells very wifely.'

Joanna spun round from the sauce she was grimly stirring. 'I am not sleeping with you tonight, Sandro!' she told him shrilly.

She looked hot, she looked bothered, she looked just about ready to fall apart at the seams. She had tied her hair back in an unattractive tight knot on the top of her head, and she had changed out of the jeans and dragged on the most unflattering items of clothing she could find in the wardrobe: white wide-legged trousers and a long black jumper that was suffocating her in the heat permeating the kitchen.

He, by contrast, looked cool and at ease and as usual,

very stylish, even though the jacket to his suit had gone, along with his tie, and the cuffs of his shirt sleeves had been unbuttoned and left to hang loose about his strong brown wrists.

'What are you making?' He walked forward, ignoring what she'd said to him. 'Gnocchi?' he quizzed, glancing over her shoulder to see the tiny dumplings gently simmering in a pan on the cooker. 'I married an Englishwoman with an Italian heart!'

'I won't sleep with you,' she repeated, turning back to the sauce she had been working on when he came in.

'Shall I find some wine to go with this, or have you already done it?'

'No wine,' she snapped, 'I don't want wine—I want you to listen to me!'

'That pan is non-stick, *cara*,' he pointed out gently. 'You will take its protective coating off if you stir it as violently as that. I'll go and find a bottle of white, in case you change your mind later…'

He moved off; she spun again. 'Sandro!' she called after him, and it was a wretched cry from the heart.

It stopped him, but he didn't turn. 'I am not listening to you, Joanna,' he informed her flatly. 'It is time to come to terms with what happened to you. Three years of your life is quite long enough to devote to the experience.' Then, *'Mamma mia!'* he added with tragic Latin drama as he continued walking. 'It is more than long enough!'

'You're so damned insensitive!' she sobbed furiously after him. 'I hate you! If you so much as touch me my skin will shrivel!'

He didn't even bother to answer that one, disappearing into a utility room off the kitchen, which led through to his impressively well-stocked wine cellar, leaving her standing there feeling bitten through to her very centre with a helpless, anguished frustration. It wasn't fair! she thought tragically. She had taken enough—more than enough—over the last two days, yet still he wouldn't listen to reason!

A tear tried to roll down her cheek but she angrily swiped it away, going back to her sauce as if her life depended on it. He came back with a bottle of wine, found an ice bucket and emptied a tray of cubes into it before adding the bottle. From her station by the stove Joanna grimly ignored him, while every single sensor she possessed was on full alert to pick up exactly what he was doing and where he was doing it as he moved around the hot kitchen.

'How long?' he asked.

'Tw—twenty minutes.'

'Then you have time to get a quick shower and change,' he opined. 'You can safely leave the rest to me.'

'I don't—'

'Don't argue, Joanna,' he interrupted, coming to stand behind her and taking the spoon right out of her hand. 'You are hot,' he stated, turning her round to face him, 'you are uptight, and you are not going to close that door on me again,' he added determinedly. 'So, be sensible and go and make yourself comfortable before we sit down to eat. You know I am not going to hurt you in any way, *amore*,' he tagged on gently. 'At least let your common sense tell you that.'

She sniffed, her unhappy face bowed, unable to let her common sense tell her anything while he was standing so close. His sleeve-cuffs were still dangling, she noticed inconsequently, which made them dangerous around a hot cooker. Automatically she reached out to fold one up his arm for him. He didn't say a word but let her tidy him, even holding out the other arm when she'd finished with the first, so she could see to that too.

'You can't possibly begin to understand how I'm feeling right now,' she said shakily.

'Then explain it to me.'

But she shook her head, watching his gold Rolex watch appear as she folded back the white cuff of his shirt, seeing brown skin and dark hair, strong muscle and sinew.

She could also picture this man naked, walking towards her, his eyes so black she could see the twin fires of a powerful desire burning brightly behind them.

Sucking in a sharp, shaken gulp of air, she moved around him, away from him, out of the room at the speed of light, that vision one she had not seen in a long time— and it scared her as much now as it had done when it actually happened. Here, in this apartment, in his bedroom, on their wedding night.

He'd been right about the shower and the change of clothes; she did feel more comfortable, though no less uptight, when she went back to find that Sandro had set the table in the small dining room just off the kitchen. Like all of his homes, this apartment had two sides to it: its homely side and its formal side. One set of rooms devoted entirely to personal creature comforts, the other for entertaining on a grand scale.

Not that she had ever been present when Sandro had entertained like that, she remembered heavily. She had been too shot through with insecurities for him to dare expose himself to the embarrassment of showing off his neurotic wife.

So they'd spent most of their year living together more or less isolated from other people—except for Molly, of course, who had lived with them for the first six months.

'Here, take these,' Sandro said as she walked into the kitchen. He was holding out two warm plates wrapped in a linen teatowel. 'I want to open the wine before I bring it in…'

All very normal, she noted. Very let's-pretend-everything-is-fine! Tight-lipped, she took the plates from him and carried them into the small dining room. She found he'd lit candles and wanted to smash the damn china over his head!

Which meant the tension between them had the same effect as nettle rash as they sat down together to eat.

'Pretty dress,' he remarked, long lashes sweeping down over his eyes as he took in the simple but classical lines of the royal-blue silk shift dress she had chosen to wear.

'You should know; you bought it,' she tossed deflatingly back.

'From now on you will dress as I want you to dress,' he smoothly declared. 'It is part of your therapy that you will dress up to your beauty and not down to your low opinion of yourself.'

There didn't seem to be any answer to that so she didn't try to look for one, because he was only telling it how it was. She did dress down, but she always had done; it wasn't something that had developed because of what had happened to her. She'd always had an aversion to pandering to vanity—perhaps because that was what her mother had done. Until she became ill, her mother's life had revolved around how to get the best from herself. It had never seemed to occur to her that she was naturally pretty; she'd felt she had to work at it constantly, to the point where more often than not she'd gone right over the top.

Not that Sandro was likely to dress *her* in over-the-top garments, because his own sense of good taste just would not let him.

'What's happened to your housekeeper?' she asked in a clear change of subject. 'She hasn't been near the place today, as far as I can tell.'

'I've given her the next couple of weeks off,' he explained, pouring a bone-dry Chianti into lead crystal wine glasses. 'I thought we could do with the privacy while we get used to each other again.'

Privacy so he could keep the pressure on her, Joanna

corrected silently. She might be neurotic but she wasn't a fool; she knew he was still a man on a mission.

Which effectively ruined any hopes of them sharing this meal with any more harmony than they had shared during lunch. By the time it was over she felt so damned uptight that when Sandro climbed to his feet she almost jumped out of her wits.

'I will go and get my shower and change now, if you don't mind,' he said coolly, ignoring her reaction.

'Fine,' she said, coming to her feet herself. 'I'll just clear up here, then I think I'll go to bed,' she told him stiffly. 'I'm very tired...'

Hint—big hint. She expected another argument; she expected him to order her to stay right where she was until he got back.

But, 'Suit yourself,' was all he said as he walked away. 'I'll use another room so I won't disturb you.'

Another room. Joanna wilted in sinking relief, only to come upright again almost immediately when it suddenly occurred to her that he was behaving out of character by saying that!

What was he up to? she wondered as she cleared away the dinner things. Why ease the pressure now, after piling it on so steadily throughout the long day?

Well, there was one thing for sure, she decided: she wasn't hanging around to find out!

So she was shut safely in her room and curled up in bed by the time she heard him come out of that other bedroom further down the hallway.

He didn't even pause to listen at her closed door as he passed by it.

She frowned, not understanding him—not understanding him one little bit! She didn't understand herself either, because there was something niggling at her insides that felt very much like disappointment.

She fell asleep like that, still niggled, still tense,

clutching a spare pillow to her front as if it were a magic charm that could ward off any unwanted callers.

Yet, if that was its function, it didn't work. The unwanted callers came in her dreams. She supposed she should have expected it after what she'd been through over the last couple of days. As it was, she woke up sweating, gasping for breath in the darkened bedroom, frightened and disorientated for the few fevered seconds it took her to remember where she was. Then she just lay there, waiting for it all to fade away again.

But it didn't fade away, and she knew she was going to have to get up and out of here while she gave herself time to get over the whole horror.

She was just about to slide out of the bed when her hand touched something very warm and alive lying next to her, and all of a sudden everything inside her went haywire, shooting her into a sitting position as her mouth opened wide and she let loose an ear-piercing scream.

It brought Sandro awake with a start that had him sitting up too, before he had even opened his eyes. 'What the hell—?' he gasped.

CHAPTER EIGHT

'OH,' JOANNA whispered in quivering relief. 'It's you.'

'Who the hell else would be sleeping next to you?' Sandro rasped, so angry that she realised he was responding to her shock, not her comments.

'Bad dream,' she breathed in an attempted explanation.

'Ah,' he said, for once sounding the disconcerted one. Then, more gently, 'Are you OK?'

She shook her head, fighting not to suffocate in air that, to her, reeked of the stench of stale beer and male body odour. It was amazing how the subconscious mind could be so brutally authentic when it wanted to torture you.

'I can't stay here,' she said, and scrambled out of bed to drag on her robe. She hurried from the room without even bothering to ask what he was doing in her bed! It didn't seem that important when other far more dreadful horrors were having a field day in her mind.

The rest of the apartment was in darkness, the quietness in itself almost as suffocating as the room she had just left. Still trembling in the aftermath, she made for the drawing room, her bare feet moving silently on cool mosaic flooring as she walked down the hall and pushed open the drawing room door.

It was dark in there, too; her hand lifted, fumbling along the wall beside the door in search of a light switch. The room came alive with a clever burst of subdued lighting from several strategically placed table lamps,

Still shaking, she moved across to a lemon sofa and

curled herself into one corner while she waited for her skin to stop crawling and her heart to stop hammering.

Yet the dream had not been as bad as it could have been. In the beginning—after she'd finally left Sandro and was living with Molly, which was when the dreams had first begun—she'd used to wake up screaming so hysterically that it used to frighten poor Molly out of her wits!

Much as she had just done to Sandro, she realised, frowning because it was just beginning to sink in that he had been in bed with her.

He came into the drawing room then, dressed in a hastily knotted short black cotton robe that did nothing to dampen his masculinity. 'What happened back there?' he demanded, the coils of sleep still showing around the lazy fringes of his eyes.

'I told you. Bad dream. What were you doing in my bed?' she countered.

Yawning, he threw himself into a chair opposite her. 'Where you sleep, I sleep,' he answered simply. 'It is what husbands and wives do.'

Well, not this husband and wife, Joanna thought. 'You said you would use another room,' she reminded him.

'To shower,' he clarified, yawned again, then had the gall to begin to fall back to sleep as he lounged in the chair!

'Go away, Sandro,' she snapped, more to wake him up than to give him his marching orders. 'I'll be OK here on my own.'

Then she frowned again, because she'd suddenly re-membered that she used to say the very same thing to Molly. Go away, I'll be OK. But she never was OK, was she? She used to shiver and shake, much as she was doing now, and poor Molly would hover anxiously, not knowing how to react.

Oh, Molly, she thought, and tipped back her head to sigh heavily as she closed her weary eyes. Why did all of this have to happen? Why did you have to die, and why did I have to end up being like this?'

'Joanna…'

'Shh,' she said. 'I'm busy missing Molly.'

Strange thing to say, yet he seemed to understand because he got up, ran a tired hand through his tumbled hair, then said quietly, 'What about a warm drink?'

'Mmm,' she accepted, 'that sounds nice.' Mainly because it was easier than saying no.

He left the room and she went back to thinking about her sister. Poor Molly had worried so much about her, she remembered. The way she'd lived, like a lifeless zombie, the way she'd snapped if Molly tried to ask questions. And the way the dreams had used to come and scare the living daylights out of both of them. So much so that in the end, she'd felt compelled to give Molly some explanation, because her sister had been ready to put all of the blame onto Sandro.

By then Molly had her own little flat, not far from the London college she'd been studying at. It had been a kind of compromise in the end, that Molly would continue her studies so long as Joanna—with Sandro's financial help—would let her live near the campus.

Her marriage had fallen into such dire straits by then that she had actually been glad to get her sister out of Sandro's home, because then they could at least be open about all the stress between them, instead of having to pretend nothing was the matter for Molly's sake.

Or maybe Molly had felt the tension anyway and had been relieved to get away from it, Joanna grimly suggested to herself. She wouldn't have blamed Molly if that was the truth of it; those first few months of her marriage had been absolutely dreadful, with Sandro insisting that they share a bed even though she spent the whole night clinging to the edge of the mattress so she wouldn't turn over and cling to him instead.

But once Molly moved out, so Joanna moved out—of his bedroom.

Now it seemed that that situation had gone into a complete reversal. She was back living with Sandro, and he was back sharing her bed.

He returned with two steaming cappuccinos liberally sprinkled with cocoa. He put them down on the coffee table but instead of going back to his own chair sat himself down right in next to her, so the firmness of his hips pressed against the curve of her stomach. Smiling down at her, he lifted a hand to gently remove a red-gold skein of hair from her cheek, then kissed her.

She didn't flinch, wasn't even close to flinching because the kiss was so openly passive.

'Feeling better?' he asked.

She nodded. 'Sorry if I frightened you,' she added.

'Don't mention it,' he murmured. 'Would you like to talk about it?'

'If I say no will you start bullying me?' she countered wryly.

'No.' His reply was deep and sincere, and it did things to her insides she found very confusingly nice. 'I find that even I am not quite that ruthless,' he admitted with a small wry grimace.

'You are ruthless enough to sleep in my bed uninvited,' Joanna pointed out.

'That's different,' he said. 'And anyway, you never even noticed me getting in it, so what are you complaining about?'

'I wasn't complaining,' she argued. 'I was merely making a protest.'

'No, you were not,' he smiled, still gently stroking that now very tidy coil of hair round her earlobe. 'You were searching for an excuse so you could let me stay there without you having to kick up a fuss.'

'What a lie!' she objected.

'Is it?' he quizzed. 'Then, what if I promise to keep

the bad dreams away if you let me stay in your bed? Will that do?'

It was stupid, she knew, but his gentle teasing caused tears to suddenly bulged in her eyes.

'Ah, don't do that, *cara*,' Sandro pleaded unsteadily. 'It cut me up enough hearing you weep this morning.'

'You never even noticed,' she choked out accusingly.

'See this fist?' he demanded, showing her the one with the plaster that still covered the bruising. 'It almost had a matching one.'

It was pure impulse that made Joanna reach out with both hands to draw his uninjured fist to her cheek for safe-keeping. It moved him; that one simple gesture seemed to move him so deeply that her tears came back all over again.

Why? Because even she realised it was the first time she had voluntarily reached out and touched him like that in so long. It was wretched.

'Come on.' He sounded suddenly unlike himself. 'I'm taking you back to bed,' he said, gathering her into his arms and standing up with her, 'where I am going to hold you close for the rest of the night. And if you argue I am going to kiss you senseless. That's the deal, *cara*,' he stated firmly, not seeming to have noticed that she wasn't arguing. 'Sleeping, or kissing.'

'No bartering. No haggling?' she said drily.

He grinned. 'You want to haggle? I should warn you first that I am very good. It is the banker in me. I can haggle the pants off the best of them,'

Wrong choice of words, perhaps, but Joanna chose to ignore them. She was too tired, for one thing. But mainly she was simply too weary of running for cover all the time. Perhaps Sandro was right, she mused sleepily as he lowered her feet to the floor by the bed so he could deal with her robe before urging her back into the bed.

He joined her in seconds, removing his own robe to reveal a pair of loose white boxer shorts that did little

to disguise his masculinity. Yet she didn't feel threatened, felt no desire to pull away from him when he collected her unresisting body to his.

Maybe he was right: the more he touched her, the
more she would grow to accept it. Maybe the baring of
her darkest secrets this morning had exorcised the
ghosts. Maybe they really did have a chance at making
a go of this, after all...

She could not have been more wrong about anything
she discovered the next morning.

Joanna awoke at dawn to the sound of a bird singing
on the ledge outside the window and lay listening to it
for ages before eventually rolling over with the intention
of drifting back to sleep again.

It was then and only then, as she found herself staring
into his face, that she remembered.

Almost instantly the alarm bells began to ring inside
her, then died away again when she realised he was still
fast asleep, with a strong brown arm thrown across the
pillow just above her resting head.

She went still, relaxing into the mattress while she
indulged herself in the rare luxury of looking at him
without having to worry about doing it.

He was, she acknowledged, as beautiful in sleep as he
was awake, and stimulatingly vital. So dark, so fea-
ture-perfect, so lean and tight—that impressive torso of
his shamelessly naked so she could lie here and feast on
firm chest muscles densely dusted by a layer of springy
black hair. Feast on this man who, for some reason she
had never been able to understand, had wanted this little
waitress when he could have had anyone.

It had been his misfortune, she thought sadly.
Because—look at him, she told herself: tall, dark and
handsome as he was, strong, stubborn and determined as
he was. And even though he had carried her back here
to this bed, and virtually coiled himself around her, there

was not a single point at which their bodies brushed now,

Why? she asked herself with an aching sadness that stemmed directly from guilt. Because she knew that he had become so well conditioned during their marriage not to let himself come close to her. Even while he slept he was still maintaining that maxim now, in his subconscious.

A sigh whispered from her, the kind that told her she should be thinking of sliding out of this bed before Sandro woke up and yet another round of mental torment would begin as he probed what she was thinking and feeling about this situation when she just didn't know how she felt about it. She was confused—extremely confused.

I love you, Alessandro, she whispered with a melancholy softness inside her head. I'm sorry for everything I've ever done to you.

She might as well have shouted the words at him because his dark lashes suddenly fluttered away from his eyes, catching her exposed and vulnerable, catching her with nowhere to run and hide.

He didn't move, he didn't speak, and neither did she. Their eyes caught in that one long knowing moment as everything that had ever gone before it flooded painfully through her then ebbed away.

'What time is it?' she asked, because she felt the need to say something and that was all she could come up with just then.

His long, lush lashes lifted higher, revealing yet more of those rich, dark, slumberous eyes as he glanced at the silk-draped window through which a golden dawn was seeping softly into the room.

'Around five at a guess,' he judged, then the eyes were back on her again. 'You had a bad dream last night,' he seemed compelled to remind her.

She nodded. 'I remember.'

Another silence fell between them. Not tense, for a
change, but wary. Because that barrier of space still lay
between them? she wondered. Neither of them had
moved so much as a finger or toe since he'd opened his
eyes. She was afraid to, too frightened of beginning what
she sensed was only just staying hidden beneath the surface of all this uncanny stillness.

'It's still early,' he murmured. 'Go back to sleep. We
have a couple more hours left before we need to think
about moving from here...'

Sleep, she repeated to herself as she watched his eyes
close, watched those lashes lower over rich brown irises
then settle against his satin-smooth cheekbones.

Sleep, when her hands wanted to reach out and stroke
him, when her lips wanted to taste that warm, dark skin.

Sleep, where she would only dream of him, instead
of lying here being able to look at the real thing.

No, she didn't want to sleep. She wanted to stay wide
awake and hoard the moment, gather it up and hold it
close as she always did with her special moments with
this special man.

Then, that strong brown arm above her head
moved—not much—but the corded muscles flexed a little and she was instantly aware of the defensive tensing
of her own muscles in response.

His eyes flicked open as if he sensed the very moment
when all the old anxieties came bubbling up inside her.
Anger sparked in their dark brown depths, and she didn't
blame him for letting it because he hadn't even touched
her! Hadn't so much as accidentally brushed a single
hair on her head!

'I'm sorry,' she jerked out anxiously.

'Too damned late,' he bit back, and suddenly he was
most definitely touching her, his naked upper torso rolling across her, hot and hard, pressing her into the mattress, big arms curving about her head so his hands could
frame her anxious face. 'One day soon,' he muttered, 'I

am going to drag you out from behind your insecurities and lay you out naked in front of me! Then I am going to devour you, *cara mia*! I am going to eat every single last morsel of you and not even bother to spit out the bones!'

'I said I was sorry!' she cried. 'I didn't mean to do it! I was just—' Engrossed in looking at you, she had been going to say, but stopped herself.

So Sandro put his own biting conclusion to her cut-off sentence. 'Reacting predictably!'

'No!' she denied. 'I was startled, that was all!'

He didn't believe her. 'Prove it,' he said. 'If you were only "startled".' He mocked the word deridingly and moved against her, his forearms taking most of his weight, though there was enough of it for her to feel completely overwhelmed by the man. 'Prove it,' he repeated challengingly. 'And convince me you were not about to run screaming for cover.'

Her heart began to hammer. This situation was quickly racing out of control. She began to wish she *had* run screaming for cover, had taken her chance when she'd had it earlier and just got the hell out of this bed before Sandro even opened his eyes!

'I don't know what it is you expect me to do to prove something that was sheer reflex!' she snapped out irritably.

'Well…' he drawled, and suddenly he was no longer angry but lazily sardonic, a much more dangerous mood when she found herself trapped beneath him. 'You could try another reflex reaction, and put your arms around my neck, then pull me down so you could kiss me.'

'I don't want to kiss you.' She stiffly rebuffed the suggestion.

'Why not?' he asked. 'You were dying to kiss me a few moments ago,' he taunted provokingly.

Her eyes flashed with comprehension. 'You were

watching me look at you!' she accused him in mortified horror.

'Mmm,' he admitted with a lazy smugness. 'I found it most arousing to have your eyes caress my body like that.'

She shut those stupid eyes, wishing herself a million miles away from here now, and tried to move out from beneath him. Only to go perfectly still when the movement made her so intensely aware of his long, lean, warm nakedness that her cheeks bloomed with heat— the same heat that began running along her veins in a helter-skelter ride of wild exhilaration.

'Are you going to kiss me?'

She shook her head, keeping her eyes tightly shut while her breasts heaved against his resting chest, and her abdomen began to curl with tension.

Did he know what was happening to her? She was sure he knew, because of the way he laid his next silken challenge before her. 'You would prefer it if I moved away from you?' he suggested. 'Give you back your own space?'

Her hands snapped up of their own volition, anchoring themselves around his neck. Sandro laughed, all male, all sexually confident male.

'You will understand, *mi amore*,' he continued in that same tormenting vein, 'that when I insist that you must kiss me, it is only because I have no wish to be accused of coercing you in any way.'

And this wasn't coercion? Having a full-blooded half-naked male resting sensually against her was not a terrible coercion in itself? Having these strong brown arms enclosing her, and that beautifully muscled torso pressing down on her, and one of those powerful thighs of his hooked across her own was just about the worst coercion she had ever experienced.

Then one of his hands gently cupped her breast and she went into emotional overload, groaning out a protest that was more a whimper of surrender as her spine arched and her hand applied the necessary pressure to bring his waiting mouth crushing down on her own.

In seconds her senses were raging wildly again. She seemed to have no control over them any longer! Her hands were doing exactly what *they* wanted to do, caressing his warm dark skin; her lips were doing what *they* were desperate to do, greedily tasting him, tasting him everywhere, anywhere she could place her hungry mouth to taste him.

'Joanna, this is too fast,' Sandro muttered in a thickened rasp as she literally caught fire beneath him.

And he was no longer taunting. He was no longer playing the sexually confident male who had just threatened to completely devour her. He was trying to subdue her, trying to stem the wild storm.

'Joanna…'

She caught his mouth in a kiss that devoured him instead, one hand clasped around his nape while the other ran in a feverish sweep down the full length of his back. He arched like a man shot by an arrow, groaned something painful, then just gave himself up to the whole bubbling turmoil, taking over, becoming the hot, hungry and passionate lover she had always known lurked beneath his impossible self-control.

As his touch grew bolder, caressing her where she'd never allowed him to caress her before, she thought elatedly, I can do this! I can actually let this happen now!

Only to feel the whole thing flip over like a spinning coin that falls to the ground to land the wrong way up. Suddenly the panic was back, sizzling along her veins and making her fight instead of encourage. She let out a choked whimper, then was pushing violently away from him, scrambling from the bed, standing swaying dizzily beside it, legs shaking, pulses frantic, her whole mind gone into a complete mental meltdown while Sandro remained where she had pushed him, watching it all happen with a kind of grimly rueful familiarity that almost tore her apart as much as her own sense of failure was managing to do.

He should have been angry, she would have preferred it if he'd got angry! But all he did, after watching her battle with herself for a while, was roll onto his back and drawl lazily, 'Well, at least that got a whole lot further than it ever did before. Things could well be looking up for us, *cara*.'

On a choke of distress she ran from the room.

The hour long drive to Orvieto along the main road out of Rome was accomplished in the most appalling tension—hers, not Sandro's. He, by comparison, seemed incredibly relaxed which, considering the way she had left him in a fierce state of physical arousal, was more distressing to her than the very unpalatable fact that she had been in no lesser state herself.

Yet, when she had eventually forced herself out of their bedroom—having had to wait until he'd decided to vacate it before she would go back in there to shower in the en suite bathroom, and get herself dressed and ready to face another day of pressure Sandro had planned for her—there he'd been, sitting at the table on the sunny breakfast terrace, reached via the small dining room, drinking coffee while he skimmed through a morning newspaper and looking just about as relaxed as anyone could look!

It was amazing. The man definitely had his emotions encased in steel, she'd decided. He had showered, shaved, and was wearing oatmeal-coloured trousers held up by a brown leather belt, and a plain white tee shirt was tucked in at his spare waist. As usual, he shrieked style, even though there was no obvious evidence of his clothes being anything special.

But there it was, Sandro in a nutshell: a man whose style came from within, but which was always evident.

'Help yourself,' he'd invited, indicating towards the coffee pot that had stood on the table next to a basket of warm bread rolls. 'We should try to leave here within the next hour,' he'd said smoothly. 'But you have time to eat and drink something before we go.'

She'd said nothing. What could she have said except, Why don't you put us both out of our misery and let me go again?

Then she'd seen it, tucked in beside her plate, and her eyes had filled with the now too-ready tears, her wretched mouth beginning to quiver. 'Sandro...' she'd whispered hoarsely.

'Shush,' he'd said, getting up from the table, then bending down to brush a kiss across her pale cheek. 'Enjoy your breakfast. I have to make a few phone calls before we leave.'

She'd watched him stride back into the apartment, leaving her sitting there feeling wretched, feeling hopeless, feeling utterly, heart-wrenchingly useless, as her fingers gently stroked along the thornless column of the short-stemmed red rose he had placed there for her.

I don't deserve him, she'd told herself—something she had always, always known.

By the time he'd come back for her the rose had disappeared, having been carefully folded into a napkin and placed inside her purse for future filing with her precious store of memorabilia. If she ever saw that store again, because she knew she would never ask Sandro for it. That would open up too many cans of wriggling worms that still had to be let loose.

'Ready?'

She'd nodded and stood up to join him, lifting very guarded eyes to his. But Sandro hadn't been looking into her face, he'd been too busy checking out what she was wearing, his dark eyes inspecting the cream linen trousers and the tiny cotton top of the same colour. She had managed to get her long hair to plait into a single braid that swung between her shoulderblades this morning. She wore no make-up. It was just too hot. So she had applied some protective cream from the very expensive-looking jar she had found in the bathroom.

Now she wished she'd piled on the make-up, because at least it would have hidden the strained pallor that was back in her face.

Together they had walked through the apartment and out into the upper foyer, where he'd paused hesitantly, then turned towards her. 'We can go down by the rear fire escape, if you would prefer it,'

It had been a concession she'd felt neither pleased about or grateful for, because it had only highlighted what a pathetic waste of time she was.

'The lift is fine,' she'd said coolly and, to prove the point, had stepped up to press the call button herself. Personally, she'd been quietly impressed with the way she'd stood calmly beside him while the lift took them to ground level.

Sandro hadn't said a word, but what he had done was reach for her hand and raise it to his mouth in a silent praise as they'd waited for the doors to open. And even that small gesture had only managed to make her feel worse, because what had she done except overcome a silly obsession she should have combated years ago?

That was why she was tense—that was why she was silent and withdrawn and very uncommunicative. She was cross with herself because living with her was like living in a minefield—you never knew where the next explosion of panic was going to come from!

She couldn't, in all fairness, put Sandro through that kind of madness a second time. He had to learn that it just wasn't worth the effort he was trying to put into it, and the best way to do that was completely freeze him out again.

She could do it, she told herself grimly. She had done it very successfully once before, hadn't she?

CHAPTER NINE

ORVIETO lay about halfway between Rome and Siena on the Umbrian-Tuscany borders. It was an area of breathtaking beauty, with lush and fertile rolling hillsides covered by row upon row of vine trees broken by thick clusters of woodland. Enchanting old towns capped incredible hilltops which seemed to rise out of the ground for no apparent reason.

Yet, picturesque as the area was, it was so obviously intrinsically rural that she began to wonder what it was here that had caught Sandro's usually very urban eye.

'The estate is just over the next hillside,' Sandro said beside her. 'Look now,' he directed.

Her gaze drifted outwards, then simply stilled while she stared open-mouthed at the lovely valley that came into view. Despite her resolve, she responded, 'Oh, Sandro!' with a gasp of unrestrained pleasure. 'This is lovely! How much of it belongs to you?'

'To us,' he smoothly corrected. Then, before she could react to that stunning correction, 'As far as you can see,' he answered her question, bringing a further gasp escaping from her parted lips.

He turned the car then, steering them in through a gap in the rows of vine trees. It was a private driveway, columned on either side by tall cypresses that led them towards the pretty villa she recognised from the brochure Sandro had shown her the day before.

As they came closer to the house itself the vines began to give way to thick fruit orchards, then the most beautiful gardens set in typically formal Italian style with terraces already blooming with well-behaved colour.

It was, Joanna decided, the most beautiful place she had ever laid eyes on, the house itself looking as though it had sat there for ever, with its red-tiled roof and its yellowing walls basking in the golden sunlight.

Sandro pulled the car to a stop on a tiny cobbled area just in front of the house. Off to one side, Joanna could see what she recognised as the stable block—again looking as if it had always been there. Behind that stood tall, narrow cypress trees, acting like windbreaks or more probably as a boundary line, planted to separate the private accommodation from the working estate.

Joanna climbed out of the car and stood gazing around her, too captivated to maintain the indifference she had been so determined upon.

'Well?' Sandro murmured quietly from the other side of the car. 'What do you think?'

Think? She couldn't think; this place was just too enchanting for her to be able to think. Feel, maybe; she could feel many things: pleasure, wonder, a yearning desire to belong to this lovely place.

'Who in their right mind would want to sell this?' she asked rather breathlessly.

'The owner's daughter married a Californian wine-grower,' Sandro explained, coming around the car to stand beside her. 'They wanted to be close to her, so they put this place up for sale and moved to California. An expedient move on their side,' he added sagely. 'For this place may look picture-perfect but in fact it needs a lot of money spending on it to bring it up to New World standards in wine-growing and processing if it is going to compete.'

'And you fancied taking on the challenge?' Joanna began to understand at last. This was Sandro being Sandro, seeing a good investment.

But he thoroughly shocked her by saying quietly, 'I did not buy this for the challenge, Joanna. I bought it for you.'

For her? Her eyes whipped around to stare at him in open-mouthed disbelief. 'But why me?' she asked in bewilderment.

He didn't answer, just smiled a rather odd smile and said, 'Come on. We may as well inspect the house first.'

Then he was striding off towards the house, leaving her to follow more slowly, with her mind thrown back into clamouring confusion because never, not once, had she ever voiced a desire to live somewhere like this!

So, what was he playing at with his clever word-games? she wondered frowningly. Then, reparation, she remembered, as she followed him into a large, cool entrance hall darkened by the wooden shutters pulled across the windows. Sandro was most definitely still a man on a mission, and that mission included reparation.

'The house requires some renovation,' he said, as she came to an uncertain halt just inside the open doorway. 'But nothing too drastic…'

He was already moving to open the shutters, throwing them back from the long narrow windows to allow light to come streaming in, dust motes dancing in the sunbeams onto disappointingly bare stone floors, plain white walls and a huge rustic fireplace. There was a spiral stairway leading up from a central situation against the far wall and several closed doors flanking either side of it.

But that seemed to be all. 'It's empty.' She voiced the absolute obvious.

'Si,' he acknowledged. 'Which is going to give you a lot to think about as you plan the refurbishing of the whole house.'

Joanna didn't answer. Her mind was boggling, her natural defensive system grinding into full action simply because she did not understand what was going on here. Yesterday he had implied that they were coming here to start their marriage properly, which meant sex, of course. But to enjoy the kind of sex Sandro had to be thinking about, there first had to be a bed, and this place did not look as if it had one stick of furniture anywhere in it.

In a daze, she moved off towards the nearest door and pushed it open to find yet another empty room darkened by wooden shutters covering the windows. 'What was this?' she enquired as he came up behind her.

His hands slid around her waist, long fingers easily spanning her. Sensation whipped like electrically charged wire in a tight coil around her whole body, and it took every ounce of self-control she possessed not to jump away from him like a severely scalded cat.

'A sitting room,' he replied. 'There are two of them—one either side of the front door…'

She nodded, unable to say another word, while he was still holding her. She didn't even dare breathe in case Sandro realised just how desperately aware she was of him.

'Shall I throw open the shutters?'

'Please,' she said, and almost wilted with relief as his hands left her so he could move past her and throw the room into dust-dancing light.

After that, she was careful to keep her distance from him as they walked from room to room, throwing open shutters and staring round the empty spaces while he described to her what they had been used for by the last owners.

The house was big—bigger than it looked on the outside. Four reception rooms in all, two office-cum-studies and a huge kitchen with quaint old-fashioned fittings that she liked on sight. Upstairs were six large bedrooms but only two bathrooms, which, Sandro informed her, would have to be put right before they could move in here permanently.

There had to be a catch to all of this, she told herself again. There just had to be—or why bring this beautiful place into the conflict at all? After all, he didn't need it to keep the pressure on her, because he was managing to do that very successfully without it!

So, she held herself tense and silent as they moved from room to room, letting him do the talking, waiting for him to get to the point and finally tell her what the catch was.

They had looked over the whole house and had come back to the hallway before he actually asked her a direct question. 'So?' he prompted. 'Do you like it?'

'I think it's delightful,' she replied. 'But I don't understand why you think I should *want* to live in a place like this?'

He didn't answer immediately. Instead he walked over to one of the windows and stood gazing outside for a while. He looked sombre suddenly, as though he was considering uttering something he wasn't sure was the right thing to say. Accordingly Joanna felt the muscles encasing her spine contract with tension.

'Molly told me that you used to live on a farm once,' he revealed. 'Until your grandfather died and your mother decided she did not want to take over his tenancy, and so she moved you all up to London to live.'

Molly had told Sandro that? Joanna was shocked. She hadn't been aware that Sandro and her sister had ever been close enough to talk about things like that!

'She said you used to love it there,' he continued, turning to watch the different expressions as they flickered across her face. 'She said you loved the clean air and wide-open spaces and the sense of freedom to come and go as you please. Apparently you had a horse of your own and used to ride him everywhere. She told me how much you missed it all once you were stuck in London...'

Silence. Joanna stood there in a dusty sunbeam while she came to terms with the disturbing fact that Sandro knew a lot more about her than she'd ever suspected he knew.

'Say something,' he prompted.

'Molly said an awful lot to you, by the sound of it,' was the only remark she could come up with.

He grimaced, hands doing their usual thing by sliding into his trouser pockets in a way that was supposed to be relaxed but which Joanna suspected meant he was the complete opposite.

'We used to meet,' he confessed. 'For lunch—perhaps once a month after you left me. I needed to know how you were coping and she was more than willing to talk about you…'

Tears washed across her eyes and stayed there, blurring out the dusty brown floor at her feet; a pain she couldn't quite interpret was tugging at her heartstrings. Grief for a much-missed Molly? Probably. Hurt for all those secret meetings she hadn't known had been going on between her sister and Sandro? Definitely. But, most of all, she felt dreadfully exposed again, as though nothing about her was sacred where Sandro and his obsession with her were concerned.

'Then…' he went on, and his voice sounded constrained now, enough to set Joanna moving restlessly, her arms wrapping themselves around her body so her fingers could pick tensely at the soft sleeves of her creamy top. 'A couple of days before I was due to fly out here to spend some time with my mother, because she had been ill and she seemed to need me more at that moment than you seemed ever likely to need me…'

He paused, she presumed it was to grimace at his own honesty, but she couldn't look at him to check that out, and, anyway, the tears were still blurring her vision.

'Molly called me up and asked me to meet her. She sounded—distressed,' he said. 'We met for lunch, and it was then that she told me what you had apparently only just told her, about what had happened to you and why you couldn't live with me. She asked me if it made a difference to how I felt about you,' he said, and then went on gruffly, 'I said, Of course it made a damned difference, but, for once, you were going to have to wait until I had given my mother the few weeks I had put aside for her to oversee her convalescence!'

Defiance, Joanna recognised. Oh, there had been a lot of angry defiance in those words just then.

'When I got back to London—' He had to stop a moment because his voice had broken, and Joanna squeezed her eyes tight shut because she knew what he was going to say next. 'You had both left the flat,' he continued. 'I could not bring myself to believe it at first, then I assumed that Molly must have told you what she had told me, and you had, predictably, made a run for it, because you couldn't stand the idea of my pursuing you again. In fact,' he concluded, 'I was so sure that was the case that I did not even bother checking any further than your flat, which is why I never got to hear about what happened to Molly.'

In other words he'd presumed the worst about her, Joanna noted hollowly. Just as she had presumed the worst about him.

'Now I want to make reparation for the last year, which must have been hell for you. And this,' he explained with a slow wave of one beautifully sculptured hand, 'is my way of making that reparation. I give you wide-open spaces, Joanna, and the freedom to enjoy it as you wish…'

The reparation was *his* reparation not *her* reparation? 'Y-you mean…?' she stammered out incredulously. 'You mean you've bought this beautiful place for me because you feel you owe me something?'

'Do I not?' he countered.

'No!' she cried 'You do not!'

'I will have to move main control of the bank back to Rome, of course,' he said, speaking right over her protest as if she hadn't voiced it. 'But I will install a full communications system here, for convenience, which will mean less commuting for me, so we can work at this place together...'

Joanna stared at him and couldn't even breathe through the pressure building in her breast. He believed she would be happy living in the country, so he had bought them a country estate to live on! And he was going to move his head operation back to Rome—again!

In other words, he was prepared to move heaven and earth to make this work for them—again.

'And what do you want, Sandro?' she asked him huskily. 'What is it you personally want from all of this for yourself?'

He shrugged, then smiled a wry kind of smile that thoroughly mocked whatever it was he had been going to say before he'd even bothered saying it. 'A wife who will be a wife to me would be nice.'

And that was all? A minor want like that? A perfectly justifiable want for any man, never mind a man like Sandro!

But, oh, good grief, it was like a mountainous obstacle to her!

'Oh, Sandro,' she sighed in shaken response, knowing she could never give him what he wanted. She had proved beyond all doubt this morning that she was incapable of being a proper wife to him! Which meant, therefore, that she could not accept anything else from him. 'Stop doing this!' she cried out in pained compulsion. 'Don't you see I'm not worth it? I don't even want it!'

'Then what do you want?' he demanded.

You, she thought hopelessly, and turned away from him so he wouldn't see that answer written in her eyes.

'No!' he objected, angry now, very angry, because once again she was letting him down with her inability to give him back what he needed from her. Striding towards her, he grabbed her arm and spun her back to face him. 'You will stop hiding from me whenever we begin to get close to the real truth!' he grated at her.

'I can't keep taking from you and giving nothing back!' she cried in pained distress.

'Then give yourself to me,' he answered simply.

'I can't!' she choked. Good grief, did he never listen to a word she said to him? 'I can't, damn it. *I can't!*'

He sighed, straightened his body as though he was containing something very intense deep down inside him, then unclipped his hands from her shoulders and moved off towards the sunny front doorway.

'Come on,' he said to her over his shoulder. 'There is a lot more to see yet outside. I think you will like the stables…'

Joanna couldn't believe it! She stood there, exactly where he had left her, and marvelled incredulously at the stubborn way he was still completely ignoring anything she said to him that he didn't like!

In the end she followed him outside and let him show her the gardens and the stable block, for which, he informed her, she was to choose her own stable of horses once they'd made the house fit to move in to permanently. In a daze she let him guide her from one thing to another, said nothing—thought nothing! Her mind had shut down completely, as though someone—namely Sandro—had turned it off for her because her thoughts didn't suit him.

An hour after that they were back at the car, and for one last time she tried to get through to him. 'Sandro—please!' she begged, 'Will you listen to me?'

'Not unless you are going to say something positive,' he replied coolly.

'I positively know I am never going to be able to let you make love to me,' she answered bluntly.

'Why not?' he challenged.

She didn't answer, her eyes lowering from his, her lips pressed grimly shut.

'Still more ghosts to uncover, Joanna?' he prodded.

You are my ghost, she answered silently. You haunt my every breathing moment. 'I've faced the ghosts,' was what she said out loud. 'Without it changing anything.'

'No, Joanna,' Sandro responded. 'There are still some ghosts lingering here that I have not managed to uncover yet. But I will,' he vowed. 'I will find that person I once fell in love with. The person who once loved me in the same exquisite way, no matter what it takes to do it. And that,' he concluded, 'is what is called positive thinking, *cara*. Not that negative stuff you keep on throwing at me.'

'You're mad,' she sighed, her red-gold hair glinting in the sunlight as she sent him a look of weary frustration. 'You have to be—if you are this pig-headed!'

'You think me mad?' He laughed. 'No—no.' He denied the charge. 'For I can remember that what we had was so damned special only a madman would let it slip through his fingers—which I am not about to do!'

'You let it go once before,' she reminded him.

'But I did not know why you drove me to do so,' he countered. 'You let me believe it was my fault, something you could not stand about me! I could not overcome your physical aversion then, Joanna, but I can now, and I will,' he stated grimly. 'I'll overcome your sad determination to punish us both for something neither of us had any control over!'

With that, he turned and climbed into the car, leaving her to follow or stay as she felt fit. She followed, because she was heavily aware that she had no real choice about it.

No choice.

She almost laughed, except the situation warranted tears, not laughter.

He already had the engine running by the time she got in beside him, his dark expression set in stone and the atmosphere so bad now that neither of them made

any attempt to ease it. They drove back down the cy-
press-lined driveway without another word passing between them.

She felt angry and guilty and cruel and petty. Maimed,
that was what she was, she told herself bitterly. Maimed
to the very roots of her persona if she could treat him
as badly as this.

It was not a very pleasant thing to know about oneself.

That was why this relationship could never work for
them. She would always be letting him down like this.
Just as she had always let him down before.

So the gulf between them seemed to get even wider,
and the antagonism to get so biting that Sandro curtly
excused himself the moment they arrived back at the
apartment late that afternoon, and disappeared behind a
slammed door to his private study.

Joanna winced, recognising the sound from three
years ago. This is it, she likened dejectedly; the slippery,
sliding slope back into emotional carnage.

And it wasn't over yet. She was just coming out of
her bedroom, after showering and changing into a cool
cotton sundress, when she heard voices in the drawing
room. With a sinking heart she recognised the voice of
their visitor, and she gritted her teeth and made herself
walk into the room.

Sandro and his mother were standing sharing soft-
voiced, angry words, by their tones. They were speaking
in Italian, so Joanna had no idea what they were actually
saying, but the moment they both noticed her standing
there they clammed up so tightly that she knew they
must have been discussing her.

'Mamma has just discovered we are here in Rome,'
Sandro informed her coolly, 'and decided to pay us a
visit.'

His mother winced, and Joanna understood her desire
to do it. Sandro's voice had been sliced through with
grating sarcasm.

'*Buona sera*, Joanna,' his mother greeted her, rather ruefully. She was a short, slender, very elegant creature, with dyed dark hair and her son's velvet brown eyes. Eyes that were fixed coolly on Joanna at the moment. 'It is good to see you again, my dear...'

Was it? Joanna didn't think so, going by the look in those eyes right at this moment. 'Thank you,' was all she said, stepping forward to allow their cheeks to brush in the expected Latin way of greeting. 'I w-was about to make some coffee,' she murmured, looking desperately for a way of escaping this awkward situation. 'Perhaps you would like to s-sit down while I go—'

She was already turning for the door when a telephone began ringing in Sandro's study. 'I need to answer that,' Sandro said grimly. 'You stay and talk to Mamma.'

Joanna stared at him in horror as he went striding by her. Don't you dare do this to me! her eyes pleaded furiously. He ignored her, still so angry with her that she supposed this was his way of getting his own back.

'Please, Joanna, come and sit by me and tell me what you have been doing with yourself since we last met.'

Oh, damn. Joanna's shoulders dropped, her bank of energy along with them. Turning with an air of dull fatalism, she made herself walk over to the sofa and sit down beside Sandro's mother.

'You are looking well,' his mother remarked politely.

'Thank you,' she replied again. 'And s-so are you,' she felt compelled to add. 'Sandro has been telling me that you've been ill recently.'

The older woman nodded. 'Last year it was necessary I underwent some open heart surgery,' she explained, with a small grimace that revealed a reluctant acceptance of her illness. 'Alessandro took me to Orvieto to convalesce afterwards. It is such a peaceful place to be, away from Rome's constant rush and noise, when one is feeling under the weather...'

'Yes.' Joanna nodded, her eyes glazing with a wistful understanding of what her mother-in-law meant.

'Of course,' his mother acknowledged. 'For you have just arrived back from visiting the old Campione estate. Alessandro was explaining why I could not reach him by telephone today. I discovered by pure accident, you see, that you were here with my son.'

And here it comes, Joanna noted, her spine straightening slightly, because she had a fairly good idea what was going to come next, like— What the hell do you think you're up to, disrupting my son's life a second time?

Yet it didn't come. 'You liked the estate?' Sandro's mother asked instead.

'Very much—who wouldn't?' Joanna found a stiff little smile from somewhere. 'It's such a beautiful place.'

The older woman nodded. 'Alessandro and I visited it several times while we were there. He was so very drawn by this idea, you see, that a country home could well be the lure he was searching for to coax you back to him.'

Joanna blinked. Sandro had been considering that beautiful place as far back as twelve months ago? She had believed it was a recent impulsive decision on his part.

'But of course,' his mother continued levelly, 'the best made plans can to go awry, even for a man like Alessandro. I was sorry to hear about the tragic death of your sister, Joanna,' she added gently. 'It must have come as a terrible blow to you.'

She knew about that too? Joanna's spine went a little straighter. 'It was at the time,' she agreed. 'But I am over it now.'

'Still…' Obviously not put off by Joanna's stiff tone, the older woman continued, 'It seems dreadfully fated that while my son was planning his campaign to reinstate

you as his wife, you were enduring such a terrible loss…
Do you believe in fate, Joanna?'

'I don't know,' she answered warily. 'I've never really
thought about it.'

'Do you believe in love, then?' the older woman persisted. 'Do you believe that a good, honest and true love
can conquer all, or do you think that even the best love
may always be fated to fall by the wayside, no matter
what the lovers try to do to hold onto it?'

'I don't think I understand what you're trying to say,'
Joanna replied carefully, while her eyes darted across the
room in the dubious hope that Sandro would reappear
and put a stop to this before it got out of hand.

But he didn't appear and, like her son, the mother was
obviously someone on a mission at the moment, because
she touched Joanna's hand to regain her attention. 'What
I am trying to ascertain, *cara*,' she said gently, 'is
whether you believe that your marriage has a better
chance at succeeding this time, or whether this is just a
sad case of Alessandro refusing to accept defeat.'

'We are working on it,' Joanna said tightly.

'The physical side?'

Joanna shot to her feet. So did Sandro's mother, her
hand closing around Joanna's wrist with a surprising
strength for such a slight person. 'I am not trying to
make trouble,' she asserted anxiously, making trouble
with every word she spoke. 'But—please, Joanna, you
have no *mamma* to talk to about these things! God
knows,' she murmured unsteadily, 'it cannot be easy for
you after what you have been through. But I do not want
to see Alessandro hurt as badly this time as he was the
last, because you could not—'

She stopped and swallowed. Joanna began to tremble
because it was beginning to hit her, really hit her, what
his mother was actually saying here.

'I would like to help, if I can.'

'No one can help.' Abruptly Joanna pulled her captured wrist free, her face turned to ice, her body cast in it. 'This is not your problem.'

'What's going on here?'

Joanna spun on her heel to stare at Sandro through eyes made of glass. 'You told her,' she accused him. 'I'll never forgive you.'

With that she went to stalk past him, but he stopped her by gripping her by the shoulders.

'Let me go,' she bit out in revulsion—the first true revulsion she had shown him since his return into her life.

'Mamma does not know it all,' he avowed. 'Only what Molly told me. I am only human, *cara*,' he added on a short sigh, when her icy expression did not alter. 'I needed to talk to someone I could trust about what had happened to us!'

It didn't matter. To Joanna, still too much had been said. 'It didn't happen to *us*, Sandro, it happened to me!'

'Us, Joanna,' he insisted grimly. 'What those animals did to you, they did to me also. And, like you, I have been paying the price for their actions ever since!'

'Well, you don't have to pay the price any more,' she said, 'because I am leaving here—even if that means I walk the streets of Rome for ever!'

'You think I will let you go?' he mocked. 'Simply because you are angry at what you see as my betrayal of a confidence?'

At last her cold eyes revealed life, flashing with anger. 'I trusted Molly to keep my confidence, but she told you,' she tightly pointed out. 'Molly trusted you to keep her confidence, but you told your mother. Who has your mother told, Sandro?' she demanded. 'How many of the great Bonetti family are by now whispering behind closed doors about the dreadful fate of your sad marriage to a ruined woman?'

'Oh—no, Joanna!' his mother put in anxiously. 'I have told no one! I would not!'

But Joanna wasn't listening; she had gone way beyond the point of listening to anything anyone had to say to her any more. 'I feel violated all over again, do you know that?'

Sandro let out a heavy sigh and tried to draw her closer to him, but she wasn't going to let him. Quite suddenly, she began to shake—shake violently. To shake with anger, horror and a soul-crushing self-revulsion that had always made up a large part of her emotional reaction to what had happened to her.

'Joanna, don't do this!' Sandro muttered, trying to once more draw her closer, but still she wasn't letting him. 'Damn it!' he cursed. 'Mamma—why could you not just leave well alone!'

'Sh-she's right, though, isn't she?' Joanna said, pushing her head up to gaze into those grim brown eyes that always seemed so angry now. 'I should not be doing this to you again. I keep trying to tell you that!'

'The only thing you are doing to me is hurting me because you hurt.'

'I am no good to you any more!'

'You will stop saying things like that!' he snapped. 'Because some animals took you against your will, that does not make you untouchable, Joanna!'

'But it does—don't you see?' she cried, her eyes bright, hot and painfully haunted. 'I had only one thing I could give to you, Sandro! One small thing that made everything perfect. Because you could give me the world where I had so little to offer you, except for that one s-small thing that you thought was so s-special. And they took it!' she sobbed, her voice lifting to a heart-wrenching shrillness. 'They stole the only thing I had that I could give to you! N-now I can't give myself at all!' she finished achingly. 'I can't do it, Sandro. I'm sorry, but I *just can't do it*!'

'Santa Maria?' Sandro's mother breathed in pained

understanding from somewhere beyond the heavy mists of Joanna's own helpless anguish.

Sandro said nothing. He just stood there in front of her with his lean dark features turned white. His mouth was clamped shut, his lips drawn inwards so there was barely an outline left on show. His jaw had locked and his eyes had gone so black they were like twin tunnels leading directly to his darkened soul. He tried to swallow but didn't quite manage it.

Above all, he was trembling—whether he was trembling with appalled comprehension at last, or trembling with sheer bloody anger was difficult to tell.

But Joanna knew she could not stay around to find out. She had to get out of there, away from the apartment, away from the hell it had all become. But, most of all, she had to get away from him.

Breaking free from his grip, she was suddenly off and running. Running before Sandro had a chance to react. Running into the hall and out of the apartment. Running into the waiting lift, where she stabbed an urgent finger at the console, then turned on shaking legs in time to glimpse Sandro angrily striding towards her as the doors closed firmly between them.

She heard his fist hit the solid door, heard him swearing and cursing until she was out of earshot. Then the doors were sliding open again and she was running again, out into the street as dusk was just beginning to turn everywhere a rich silken red, and still she kept going, on feet that seemed to have been given wings.

CHAPTER TEN

How far she got away from the building before Sandro eventually managed to catch up with her, Joanna didn't know. She had no idea where she was even running to! But she pulled to a panting halt when a familiar black car sped by and skidded to a screeching halt several yards in front of her.

Its door flew open even before the car engine had shuddered its last jolting breath, then Sandro was climbing angrily out.

Tall, lean, heart-rendingly handsome and excruciatingly special, he began striding towards her with that same look of whitened anger etched into his face.

He said not a word, his mouth nothing more than a thin, tight line, as he reached out and took a firm grip on her wrist, turned on his heel and began pulling her behind him back to the car.

His free hand tugged the passenger door open. He urged her inside, shut the door with a muted slam that made her wince, then was striding around the car's shining bonnet to climb in beside her.

His door slammed them in. Reaching out with a long finger, he touched a switch that sent all the locks shooting into their housing, then he just sat there, one hand clenched into a fist on his thigh, the other pressed into the line of his tightly held mouth, while Joanna sat beside him, gasping for breath after her wild bid for escape and sweating so badly that her skin glistened with it.

'I...'

'Don't!' he gritted. 'Don't say a bloody word.'

She blinked and was thoroughly silenced by the power

of emotion he'd infused into that command. In the midst
of that emotion, he started the car engine, threw it into
gear, then jettisoned them off down the road.

The journey back to his apartment was achieved so
quickly that Joanna wondered deliriously why she had
bothered to run at all! They jerked to a stop and he got
out, came round and opened her door to pull her out. He
didn't look at her, hadn't looked at her since the car
skewed to a halt in the road. He hauled her into the
building, then into the waiting lift.

They shot upwards. She didn't even notice, she was
so busy worrying what was coming next. He opened the
apartment door, hauled her inside there also, slammed
the door shut, then made a grim point of firmly locking
them in. Then and only then did he seem to pause to
take stock of the whole crazed, wretched experience.

But Joanna didn't feel like hanging around to wait for
whatever conclusions he eventually came to. She made
a second bolt for it, flying down the hall and into the
bedroom, hurriedly shutting the door behind her before
going to sink down weakly on the side of the bed, wishing the door had a lock on it so she could make sure she
kept him out.

But there was no lock, and she was trembling with
reaction now, shaken to the very core by her own wild,
naked confession and the tearing run that had followed
it.

'Oh, God,' she sobbed, and dropped her face into her
hands—only to fly jerkily to her feet again because she
could hear him just outside her door and she couldn't
face him yet; she just couldn't!

The bathroom door had a lock on it! she remembered,
and moved off on shaky legs towards it—

'Try it,' a super-grim voice behind her invited, 'and
watch me break it down if I have to.'

'I n-need a shower,' she improvised, tossing the sup-
posedly casual words over her shoulder so she did not

have to turn and face him. 'I'm sweating and the air-conditioning is on. It's ch-chilly in here.'

'What it is, *cara*,' Sandro drawled, 'is you on the run again. But, as you see, I am not going to let you. So you may as well turn and face me yourself, rather than have me make you do it.'

And he meant every silkily threatening word of it, Joanna acknowledged sinkingly. Sandro was that man on a mission again, and her innermost soul laid out for his inspection was that mission's goal.

'Y-your mother—'

'Is very relieved to know that I have you safely back here with me,' he inserted. 'And has gone home to recover from the whole wretched scene you threw!'

I threw! Joanna repeated in silent scorn. And who had instigated the wretched scene? His mother, that was who!

'Turn, Joanna.'

Her hand was at her aching eyes again, but almost instantly dropped to her side. Making a small fist, she grimly straightened her shoulders before she spun abruptly on her heel. 'Happy now?' she tossed at him defiantly.

'No,' he replied. 'You look dreadful.'

He didn't look too good himself, she noticed with a terrible ache inside her. His face was still pale, still drawn, his eyes too black, his lips still held in a thin, tight, angry line.

'I'm sorry,' she whispered, unable to stop herself.

As usual he wasn't impressed by the apology. 'Has it never occurred to you, *cara*, that there is a hell of a lot more to loving someone than the size of their bank balance?'

'I've never wanted your money!' She denied that implication hotly.

'Quite,' he said, throwing her into a mind-numbing confusion as to what he was trying to get at here!

Then she found out. 'As I never wanted your virginity,' he declared, watching almost detachedly as she went white at the very mention of the word. 'Although I do admit that once I believed I was getting it I felt honour-bound to treat such a gift with the respect it clearly deserved. No, don't you dare turn away from what I am saying here!' he rasped out, when she went to do just that. 'You will keep facing me and listen!' he commanded, levering himself away from the door to start towards her. 'You will listen, Joanna,' he gritted. 'As I had to stand and listen to your heart-rending little speech just now!'

'I knew you would never understand how I feel!' she cried, backing away as he came nearer.

'Oh, I understand that you truly believe I held your innocence in a higher regard than the love I felt for you!' he snapped. 'And you insult me with that opinion, do you know that? You insult what we had together and you insult the way I loved you!'

Fine words, three years after the event, Joanna thought bitterly. She could still remember the fuss he'd made about her virginity then—and the way he'd changed towards her! Goodnight pecks on the cheek, instead of long, passionate embraces! Holding her hand instead of letting his hands roam all over her!

In fact, she had begun to wonder if he would actually bring himself to take that precious virginity from her once it was his for the taking!

'And you're turning it all round to suit your own view of things again,' she threw angrily back at him. 'It is always how you feel, Sandro! How I let you down all the time—as if you think I don't already know exactly how badly I failed you!'

'Not with this virginity thing, you do not,' he denied. 'For what is a thin veil of skin in reality, *cara*? It is there for the practical purposes of protecting the female womb against infection and disease until the said female

is ready to go forth and produce children. Nothing
more—' he shrugged '—nothing less. Unless you are
some kind of purity-obsessed barbarian, of course, which
I am not,' he declared.

'But it was mine to bestow where I wanted to bestow
it,' she reasoned shakily. 'And I wanted to give it to
you!' It was a cry from the very heart of her. 'When
they stole that right from me, they stole my special gift
to you!'

'And once it was gone, it was gone for ever, Joanna,'
Sandro grimly pointed out. 'Yet the importance you
place upon it seems to suggest that once you had given
this precious gift to me, you would have had nothing
else left to give!'

'Which doesn't alter the truth, Sandro! That I find I
cannot even think of letting you m-make love to me
without it tearing me apart inside because of the loss of
that gift!'

'You think I will miss it?' he demanded. 'That I will
mourn its loss and think less of you for that loss?' He
had the gall to laugh, albeit contemptuously. 'I would
have thought it was damned obvious that I would rather
be allowed to make love to my wife than live the bloody
frustrating life I have been living without being allowed
to touch her!'

'I told you you wouldn't understand,' she sighed out
shakily.

'Oh, I understand a whole lot more than you give me
credit for,' he came right back. 'I understand very well
that you are really nothing more than a very frightened
virgin at heart.'

Joanna jumped, shocked and hurt by the interpretation.

'What those two animals did to you does not count,'
he dismissed with a deriding flick of his hand. 'That was
a mere technicality beside the real issue that keeps you
in this pathetic state of high anxiety. And what is the

real issue?' he proposed. *'You,'* he answered for himself. 'You have difficulty finding enough courage to give yourself to me. *Yourself*, Joanna,' he repeated forcefully. 'Your *virgin* self! The self you give freely to me—which is the real gift of love from one person to another. Not that fine veil of skin you set so much store by. And if you continue like this,' he concluded as he turned towards the door again, so obviously sick to death of her that it showed in every distasteful line on his face, 'then you are condemning us both to lot of misery,' he warned. 'Because you will be condemning me to a life of frustrating celibacy, and yourself to a life of guilt and anguish while you watch me suffer like that!'

'W-what do you mean?' she whispered, not liking at all what she suspected he was saying.

'Exactly what your horrified mind is telling you,' he replied. 'That this marriage is for life. I am not letting you push me out of it a second time. Unless, of course,' he tagged on grimly, as he pulled open the door, 'you cling so tenaciously to what is in effect a damned lost cause, I may decide it is more than time to let go of my own lost cause!'

Which so obviously meant her that Joanna just stood there staring as the door closed behind him, his words having had such a profound effect on her that she could barely draw in breath!

Lost cause? Was that what she was? Was that what this whole wretched state of affairs was really all about—a lost cause?

Her legs gave out, sinking her weakly onto the bed because she had suddenly realised that Sandro was oh, so right!

In her own case, what was gone was indisputably gone! Pining over its loss was never going to bring it back again!

She *had* been clinging to the principles of a long-lost cause! She truly *was* a frightened virgin at heart, afraid to give herself freely to the man she loved in case he took and found her wanting!

And what those two men had done to her *didn't* count, not any more.

It couldn't count, she realised suddenly, if she was going to salvage anything at all from this mess she had made of both her own and Sandro's lives!

Because that was something else he had been right about, namely, why should he continue clinging to something that was so clearly becoming his own lost cause?

Abruptly she was on her feet again, shivering, cold— so cold it struck at the very heart of her. Cold with fear. But this fear was different from the one she was used to feeling, because it came from a fear of losing, not the old fear of giving.

Sandro was beginning to see her as a lost cause. He was going to give up on her!

That was when the panic flared—again, not the old panic but a new panic, which set her moving jerkily towards the bathroom with the certain knowledge of what she had to do if she wanted to make things right between them ringing like a warning bell inside her head. It had her quickly stripping off and showering her clammy body. Had her hurriedly tugging a long white bathrobe over still damp skin with shaking fingers

She didn't know if she could carry it right through to its natural conclusion, but she was certainly going to try!

The rest of the apartment was quiet when she stepped out of her room, so quiet she began to fear that Sandro might well have left it altogether! That fear tagged itself on to the end of every other fear she was desperately trying to wage war with as, to the pulsing rhythm of her own tense heartbeat, she made herself walk down the hallway to the room she had not let herself enter in three long years.

Pressing anxious teeth into her trembling lower lip,

she reached for the door handle and made herself turn it.

Her eyes honed directly in on him the moment she stepped inside. It was such a relief to find him there that she never even noticed the once-daunting quality of high ceilings and grey-painted walls washed over with eau-de-nil and gold leafed features.

She didn't see the majestic bed, or recall that the last time she had been in this room she had enacted the kind of horrified scene that had left Sandro utterly shaken.

None of that seemed to matter any more, because he was all that mattered. This man who was standing there, staring out of the window, lost in his own grim train of thought. He had showered too, she noticed, his long lean body wrapped in a short white towelling bathrobe similar to her own.

He had heard her enter, because he was turning abruptly, his dark eyes still those two pinpoints of anger lancing into her, until he grimly hooded them over with his lids, closing her out.

Was it too late? Had she already left it too late to salvage this precious marriage of theirs? Her heart flipped over, all those fears and uncertainties centering on that closed, grim face, the knowledge of what she had to do next making her fingers tremble as they reached up to the knot that was holding her bathrobe in place.

The action stiffened his body slightly. His eyes flicked upwards to clash with hers in a question that brought a flood of heat rushing to her cheeks.

But she determinedly continued with what she was intending to do. Heart hammering, lungs tight, she let her fingers loosen the robe belt and slowly parted the heavy fabric, sliding it from her slender shoulders until its weight sent it falling from her body to land in a snowy heap around her feet.

Naked.

Married for three years, wildly in love for even longer than that, yet this was the first time she had stood in front of Sandro naked.

It was such a dramatic gesture. So in keeping with the dramatic way Joanna dealt with all situations in her life, be it love, fear, pleasure or trauma.

Which category this particular gesture fell into, she wasn't sure; she had a suspicion it was a mad tangle of all four emotions as she stood there, watching the way those long, lush lashes lowered over the dark burn in his eyes as they swept slowly over her, from satin-smooth shoulders to the high, firm thrust of her rounded breasts.

They responded by tightening, the rosebud tips stinging into prominent life under his hooded gaze. The silence in the room was stunning; neither moved, neither breathed as Sandro slid his gaze lower, over the slender ribcage that led to her narrow waist and flat stomach, where the hollow of her navel quivered slightly under stress. Then on, further on, down across the gentle swell of her hips to linger finally on the soft cluster of red-gold curls that defined the heart-shaped apex where her long, shapely thighs met with the very core of her sex.

That part of her began to throb softly, her bare toes curling in response. Did he understand what she was trying to do here? she wondered tensely. Did he see that she was trying to give back to him something she had taken away from him, right here in this very room three years ago?

His face told her nothing, nor his stone-still stance.

'I love you so much, Sandro,' she burst out anxiously. 'Please don't give up on me yet. At least let me try to be a proper wife to you!'

Nothing. He came back with nothing. And in the growing tension Joanna waited, exposed, vulnerable, achingly unsure of herself, breath held, heart pounding, soft lips parted and quivering, her whole person quivering like some helpless sacrifice standing there waiting to hear its final fate. His gaze drifted over her one more time, lowering, then lifting, lifting until at last he let his eyes clash with her eyes…

Then he sighed, the sound seeming to come from some deep, dark well inside him. 'Come here, you crazy mixed-up creature,' he commanded huskily.

Relief broke from her on a stifled sob, then she was across the room and throwing herself against him, feeling his arms close around her, wrapping her own arms tightly around him.

Their mouths met in a hot fuse of raging hunger. There was no in-between. With typical drama she had let go of all her old prejudices and now she was wild for him. The kiss went on and on, consuming them both, consuming the room and the air inside it until she felt as if there was only herself and Sandro left to hold the whole world together.

His hands were all over her, touching, stroking, learning—claiming what she was offering, accepting it as his for the taking at last.

Eager to learn, desperate to please, she matched him kiss for passionate kiss, caress for each agonisingly arousing caress, which saw the last of the barriers between them collapse as his robe fell from his own broad shoulders. Naked together at last. She leaned against him, pressing herself into the full hard, hot length of him.

It was a revelation: her skin seemed to sizzle in response, her senses coming vibrantly alive to rush hungrily to the surface with a need to grab their share of a new and glorious sensation. Her breasts pushed themselves into the silken whorls of dark hair that covered the rock-solid wall of his wonderful chest; her spine arched her closer to him so her hips could mould themselves to the rigid power of his hips.

She felt the force of his response answer everything she was feeling; felt the heavy pound of his heart against the press of her eager breasts; felt the full, throbbing rise of his passion push against her arching hips; felt his arms tighten round her as if he was afraid she might turn tail and run; felt a groan of impassioned agony roll through him and the sting of his heated breath as he broke their mouths apart so he could mutter something barely distinguishable in shaken reaction to the whole wild experience.

'Bellisima,' it sounded like. *'Bellisima…'*

Then their lips were fusing again, with an electric pleasure that had her arms hooking urgently around his neck to keep him locked in a heated embrace so intense that it left no room for the old ghosts to appear.

When he picked her up and carried her to the bed, she clung to him, allowing him no space to move away from her as they fell in a tangle of limbs onto the mattress, where it all continued with barely a pause.

'Slow down,' he muttered at one point. 'We should take this very slowly, step by step. It does not have to be a conflagration, *cara mia.*'

'Yes it does,' she argued, skimming her eager fingers over his tight satin shoulders and into that mat of crisp dark hair on his chest. 'We took it step by slow step last time and look what happened. You lost something that belonged to you and I lost my way.'

'You belong to me,' he murmured. 'It is all I have ever wanted, *cara.*'

She nodded. 'I understand that now. But don't hold back from me, Sandro, for fear of frightening me,' she begged him. 'I need you to overwhelm me, to give me no time to change my mind, because I still have this horrible fear that at the final moment I am going to let you down again!'

She didn't let him down. She enchanted him. She made him fall in love with her ten times over.

'You have to stop that,' he murmured, gently removing her stroking fingers from where they were causing such havoc.

'Why?' she asked guilelessly, moving her hands to some other part of him she had already learned gave him pleasure.

'This is why,' he laughed softly, and ran his finger into the warm, moist crevice of her body that set her gasping while he lay beside her, watching her catch fire for him, watching her respond in complete abandonment to what he was making her feel.

It moved him—moved him fiercely to see how completely she was giving herself over to him. It was as if someone had opened a box containing all her stifled emotions and now they were out and flying free: no inhibition, just pure sensual freedom.

And it was all for him.

'Sandro,' she gasped, and he knew exactly why. But now it was his turn to feel uncertain, his turn to worry that he might just be the one to let her down.

Maybe she sensed that, maybe she knew that there was more at stake here than just her own old feelings of inadequacy. She had treated him too badly, and for too long, for those feelings of rejection to simply melt away.

Her eyes fluttered open and her hands reached up to mould his flushed, dark, passion-intense features. 'If you don't do it, I'll die,' she warned him softly.

Another laugh broke from him, gruff and rueful, maybe even a little shaken, as he shifted his body over hers, letting her feel his weight, the power of his passion, before he made that vital contact and began to push slowly, slowly inside her.

She was hot and she was tight, the untutored muscles of her pulsing silk sheath closing all around him as her slender body arched on a fierce intake of air; then—nothing.

She simply stopped breathing, her body held in a state of complete suspension that made him pause, his dark eyes fixing on her worriedly because he couldn't tell why she was responding like this.

'Cara?' he murmured in a thick-voiced question. 'Do I hurt you?'

She couldn't answer, was too thoroughly lost in the whole new experience. The feel of him, hard and strong and so completely filling her. The heat of him, mingling with her own burning heat, fusing them together as if to make them one entity. The very intimate scent of him, blending so perfectly with the scent of herself. And, most exquisite of all, the clear, sharp, sparkling knowledge that here she was, joined at last with this man she loved so much.

It was wonderful, like being set free of every single constraint that life had had to offer. On a sudden sunburst of unrestrained triumph, she laughed, her arms wrapping around his neck, her long legs wrapping themselves around his lean tight hips.

'I feel you, Sandro,' she confided in silken wonder. 'I can feel you throbbing deep inside me.'

The words moved him. Emotionally they moved him, sending the air rushing from his lungs on a shaken gasp. Physically they moved him, adding extra substance to his masculine potency. In the next moment he was kissing her, long and deeply, his tongue matching the powerful thrust of his body as he began to move, merging both acts into one glorious experience that held her completely captivated in its exciting thrall.

Then the sun-burst taking place inside her was no longer one of mere triumph, but a sun-burst of sensation—pure, sexual sensation. It opened like a budding flower, spreading its petals wider and wider on the rippling winds of an incredible pleasure, until—on a sharp indrawn gasp—she burst forth into full bloom, those delicate petals of sensation quivering out to encompass every nerve-end, every corner of her acutely responsive flesh.

Above her, Sandro was trembling with the constraint it was costing him to make this happen for her. With his hot mouth buried in her throat he moved on her, inside her, all around her. On fire, as she was on fire, so ultra-sensitised to every muscle pulse it was almost an agony to complete each sensual thrust of his body.

When her fingers caressed him, he shivered—not with cold, but with excruciating pleasure. When she kissed him, he groaned in anguish, but urgently kissed her back. But when the flower-burst began to happen inside her, he stopped moving altogether, watched her begin to bloom, felt the initial quivers of that final sensation take fierce hold of her, and with smooth, slow, careful timing, he guided her into that earth-shattering climax. Then he felt his own sun-burst begin to grow ever stronger, but only when she leapt did he give in to it; only when she cried out his name did he let go.

Reparation. It was his own reparation to hear the woman he loved so much crying out his name at this point of intense exaltation.

After that, everything splintered into a wild electric storm of pure feeling.

And neither had let the other down. Both lay there, still clasped tightly together in the prolonged and powerful aftermath, unable to move, their two hearts pounding as one.

'OK?' Sandro murmured when he could manage to speak at all, pushing up on his forearms so he could lay slightly trembling fingers against her flushed, damp cheek.

For an answer she kissed the hand, because it was impossible for her to use her voice yet. The biggest obstacle in her life had been surmounted at last and she was no longer a virgin—not in heart, not in mind, and definitely not in body.

'They were pretty inadequate, weren't they?' she whispered eventually.

'Who?' he demanded, already stiffening because he sensed rejection on the way.

'Those animals,' she explained, and opened her love-enriched blue eyes to gaze in wonder up at him. 'They had no idea what this is really all about.'

She thought he might get angry, was aware that he had a right to be angry with her for bringing that incident up at such a special moment. But Sandro was Italian, and Italian men were by nature very macho. He grinned—the kind of lazily smug grin that was ready to accept a compliment even if it was a very back-handed one.

'See what you have been missing out on all of these years?' he said arrogantly. 'Now, perhaps, I will get a little respect around here.'

'Ah,' she said, and suddenly the old Joanna was looking up at him, the blue-eyed, saucy minx he had first fallen in love with. 'But can you repeat the performance?' she challenged him. 'That's what I want to know.'

He repeated it, several times in fact, during that long, dark, steamy night.

The next morning she awoke to find herself curled around him. His arm was resting in the hollow of her waist, just below her ribcage, and his other was beneath her pillow, beneath her head, long fingers tangled amongst the tumbled silk flow of her hair.

She had never seen him look so wonderful, or so content, and she lay there for ages just gazing at him, basking in the full, glorious beauty of what they had shared the night before.

Then another need began to demand supremacy. Hunger pangs bit at her with a ravenousness she hadn't felt in days, weeks, months—years! She got up, stealthily sliding herself away from him so she wouldn't wake him, before padding softly across the bedroom with the intention of going to her old room to get dressed.

Then she spied his discarded tee shirt, lying where he must have angrily tossed it the night before, half on the back of an upright chair, half trailing on the floor. Sheer impulse made her snatch it up and take it with her out of the room.

She pulled it on over her head. It was huge, the hemline reaching well down her slender thighs. Grinning to herself, she continued on her way to the kitchen with her bare feet pressing into the cool mosaic tiling floor, aware of every tiny nook and cranny. In fact, she felt so super-sensitive to everything that even the brush of the soft, smooth cotton across her breasts was unutterably electrifying.

Freedom, that was what all this elation was, she recognised. She felt as if she'd been set free from eternal bondage. Reborn overnight into a completely different person.

A person who could even hum happily to herself while she prepared freshly squeezed orange juice to have with her breakfast of hot buttered toast.

'You sound cheerful,' a deep voice said.

She turned from what she was doing to find him leaning in the open doorway. He had already taken a shower and shaved, and he was wearing a pair of old boxer shorts and nothing else—except for the short-stemmed red rose he had stuck into the elasticated waistband.

Her senses began to sizzle, memories of the night before surging up like a fire to almost engulf her. This man, she thought breathlessly, this wonderful, sexy, dynamic man—is *my* lover!

My lover.

Possession gushed through her, plus a fierce sense of heart-bursting pride and a far more unrighteous sense of feline power—for, no matter how incredible he had made her feel last night, Joanna knew without a doubt that Sandro had felt it all just as deeply.

It was that same sense of power that brought on the very provocative response he received from her.

'Nice legs,' was all she remarked, before turning casually back to what she had been doing with a pile of fresh oranges and a juice-squeezer, deliberately ignoring the rose—just as she'd used to do.

She heard him move, felt the tingle of anticipation begin at her toes and start to run through her as his bare feet brought him to stand behind her. His hands slid around her waist and his dark head bent to nuzzle her nape, making her smile as she tilted her own head to give him better access.

'Mmm, this is the life,' he murmured. 'My sexy wife smelling of oranges and wearing my cast-off shirt.'

She turned within his arms so she was facing him. 'Here,' she said, and held her sticky fingers up for him to suck clean.

He did so quite happily, while his eyes held onto hers, filled with dark, lazy promises. But, for all her nonchalance, she felt a shy blush coming on, and she lowered her gaze to watch her slicked fingers collect the rose from the waistband of his shorts.

'Where do you keep producing these from?' she asked curiously.

'Secret,' he said. Then he was suddenly very serious. 'No more ghosts left now?' he questioned gently.

She shook her head, smoothing the deep red rose across her lips, then absently doing the same thing with it down the centre of his hair-roughened chest. 'Do you forgive me for the hell I've put you through?' she countered.

'There is nothing to forgive,' he said. 'You were in trauma. It closed you in behind a wall no one else could get through. I tried. Molly tried. And, although we did not understand why you were like you were, we were perceptive enough to realise something pretty dreadful must have happened to you to change you so radically, what seemed like overnight.'

'Did you ever guess at the truth?'

'I considered it as the most logical option,' he said. 'But, as you yourself pointed out, you had no cuts, no bruises, no evidence that pointed to a physical assault on your person…'

She shivered, then sighed and moved closer to him, so she could wrap her arms tightly round him. 'I want to forget it now,' she whispered sadly.

'Sure,' he agreed. 'Why not? Three years is more than long enough to let something as bad as that obsess your mind.'

'And today is the—fourth day of my new life,' she said, lifting her face so she could smile at him. 'What shall we do with it?'

His eyes began to gleam. She blushed again.

'Are you insatiable or what?' she chided.

'With you, satiation holds no bounds,' he murmured huskily. 'And I have three long years of wretched celibacy to catch up on.'

'Oh, Sandro—no!' she groaned in remorseful protest.

He actually looked shocked at her response. 'You think I would accept less than the best?' he demanded.

'But you told me you had a mistress!' she cried.

'You would have preferred it if I had used another woman as a substitute for you?'

'No,' she confessed huskily. 'But I would have understood it if you had done.'

'My pride may have demanded I mention a mistress,' he ruefully conceded, 'but I could not even bring myself to look at another women—never mind fancy one! But—hell,' he added on a small sigh, 'I was bitter about it. Especially during this last year, when you had disappeared altogether. I felt you had stripped me clean of my ability to be a man, *amore*,' he disclosed heavily. 'It was not a nice feeling, I promise you!'

'I do love you so,' Joanna informed him anxiously. 'I never wanted to treat you like that; I just couldn't help myself!'

'I was actually beginning to convince myself that I was much better off without you when you called,' he admitted.

Joanna groaned and hugged him tightly, in case he might decide he was still better off without her—in which case it would be her turn to refuse to let go!

'But the moment I heard your voice on the telephone it was as if something inside me caught alight,' he went on softly. 'I felt alive again suddenly—bursting with it, sizzling with it. So much so that even before you arrived at my place of work I had decided that you were never going to escape me again, even if I had to imprison you to keep you there! Then I was going to chip away at every last damned bloody stone in the wall you stood behind until I found the woman I fell in love with!'

'She's here,' Joanna assured him quickly.

He glanced down into her brimming blue eyes. 'All of her?'

'Yes.'

'Then let's go back to bed,' he said, reaching behind him to capture her hands so he could pull her with him out of the kitchen.

'But what about breakfast?' she protested. 'I'm hungry! I was just going to make you—'

'I've had mine,' he inserted arrogantly. 'I licked it from your fingers.'

Then they were inside his bedroom and the door was closing, and his hands were already beneath the shirt-hem and sliding it upwards and over her head, stripping her clear of any barriers.

His eyes glowed over her slender, pale, beautifully proportioned body, with its high, thrusting breasts and its intensely alluring cluster of dark gold between her thighs.

'You are so lovely you make my heart ache,' he told her huskily.

'So are you,' Joanna said, holding her arms up to collect him in. 'All my dreams come true.'

Lucy Gordon cut her writing teeth on magazine journalism, interviewing many of the world's most interesting men, including Warren Beatty, Richard Chamberlain, Roger Moore, Sir Alec Guinness, and Sir John Gielgud. She also camped out with lions in Africa, and had many other unusual experiences which have often provided the background for her books. She is married to a Venetian, whom she met while on holiday in Venice. They got engaged within two days.

Two of her books have won the Romance Writers of America RITA® award, SONG OF THE LORELEI in 1990, and HIS BROTHER'S CHILD in 1998 in the Best Traditional Romance category.

Lucy Gordon is a star of Tender Romance™
and her brand-new trilogy
THE COUNTS OF CALVANI
is not to be missed:

THE VENETIAN PLAYBOY'S BRIDE
– April 2003

THE ITALIAN MILLIONAIRE'S MARRIAGE
– June 2003

THE TUSCAN TYCOON'S WIFE
– August 2003

FARELLI'S WIFE

by

Lucy Gordon

PROLOGUE

THE headstone stood in the shadow of trees. A small stream rippled softly past, and flowers crept up to the foot of the white marble. The engraving said simply that here lay Rosemary Farelli, beloved wife of Franco Farelli, and mother of Nico. The inscription showed that she had died exactly a year ago, aged thirty-two, and with her, her unborn child.

There were other headstones in the Farelli burial plot, but only this one had a path worn right up to it, as though someone was drawn back here time and again, someone who had yet to come to terms with the heartbreaking finality of that stone.

Three figures appeared through the little wood that surrounded the plot. The first was a middle-aged woman with a grim expression and upright carriage. Behind her came a man in his thirties, whose dark eyes held a terrible bleakness. One hand rested lightly on the shoulder of the little boy walking beside him, his hands full of wild flowers.

The woman approached the grave and stood regarding it for a moment. Her face was hard and expressionless. A stranger, coming upon the group, might have wondered if she'd felt any affection for the dead woman. At last she stood aside and the man stepped forward.

'Let me take Nico home,' she said. 'This is no place for a child.'

The man's face was dark. 'He is Rosemary's son. This is his right—and his mother's.'

'Franco, she's dead.'

'Not here.' He touched his breast and spoke softly. 'Not ever.' He looked down at the child. 'Are you ready, *piccino?*'

The little boy, as fair as his father was dark, looked up and nodded. He laid the flowers at the foot of the grave. 'These are for you, Mama,' he said.

When he stepped back his father's hand rested again on his shoulder.

'Well done,' he said quietly to his son. 'I'm proud of you. Now go home with your grandmama.'

'Can't I stay with you, Papa?'

Franco Farelli's face was gentle. 'Not now. I must be alone with your mother.'

He stood quite still until they had gone. Not until their footsteps faded into silence did he move towards the gravestone and kneel before it, whispering.

'I brought our son to you, *mi amore.* See how he has grown, how strong and beautiful he is. Soon he will be seven years old. He hasn't forgotten you. Every day we talk together about "Mama". I'm raising him as you wished, to remember that he is English as well as Italian. He speaks his mother's tongue as well as his father's.'

His eyes darkened with pain. 'He looks more like you every day. How can I bear that? This morning he turned to me with the smile that was yours, and it was as though you were there. But the next moment you died again, and my heart broke.

'It is one year to the day since you died, and still the world is dark for me. When you left you took joy with you. I try to be a good father to our child, but my heart is with you, and my life is a desert.'

He reached out a hand to touch the unyielding marble. 'Are you there, my beloved? Where have you gone? Why can I not find you?'

Suddenly his control broke. His fingers grasped the marble convulsively, his eyes closed and a cry of terrible anguish broke from him.

'Come back to me! I can bear it no longer. *For God's sake, come back to me!*'

CHAPTER ONE

IF JOANNE concentrated hard she could bring the brush down to the exact point, and turn it at the very last minute. It took great precision, but she'd rehearsed the movement often, and now she could do it right, every time.

The result was perfect, just as the whole picture was perfect—a perfect copy. The original was a little masterpiece. Beside it stood her own version, identical in every brush stroke. Except that she could only trudge slowly where genius had shown the way.

The dazzling afternoon sunlight streaming through the windows of the Villa Antonini showed Joanne how well she'd performed her allotted task, and how mediocre that task was.

'Is it finished?' Signor Vito Antonini had crept into the room and come to stand beside her. He was a tubby man in late middle age who'd made a huge fortune in engineering and was now enjoying spending it. He showered gifts on his plain little wife, whom he adored, and had bought her this luxurious villa on the outskirts of Turin.

Then he'd purchased some great paintings to adorn it. But because they were valuable the insurers had insisted that they should all be locked away in the bank, which wasn't what he'd wanted at all. So he'd sent for Joanne Merton, who, at only twenty-seven, had a fast-rising reputation as a copyist, specializing in Italian paintings.

'Your copies are so perfect that nobody will know the difference, *signorina*,' he said now, gleefully.

'I'm glad you're satisfied with my work,' Joanne said, with a smile. She liked the little man and his wife, who'd welcomed her into their home and treated her like an honoured guest.

'Do you think,' he asked wistfully, 'that we could put your pictures in the bank vaults and keep the originals on my walls?'

'No,' she said hastily. 'Vito, I'm a copyist, not a forger. You know the condition of my work is that it's never passed off as the original.'

Vito sighed, for he was a risk-taker, but just then his wife came into the room and Joanne appealed to her.

'*Cretino*,' she admonished her husband briskly. 'You want this nice girl to go to gaol? Forget this silly idea and come and eat.'

'More food?' Joanne protested, laughing. 'Are you trying to make me fat, Maria?'

'I'm trying to stop you fading away,' Maria said. 'No girl should be as thin as you are.'

Joanne wasn't really thin, but elegantly slim. She was fighting to stay that way, but Maria made it hard.

The table was groaning under the fruit of her labours: garlic bread and tomatoes, black olive pâté and fish soup, followed by rice and peas.

Despite her concern for her figure, Joanne couldn't resist this mouth-watering repast. She'd loved Piedmont cooking since she was eighteen and had won a scholarship to study art in Italy. She'd been blissfully happy, tucking into the rich, spicy meals, or wandering through Turin, drunk on great paintings, dreaming that one day she would contribute to their number. And she'd fallen wildly, passionately in love with Franco Farelli.

She'd met him through his sister, Renata, an art student in the same class. They'd become good friends, and Renata had taken her home to meet her family, wine growers with huge vineyards just north of the little medieval town of Asti. Joanne had fallen in love with Isola Magia, the Farelli home, and been instantly at ease with the whole family: Giorgio, the big, booming papa who laughed a lot, and drank a lot and bawled a lot; Sophia, his wife, a sharp-faced, sharp-tempered woman who'd greeted Joanne with restraint, but made her welcome.

But from the moment she'd met Franco she'd known she'd come home in a totally different way. He'd been twenty-four, tall and long-boned, with a proud carriage that set him apart from other men. His height came from his father, a northern Italian. But his mother hailed from Naples down in the south, and from her he derived his swarthy looks, dark chocolate eyes and blue-black hair.

In other ways, too, he was an amalgam of north and south. He had Giorgio's easygoing charm, but also Sophia's volcanic temper and quick, killing rages. Joanne had seen that rage only once, when he'd found a young man viciously tormenting a dog. He'd knocked the lout down with one blow, and for a moment his eyes had contained murder.

He'd taken the dog home and tended it as gently as a woman, eagerly assisted by Renata and Joanne. That night the dog's owner had returned with his two brothers, drunk and belligerent, demanding the return of their 'property'. Joanne would never forget what had happened next.

Calmly Franco had taken out a wicked-looking stiletto, thrust the blade through some paper money and held it out to them.

'This will pay for the dog,' he'd said coldly. 'Take it and never trouble me again.'

But the brothers hadn't touched the money. Something they'd seen in Franco's eyes had sent them fleeing out into the night, yammering with fear, never to return. The dog had been named Ruffo, and become his inseparable companion.

But such incidents had been rare. Franco had been more concerned with enjoying himself than fighting. For him there had always been a joke to be relished, a song to be sung, a girl to be wooed, and perhaps more than wooed, if she was willing. When he'd smiled his white teeth had gleamed against his tanned skin, and he'd seemed like a young god of the earth.

Until then Joanne hadn't believed in love at first sight, but she'd known at once that she belonged to Franco, body and soul. Just looking at him had been able to make her flesh grow warmer, even in that fierce Italian heat. His smile had made her feel she were melting, and she would gladly have melted if, by doing so, she could have become a part of him.

His smile. She could see it now, slow and teasing, as though the world were his and he was wondering whom to share it with. And she knew, by instinct, what kind of a world it was: one of desire and satiation, of sinking his strong teeth into life's delights while the pleasure overflowed, of heated taking and giving, living by the rhythms of the earth that received the seed so that there should be growing, reaping and growing again. She had known all this the first time she'd seen him, striding into the flagstoned kitchen and standing

near the door, his black hair turned to blue by a shaft
of light, calling, 'Hey, Mama—' in a ringing voice.

How could anyone resist that voice? It was rich with
all the passion in the world, as though he'd made love
to every woman he'd met. And Joanne, the girl from
a cool, rainy country, had known in a blinding instant
that he was her destiny.

Sadly, she had no illusions that she was his destiny.
The estate was filled with lush virgins and ripe young
matrons who sighed for him. She knew, because
Renata had confided, between giggles, that Franco took
his pleasures freely, wherever they might be found, to
the outrage of his mother and the secret envy of his
father.

But he had never even flirted with Joanne, treating
her just as he had his sister, teasing her amiably before
passing on his way, his exuberant laughter floating behind him. And her heart had been ready to burst with
joy at his presence and despair at his indifference.

'I couldn't eat another thing,' Joanne declared, regarding her clean plate.

'But you must have some cream cheese and rum
pudding,' Maria said. 'You're working her too hard,'
she scolded her husband.

'It's not my fault,' he protested. 'I show her the pictures and say, ''Work as you like,'' and in a week she
has finished the copy of the Carracci Madonna.'

'Because she works too much,' Maria insisted, slapping cream cheese on Joanne's plate. 'How many are
still to do?'

'Four,' Joanne said. 'Two more by Carracci, one
Giotto and one Veronese. I'm saving the Veronese until
last because it's so large.'

'I can't believe that an English girl understands Italian paintings so well,' Vito mused. 'At the start I had the names of several Italians who do this work, but everyone said to me, "No, you must go to Signorina Merton, who is English, but has an Italian soul."'

'I studied in Italy for a year,' Joanne reminded him.

'Only for a year? One would think you had lived here all your life. That must have been a wonderful year, for I think Italy entered deep into your heart.'

'Yes,' Joanne said slowly. 'It did...'

Renata began inviting her every weekend and Joanne lived for these visits. Franco was always there because the vineyard was his life and he'd learned its management early. Despite his youth he was already taking the reins from his papa's hands, and running the place better than Giorgio ever had.

Once Joanne managed to catch him among the vines when he was alone. He was feeling one bunch after another, his long, strong fingers squeezing them as tenderly as a lover. She smiled up at him. She was five feet nine inches, and Franco was one of the few men tall enough to make her look up.

'I came out for some fresh air,' she said, trying to sound casual.

'You chose the best time,' he told her with his easy smile that made her feel as if the world had lit up around her. 'I love it out here at evening when the air is soft and kind.'

He finished with an eyebrow raised in quizzical enquiry, for he'd spoken in Italian, a language she was still learning.

'*Morbida e gentile,*' she repeated, savouring the

words. 'Soft and kind. But it isn't really that sort of country, is it?'

'It can be. Italy has its violent moods, but it can be sweet and tender.'

How deep and resonant his voice was. It seemed to vibrate through her, turning her bones to water. She sought something to say that would sound poised.

'It's a beautiful sunset,' she managed at last. 'I'd love to paint it.'

'Are you going to be a great artist, *piccina?*' he asked teasingly.

She wished he wouldn't call her *piccina.* It meant 'little girl' and was used in speaking to children. Yet it was also a term of affection and she treasured it as a crumb from his table.

'I think so,' she said, as if considering the matter seriously. 'But I'm still trying to find my own style.'

She hadn't yet learned that she had no individual style, only a gift for imitation.

Without answering he pulled down a small bunch of grapes and crushed a few against his mouth. The purple juice spilled out luxuriantly down his chin, like the wine of life, she thought. Eagerly she held out her hands and he pulled off a spray of the grapes and offered them to her. She imitated his movement, pressing the fruit against her mouth, then gagged at the taste.

'They're sour,' she protested indignantly.

'Sharp,' he corrected. 'The sun hasn't ripened them yet. It'll happen in its own good time, as everything does.'

'But how can you eat them when they taste like this?'

'Sharp or sweet, they are as they are. They're still

the finest fruit in all Italy.' It was a simple statement, unblushing in its arrogance.

'There are other places with fine grapes,' she said, nettled at his assurance. 'What about the Po valley, or the Romagna?'

He didn't even dignify this with an answer, merely lifted his shoulders in a slight shrug, as if other vineyards weren't worth considering.

'What a pity you won't be here to taste them when they're ripe,' he said. 'That won't be until August, and you'll have returned to England.'

His words brought home to her how near their parting was. Her time in Italy was almost over, and then she wouldn't see him again. He was the love of her life but he didn't know, would never know.

She was desperate for something that would make him notice her, but while she was racking her brains she saw a movement among the vines. It was Virginia, a voluptuous and poorly named young woman who'd occupied a lot of Franco's attention recently.

Franco had seen Lucy and turned laughing eyes on Joanne, not in the least embarrassed. 'And now you must go, *piccina*, for I have matters to attend to.'

Crushing disappointment made her adopt a haughty tone. 'I'm sorry if I'm in the way.'

'You are,' he said shamelessly. 'Terribly in the way. Run along now, like a good girl.'

She bit her lip at being treated like a child, and turned away with as much dignity as she could muster. She didn't look back, but she couldn't help hearing the girl's soft, provocative laughter.

She lay awake that night, listening for Franco. He didn't return until three in the morning. She heard him humming softly as he passed her door, and then she buried her head under the pillow and wept.

The time began to rush past and the end of her final term grew inexorably nearer. Joanne received a letter from her cousin Rosemary who would be taking a vacation in Italy at that time. She wrote:

I thought I'd come to Turin just before you finish, and we can travel home together.

Joanne and Rosemary had grown up together, and most people, seeing them side by side, had thought that they were sisters. They'd actually lived as sisters after Joanne's parents had died and Rosemary had urged her widowed mother to take the girl in.

She'd been twelve then, and Joanne six. When Rosemary's mother had died six years later Rosemary had assumed the role of mother. Joanne had adored the cousin who'd given her a home and security, and all the love in her big, generous heart.

As Joanne had grown up they'd become more alike. They had both been unusually tall women, with baby blonde hair, deep blue eyes and peach colouring. Their features had been cast from the same mould, but Rosemary's had been fine and delicate, whereas Joanne's had still been blurred by youth and teenage chubbiness.

But the real difference, the one that had always tormented Joanne, had lain in Rosemary's poise and charm. She had been supremely confident of her own beauty and she'd moved through life dazzling everyone she met, winning hearts easily.

Joanne had been awed by the ease with which her

cousin had claimed life as her own. She'd wanted to be like her. She'd wanted to *be* her, and it had been frustrating to have been trapped in her own, ordinary self, so like Rosemary, and yet so cruelly unlike her in all that mattered.

At other times she'd wanted to be as different from Rosemary as possible, to escape her shadow and be herself. When people had said, 'You're going to be as pretty as Rosemary one day,' she'd known they'd meant to be kind, but the words had made her grind her teeth.

She could remember, as if it were yesterday, the night of the party, given by a fellow student. Joanne and Renata had been going together, with Franco escorting them, but at the last minute Renata had sprained her ankle and dropped out. Joanne had been in ecstasies at having Franco all to herself.

She'd bought a new dress and spent hours putting up her hair and perfecting her make-up. Surely that night he would notice her, even perhaps ask her to stay in Italy? Her heart had been singing as she'd gone down to where he'd been waiting outside on the terrace.

He'd been dressed for the evening. She'd never seen him formally attired before, but then she'd been struck afresh by how handsome he'd been with his snowy shirt against his swarthy skin. He'd looked up and smiled, raising his eyebrows in appreciation of her enhanced appearance.

'So, *piccina,* you've decided to take the world by storm tonight?' he teased.

'I just dressed up a little,' she said, trying to be casual, but with a horrible suspicion that she sounded as gauche as she felt.

'You'll break all their hearts,' he promised her.

'Oh, I don't know about *all* their hearts,' she said with a shrug.

'Just the one you want, eh?'

Could he have suspected? she wondered with sudden excitement. Was this his way of saying that he'd finally noticed her?

'Maybe I haven't decided which one I want,' she said archly, looking up at him.

He chuckled, and the sound filled her with happy expectation. 'Perhaps I should help you decide,' he said, and reached out to take gentle hold of her chin.

At last! The thing she'd prayed for, wept for, longed for, was happening. He was going to kiss her. As he lifted her chin and his mouth hovered above hers she was on the verge of heaven. She raised her hands, tentatively touching his arms.

And then it was all snatched away. There was a step in the passage, and a woman's voice floated out to them.

'I'm sorry to arrive without warning—'

Franco stopped, his mouth an inch above hers, raising his head, alerted by the voice. Joanne felt the shock that went through his body. He'd heard only Rosemary's voice, but already some special timbre in it seemed to tell him what was about to happen. He stepped away from Joanne, towards the door.

The next moment Rosemary appeared. Joanne, watching with jealous eyes that saw every detail, knew that all the breath had gone out of him, so that he stood like a man poised between two lives. Later she realized that this was literally true. Franco had seen his fate walk through the door, with long blonde hair and a dazzling smile. And he'd instantly recognized that this was what she was. He was no longer the same man.

Dazed, hardly able to believe what had happened, Joanne turned her eyes to see Rosemary staring at Franco with the same look that he was giving her. It was all over in a flash, and there was nothing to be done about it.

There were hasty introductions. Rosemary greeted everyone and threw her arms about Joanne, while somehow never taking her eyes off Franco. He was like a man in a dream. It was his idea that Rosemary come to the party with them. Joanne wanted to cry out at having come so close to her desire, but what would be the use of that? Even she could see that what was happening had always been meant.

At the party Franco monopolized Rosemary, dancing almost every dance with her, plying her with food and wine. His good manners made him attend to Joanne's comfort, watching to make sure that she wasn't a wallflower. There was no danger of that since she was popular. She danced every dance, determined not to show that her heart was breaking, and when Franco saw that she had a supply of partners he forgot her and spent every moment with Rosemary.

Many times she wondered what would have happened if Rosemary had seen her in Franco's arms. Would she have taken him, knowing how Joanne loved him? But the question was pointless. Franco pursued Rosemary fiercely through the evening that followed and every day afterwards until he made her his own. He was like a man driven by demons until he came to the safe haven of his love.

It was still painful to recall how she slipped away from the dance and stumbled across them in each other's arms, in the darkness. She backed away, but not before she heard Franco murmuring, '*Mi amore*—I will love you until I die,' and saw him kiss her passionately. It was so different from the teasing kiss he'd almost bestowed on herself, and she fled, weeping frantically.

Apart from herself, the only person not pleased by the wedding was Sophia. Joanne overheard the family scene in which Sophia begged Franco to marry a local girl, and not 'this stranger, who knows nothing of our ways'. Franco refused to quarrel with his mother, but he insisted on his right to marry the woman of his choice. He also demanded, quietly but firmly, that his bride should be treated with respect. Joanne was struck by the change in him. Already the easygoing lad who'd once let his mother's tirades wash over him was turning into a man of serious purpose. Sophia evidently felt it too, for she burst into angry tears.

'Poor Mama,' Renata observed. 'Franco's always been her favourite, and now she's jealous because he loves Rosemary best.'

The whole neighbourhood was invited to their wedding. Joanne longed not to be there, but Rosemary asked her and Renata to be her bridesmaids. Joanne was afraid that if she refused everyone would guess why.

When the day came she put on her pink satin dress, smiled despite her heartbreak, and walked behind Rosemary as she went down the aisle to become Franco's wife. Joanne saw the look on his face as he watched his bride's approach. It was a look of total, blind adoration, and it tore the heart out of her.

A year later she pleaded work as an excuse not to attend the baptism of their son, Nico. Rosemary wrote to her affectionately, saying how sorry she was not to see her again, and enclosing some christening cake and photographs. Joanne studied them jealously, noting how the same look was still on Franco's face when he looked at his wife. Even in the flat photographs it blazed out, the gaze of a supremely happy man whose marriage had brought him love and fulfilment. She hid the pictures away.

After that there were more pictures, showing Nico growing fast out of babyhood, becoming an eager toddler learning to walk, held safe by his father's hands. Franco's face grew a little older, less boyish. And always it bore the same look, that of a man who'd found all he wanted in life.

Rosemary stayed in touch through occasional telephone calls, and long letters, with photographs enclosed. Joanne knew everything that happened on the Farelli farm, almost as well as if she'd been there. Renata married an art dealer and went to live in Milan. Franco's father died. Two years later his mother visited her sister in Naples, where she met a widower with two children and married him. Franco, Rosemary and baby Nico were left alone on the farm: alone, that was, except for a woman who helped with the housework, and the dozens of vineyard workers who wandered in and out of the house.

Rosemary often repeated her loving invitations. She wrote:

It seems so long since we saw you. You shouldn't be a stranger, darling, especially after we were so close once.

Joanne would write back, excusing herself on the grounds of work, for her skill in copying paintings to the last brush stroke had made her a successful career. But she never gave the true reason, which was that she didn't trust herself to look at Rosemary's husband without loving him. And that was forbidden, not only because he cared nothing for her, but because Joanne also loved Rosemary.

She had no other close family, and the cousin who was also sister and mother was dearer to her than anyone on earth, except Franco. She owed Rosemary more than she could repay, and her fierce sense of loyalty made her keep her distance.

She was lonely, and sometimes the temptation to pay a visit was overwhelming. Surely it could do no harm to meet little Nico, enjoy the farm life for a while, and be enveloped in the warmth and love that Rosemary seemed to carry with her at all times?

But then Rosemary would write, innocently ending the letter, 'Franco sends his love'. And the words still hurt, warning her that the visit must never be made.

She'd been eighteen when she'd fallen in love with him, and it should have been one of those passing teenage infatuations, so common at that age. Her misfortune was that it wasn't. Instead of getting over Franco she'd gone on cherishing his image with a despairing persistence that warned her never to risk seeing him.

To outward appearances Joanne was a successful woman, with a string of admirers. The chubbiness of her early years had gone, leaving her figure slender and her face delicate. There were always men eager to follow her beauty and a certain indefinable something in her air. She let them wine and dine her and some of them, blind to the remote signals she sent out without knowing it, deceived themselves that they were making progress. When they realized their mistake they called her heartless, and to a point it was true. She had no heart for them. Her heart had been stolen long ago by a man who didn't want it.

Then Rosemary returned to England for a visit, bringing her five-year-old son. They stayed with Joanne for a week, and some of their old closeness was restored. They talked for hours into the night. Joanne was enchanted by the little boy. He looked English, but he had the open-heartedness of his Italian father, and would snuggle on her lap as happily as on his mother's.

Rosemary watched the two of them fondly, while she talked of her life in Italy with the husband she adored. The only flaw was Sophia's continuing hostility.

'I don't know what I'd have done if she hadn't re-married,' she confessed. 'She hates me.'

'But she was always nagging Franco to get married,' Joanne recalled.

'Yes, but she wanted to choose his wife. She'd have picked a local girl who wouldn't have competed with her for his heart, and given him lots and lots of children. Franco really wants them. Sophia never lets me forget that I've only managed to give him one.

'I've tried and tried to make her my friend, but it's useless. She hates me because Franco loves me so much, and I couldn't change that—even if I wanted to.'

Her words made Joanne recall how Sophia's manner to herself had altered without warning. She'd been friendly enough, in her sharp manner, until one day she'd caught Joanne regarding Franco with yearning in her eyes. After that she'd grown cool, as though nobody but herself was allowed to love him.

Rosemary's face was radiant as she talked of her

husband. 'I never knew such happiness could exist,' she said in a voice full of wonder. 'Oh, darling, if only it could happen for you too.'

'I'm a career woman,' Joanne protested, hiding her face against Nico's hair lest it reveal some forbidden consciousness. 'I'll probably never marry.'

She was the first to learn Rosemary's thrilling secret.

'I haven't even told Franco yet, because I don't want to raise false hopes,' she admitted. 'But he wants another child so badly, and I want to give him one.'

A week after her return to Italy she telephoned to say she was certain at last, and Franco was over the moon.

But the child was never born. In the fifth month of her pregnancy Rosemary collapsed with a heart attack, and died.

Joanne was in Australia at the time, working against a deadline. It would have been impractical to go to Italy for the funeral, but the truth was she was glad of the excuse to stay away. Her love for Rosemary's husband tormented her with guilt now that Rosemary was dead.

The year that followed was the most miserable of her life. Despite their long parting, Rosemary had stayed in touch so determinedly that she had remained a vital part of her life. Joanne only truly understood that now that she was gone, and the empty space yawned.

She had several requests to work in Italy, but she turned them all down on one pretext or another. Then a debilitating bout of flu left her too weak to work for some time, and her bank balance grew dangerously low. When the offer came from Vito Antonini she was glad of the chance to make some money.

He lived only sixty miles away from Franco. But she

could shut herself up to work, and never venture into the outside world. There was no need to see him if she didn't want to. So, despite her misgivings, she accepted the job and flew to Italy, telling herself that she was in no danger, and trying to believe it.

CHAPTER TWO

'WHY you never take the car?' Maria demanded one day. 'When you arrive I say, 'We don't need the second car. You use it.' But you never do. Is very unkind.'

'Don't be offended, Maria, please,' Joanne begged. 'It's just that I've been so busy.'

'Don't you have any friends from when you were here before?'

'Well—my cousin's family lives near Asti—'

'And you haven't visited?' Maria shrieked in horror, for like all Italians she was family-minded. 'You go now.'

Vito backed his wife up, and the two of them virtually ordered her out of the house.

'You stay away tonight,' Maria ordered. 'You won't have time to drive back.'

'I'll have plenty of time,' Joanne insisted. 'I'm only going for a couple of hours.'

They argued about this until the last minute, Maria demanding that she pack a bag, Joanne firmly refusing. She was going to make this visit as brief as possible, just to prove to herself that she could cope with meeting Franco. Then she would leave and never go back.

She was dressed for the country, in trousers and sweater. But both had come from one of Turin's most expensive shops, and she added a gold chain about her waist and dainty gold studs in her ears. She didn't realize that she was making a point, but the costly elegance of her attire marked her out as a different person from the gauche girl of eight years ago.

As soon as she got out onto the road and felt the beauty of the day, and the sun streaming in through the open window, Joanne was glad. She'd been shut up too long with the smell of oil paint and turpentine, and she needed to breathe fresh air.

She took the route through the little medieval town of Asti. Already there were posters up advertising the *palio,* the bareback race that was run every year around the *piazza.* The jockeys were all local lads, and Joanne's mind went back to the time Franco had taken part.

She'd been nervous as she'd taken her place in the stands with the family and almost every worker from the Farelli vineyard. The *palio* was so fierce that mattresses were fixed to the walls of all the surrounding buildings to save the riders and horses who crashed into them. Even so, injuries were common.

After the first lap it had been clear that the race was between Franco and another rider.

'That's Leo,' Renata said excitedly. 'He and Franco are good friends—except today.'

It was neck and neck on the last lap. Then Leo went ahead. Franco made a desperate attempt to catch up. The crowd's cheers turned to screams as the horses collided and both riders were thrown. Miraculously the following riders managed to jump over them, and neither man was hurt. But Joanne's heart was in her mouth as they all hurried around to see Franco afterwards.

Sophia clung to him, almost suffocating him until Giorgio gently prised her away. Leo hurled his whip to the ground, complaining, 'I was winning. I had the race in the palm of my hand. And he robbed me.'

Franco offered Leo his hand. Leo stared at it until
everyone thought he would refuse to shake. At last he
put out his own hand, saying through a forced smile,
'I'll get even with you next year, Farelli. See if I don't.'

But Franco had never competed again. By the next
race he'd been married to Rosemary, looking forward
to starting a family.

Joanne parked the car and spent an hour wandering
the streets she'd once known so well. She decided she
might as well have lunch here too, and enjoyed a lei-
surely pizza. She would have denied that she was putting off her meeting with Franco, but she didn't hurry.

But when she resumed the journey she was further
delayed by a traffic jam. For two hours she fretted and
fumed behind a trail of trucks, and it was late afternoon
before she neared the Farelli vineyards. She parked the
car off the road and got out to lean over a fence and
survey the land. The vines were growing strongly and
everywhere she looked she saw the brightness of summer. It reminded her of her year in Italy when she'd
fallen in love with Franco.

What would he be like now? Her last picture of him
had been taken eighteen months ago and showed him
older, more serious, as befitted a man of responsibili-
ties. Yet even then a mischievous devil still lurked in
his eyes. But he must have changed again since the
death of his beloved wife. Suddenly she was afraid to
see him. He would be a stranger.

But she couldn't give up now. Courtesy demanded
that she see Rosemary's widower and child before she
left the district. She started up again and drove on to
the turning that led to the house. At once memory began to play back. The dirt track was still the one she'd
seen the day Renata had brought her here for the first

time. There were the ruts left by the trucks that regularly arrived and departed.

The big, sprawling house too was the same, yellow ochre in the blazing sun, the dark green shutters pulled closed against the heat, the roof tiles rusty red. And everywhere there were geraniums, the brightly coloured flowers without which no Italian country home seemed complete. Geraniums around the doors, in window boxes, in hanging baskets: red, white, pink, purple, every petal glowing vividly in the brilliant light.

Chickens strutted pompously back and forth in the yard, uttering soft, contented clucks. The Farelli family was wealthy, but the house was that of a prosperous farmer, with homeliness prevailing over luxury. That was its charm.

Did nothing ever change here? There was the long table under the trees with the benches at either side. Above it stood the wooden trellis roof with flowers wreathing in and out and hanging down from it. How many times had she sat beneath those flowers, as if in paradise, listening to the family backchat over a meal? Paradise that might have been hers, that could never have been hers. Paradise lost.

The front door was open and she walked inside. Rosemary had made this place her own, but it still felt familiar. The few new pieces of furniture blended in with the warm red flagstones. The huge fireplace, where the family had warmed themselves by log fires, was unchanged. The old sofa had been re-covered, but was otherwise still the same, the largest one Joanne had ever seen.

The staircase led directly out of the main room. An old woman whom Joanne had never seen before came bustling downstairs, wiping her hands on her apron.

She was dressed in black, save for a coloured scarf covering her hair. She stopped very still when she saw Joanne.

'I'm sorry to come in uninvited,' Joanne said quickly. 'I'm not prying. My cousin was Signor Farelli's wife. Is he here?'

'He is with the vines on the south slope,' the woman said slowly. 'I will send for him.'

'No need. I know where it is. *Grazie.*'

In the poor light of the stairs she hadn't noticed the old woman's face grow pale at the sight of her. And she went out too quickly to hear her murmur, *'Maria vergine!'* or see her cross herself.

She remembered the way perfectly. She followed the path to the stream, stepping gingerly across the stones that punctuated the fast-running water. Once she'd pretended to lose her nerve in the middle of those stones so that Franco came back and helped her across, steadying her with his strong hands.

After that the path lay around by the trees until the first slope came into view, covered in vines basking in the hot sun. Here and there she saw men moving along them, checking, testing. They turned to watch her and even at a distance she was aware of a strange *frisson* passing through them. One man looked at her in alarm and hurried away.

At last she reached the south slope. Here too there were memories everywhere, and she stopped to look around her. This was where she'd walked one evening to find Franco alone, and their brief tête-à-tête had been interrupted by one of his light-o'-loves.

Lost in her reverie, she didn't at first see the child appear and begin moving towards her, an incredulous expression on his face. Suddenly he began to run. Joanne smiled, recognizing Nico.

But before she could speak he cried, 'Mama!' and hurled himself into her arms, hugging her tightly about the neck.

Dismay pervaded her. 'Nico, I—I'm not—'

'Mama! Mama!'

She could do nothing but embrace him back. It would have been cruel to refuse, but she was in turmoil. She'd barely thought of her resemblance to Rosemary, and Nico had met her before. But that had been eighteen months ago, an eternity in the life of a young child. And the likeness must have grown more pronounced than ever for him to confuse them.

She should never have come here. It had all been a terrible mistake.

'Nico.'

The man had approached while she was unaware, and stood watching them. Rosemary looked up and her heart seemed to stop. It was Franco, but not as she had ever seen him.

The light-hearted boy was gone for ever, replaced by this grim-faced man who looked as if he'd survived the fires of hell, and now carried them with him.

He'd filled out, become heavier. Once he'd been lean and rangy. Now there was power in every line of him, from his thickly muscled legs to his heavy shoulders. He wore only a pair of shorts, and the sun glistened off the sweat on his smooth chest. An outdoor life had bronzed him, emphasizing his clear-cut features and black hair.

One thing hadn't changed and that was the aura of vivid life he carried with him, so that his surroundings paled. But it was belied by the bleakness of his expression.

'Nico,' he called harshly. 'Come here.'

'Papa,' the child called, 'it's Mama, I—I think—'

'Come here.' He didn't raise his voice, but the child obeyed him at once, going to his side and slipping his hand confidingly into Franco's big one.

'Who are you?' Franco whispered. 'Who are you that you come to me in answer to—?' He checked himself with a harsh intake of breath.

'Franco, don't you know me?' she begged. 'It's Joanne, Rosemary's cousin.'

'Cousin?' he echoed.

She went closer and his eyes gave her a shock. They seemed to look at her and through her at the same time. Joanne shivered as she realized that he was seeing something that wasn't there, and shivered again as she guessed what it was.

'We met, years ago,' she reminded him. 'I'm sorry to come on you suddenly—' She took a step towards him.

'Stop there,' he said sharply. 'Come no closer.'

She stood still, listening to the thunder of her own heartbeat. At last a long sigh escaped him and he said wearily, 'I'm sorry. You are Joanne, I can see that now.'

'I shouldn't have just walked in like this. Shall I leave?'

'Of course not.' He seemed to pull himself together with an effort. 'Forgive my bad manners.'

'Nico, don't you remember me?' Joanne asked, reaching out her arms to the little boy. A light had died in his face, and she could see that he did now recall their first meeting.

He advanced and gave her a tentative smile. 'I thought you were my mother,' he said. 'But you're not, are you?'

'No, I'm afraid I'm not,' she said, taking his hand.

'You look so like her,' the little boy said wistfully.

'Yes,' Franco said in a strained voice. 'You do. When my people came running to me crying that my wife had returned from the dead, I thought they were superstitious fools. But now I can't blame them. You've grown more like her with the years.'

'I didn't know.'

'No, how should you? You never troubled to visit us, as a cousin should. But now—' he gazed at her, frowning '—after all this time, you return.'

'Perhaps I should have stayed away.'

'You are here now.' He checked his watch. 'It grows late. We'll go home and eat.' He gave her a bleak look. 'You are welcome.'

Franco's workers gathered to watch them as they walked. She knew now why she aroused such interest, but still it gave her a strange feeling to hear the murmurs, *'La padrona viva.'* The mistress lives. Out of the corner of her eye she saw some of them cross themselves.

'They are superstitious people,' Franco said. 'They believe in ghosts.'

They'd reached the stream now and Nico bounded ahead, jumping from stone to stone, his blond hair shining gold in the late afternoon sun. It was the same colour that Rosemary's had been, as Joanne's was.

A man called to Franco and he turned aside to talk to him. Nico jumped up and down impatiently. 'Come on,' he called to Joanne, holding out a hand for her.

She reached out her own hand and felt his childish

fingers grip her. 'Hey, keep still,' she protested, laughing, for he was still bounding about.

'Come on, come on, come on!' he carolled.

'Careful!' Joanne cried as she felt her foot slip. The next moment they were both in the stream.

It was only a couple of feet deep. Nico was up first, holding out his hands to help her up. *'Perdona me,'* he pleaded.

'Of course,' Joanne said, blowing to get rid of the water and trying to push back wet hair from her eyes. 'Oh, my goodness! Look at me!'

Her soft white sweater had become transparent, and was clinging to her in a way that was revealing. Men and women gathered on the bank, chuckling. She joined in, sitting there in the water and laughing up into the sun. For a moment the light blinded her, and when she could see properly she caught a glimpse of Franco's face, and its stunned look shocked her. She reached out a hand for him to help her up, but it seemed that he couldn't move.

'Will anyone help me?' she called, and some of the men crowded forward.

'Basta!' The one word from Franco cut across them. The men backed off, alarmed by something they heard in his voice.

He took Joanne's hand and pulled her up out of the water and onto the bank. As she'd feared, her fawn trousers also clung to her in a revealing fashion. To her relief the men had turned their heads away. After Franco's explosion not one was brave enough to look at her semi-nakedness.

'I'm sorry, Papa,' Nico said.

'Don't be angry with him,' Joanne said.

Franco gave her a look. 'I am never angry with

Nico,' he said simply. 'Now let us go home so that you can dry off.'

'I went to the house first,' Joanne said, hurrying to match her steps to Franco's long strides, 'and the old woman there told me where you were.'

'That's Celia, she's my housekeeper.'

Celia emerged from the house as they approached and stood waiting, her eyes fixed on Joanne. She exclaimed over her sodden state.

'Celia will take you upstairs to change your clothes,' Franco said.

'But I don't have anything to change into,' she said in dismay.

'Didn't you bring anything for overnight?'

'I'm not staying overnight. I mean—I didn't want to impose.'

'How could you impose? You are family.' Franco spoke with a coolness that robbed the words of any hint of welcome. 'But I was forgetting. You don't think of yourself as family. Very well, Celia will find you something of her own to wear while your clothes dry off.'

Celia spoke, not in Italian but in the robust Piedmontese dialect that Joanne had never quite mastered. She seemed to be asking a question, to which Franco responded with a curt *'No!'*

'Your clothes will soon dry,' he told Joanne. 'In the meantime Celia will lend you something. She will show you to the guest room. Nico, go and get dry.'

It was the child who showed her upstairs, taking her hand and pulling her up after him. Celia provided her with a huge white bath towel and some clothes. She bore Joanne's garments away, promising to have them dry in no time.

An unsettling playback had begun in Joanne's head. This was the very room she'd shared with Renata when she'd first come here. There were still the same two large beds, and a roomful of old-fashioned furniture. As with the rest of the house the floor was *terrazzo,* the cheap substitute for marble that Italians used to keep buildings cool.

The floor-length windows were still shielded from the sun by the green wooden shutters. Celia drew one of these back, and opened the window so that a breeze caused the long curtains to billow softly into the room. Joanne went to stand there, looking out over the land bathed in the setting sun. It was as heartbreakingly beautiful as she remembered it, the Italy of her dreams, blood-red, every colour more intense, every feeling heightened.

She tried on the dress. It was dark, made of some thin, cheap material, and it hung loosely on her slender frame, evidently made for someone wider and shorter. It was a pity, she thought, that Franco hadn't kept some of Rosemary's clothes, but, after all, it had been over a year.

And then, with a prickle up her spine, she remembered the words he'd exchanged with Celia. And she suddenly understood that he did, indeed, have some of Rosemary's clothes, and Celia had wanted to fetch them, and Franco had forbidden it.

She went down to find Nico waiting for her at the foot of the stairs. After the initial confusion he seemed less disturbed than anyone at seeing his mother's image, and Joanne blessed the instinct that had made Rosemary bring him to England. Clearly he remembered her from that visit.

He proved it by holding up a colouring book she'd given him. 'I've done it all,' he said. 'Come and see.'

He seized her hand and pulled her over to a small table in the corner. Joanne went through the pages with him, noticing that he'd completed the pictures with a skill unusual in children of his age. He had a steady hand, taking colours up to the lines but staying neatly within them in a way that suggested good control. It reminded her of her own first steps in colouring, when she'd shown a precision that had foreshadowed her later skill in imitating.

When they'd been through the book Nico shyly produced some pages covered in rough, childish paintings, and she exclaimed in delight. Here too she could see the early evidence of craftsmanship. Her genuine praise thrilled Nico, and they smiled together.

Then she looked up and found Franco watching them oddly. 'Nico, it's time to wash your hands for supper,' he said. He indicated the pictures. 'Put everything away.'

'Yes, Papa,' Nico said, too docilely for a child. He tidied his things and went upstairs.

'It's strange to find the house so quiet,' Joanne said wistfully. 'When I first came here there were your parents and Renata, with everyone shouting and laughing at the same time.'

'Yes, there was a lot of laughter,' Franco agreed. 'Renata visited us recently, with her husband and two children. They made plenty of noise, and it was like the old days. But you're right, it's too quiet now.'

'Nico must be a lonely little boy,' Joanne ventured.

'I'm afraid he is. He relies on Ruffo a lot for company.'

'Is Ruffo still alive?' she asked, delighted.

Franco gave a piercing whistle out of the window.
And there was Ruffo, full of years, looking vastly wise
because the black fur of his face was mostly white now.
At the sight of Joanne he gave a yelp of pleasure and
hurried over to her.

'He remembers me. After all this time.'

'He never forgets a friend,' Franco agreed.

She petted the old dog with real pleasure, but she
also knew she was using him to cover the silence that
lay between herself and Franco. She began to feel desperate. She'd known that Franco would be changed,
but this grave man who seemed reluctant to speak was
a shock to her.

'So tell me what happened to you,' he said at last.
'Did you become a great artist?'

His words had a faint ironical inflection, and she
answered ruefully, 'No, I became a great imitator. I
found that I had no vision of my own, but I can copy
the visions of others.'

'That's sad,' he said unexpectedly. 'I remember how
badly you wanted to be an artist. You couldn't stop
talking about it.'

It was a surprise to find that he recalled anything
she'd said in those days.

'I have a good career. My copies are so perfect that
you can hardly tell the difference. But, of course,' she
added with a sigh, 'the difference is always there, nonetheless.'

'And do you mind that so much?'

'It was hard to realize that I have no originality.'
She tried to turn it aside lightly. 'Doomed to wander
for ever in someone else's footsteps, judged always by
how much I echo them. It's a living, and a good one
sometimes. It just isn't what I dreamed of.'

'And why are you in Italy now?'

'I'm copying some works for a man who lives in Turin.'

'And you spared us a day. How kind.'

She flushed under his ironic tone. Franco plainly thought badly of her for keeping her distance, but how could she tell him the reason?

'I should have called you first,' she began.

'Why should you? My wife's cousin is free to drop in at any time.'

She realized that his voice was different. Once it had been rich, round and musical. Now it was flat, as though all the music of life had died for him.

A harassed-looking girl came scurrying out of the kitchen carrying a pile of clean plates, pursued by Celia's voice bawling instructions. The girl fled outside and began laying plates on the table.

'Despite the short notice Celia is preparing a banquet in your honour,' Franco informed her. 'That's why she's a little tense. My foreman and his family are eating with us tonight.'

'I love to remember the meals we had under the trees.'

'You were always nervous about the flowers hanging from the trellis. You said they dropped insects over you.'

'*You* did that. You slipped a spider down the back of my dress once.'

'So I did,' he said with a slight smile. 'That was to punish you for revealing to my mother that you'd seen me with a woman she disapproved of.'

'I didn't mean to betray you,' Joanne protested. 'It slipped out by accident.'

'I paid for your accident. My mother slapped me and

screamed at me. I was twenty-four, but that didn't impress her.'

They shared a smile, and for a brief moment there was a glimpse of the old, humorous Franco. Then he was gone.

'Why don't you have a look around, while I wash up?' he said. 'You'll find the house much the same.'

'I'd already begun to notice that. I'm glad. This was a happy place.'

She could have bitten her tongue off as soon as the words were out. It was as if Franco were turned to stone. His face was like a dead man's. Then he said simply, 'Yes, it was happy once.'

He walked away, leaving her blaming herself for her own clumsiness. This visit was turning into a disaster. Franco had said his foreman's family was eating with them 'tonight', which suggested that they'd been invited specially. Obviously her presence was a strain, and he needed some relief.

It had been madness to come here.

CHAPTER THREE

JOANNE wandered outside. The fierce heat of the day had subsided and a soft breeze had sprung up. At such times life at Isola Magia had always been at its most relaxed and contented, but now she could feel the growing tension. Even so, the beauty of the land struck her afresh.

Here was the terrace and the exact same place where Franco had nearly kissed her on that fateful night. Geraniums still hung from above, trailing in gorgeous purple majesty. A glance showed Joanne that it was the same plant that had flowered faithfully year after year, always putting forth the same beauty while life and death passed underneath.

There was the apple tree just under the window of the guest bedroom. Joanne had seen Franco stand beneath that tree on the night before his wedding, looking up at Rosemary's window. His bride had come to the window and gazed down at him with her heart in her eyes, and neither had moved for a long time. Joanne had crept away, feeling that it was sacrilege to watch.

She tried not to be self-conscious at the glances she received, wondering whether people were staring at her face or the unflattering dress. It was a relief when Franco and Nico emerged from the house and indicated for everyone to gather around the table.

Nico slipped his hand into Joanne's. 'Can I call you *Zia?*' he asked shyly, using the Italian word for 'Aunt'.

'I'd love that,' Joanne said. 'Will you show me where to sit?'

He led her to the table, and introduced her to everyone as 'Zia Joanne'. Umberto, the foreman, was there, with his wife and three children. The family greeted her politely, but with the look of awe that she was beginning to recognize. Franco sat at the head of the table, and Nico placed her between his father and himself. Franco poured her a glass of wine. His manner was attentive, but his eyes didn't meet hers.

As he'd said, Celia had whipped up a banquet in an amazingly short time, black olive pâté, spinach and ricotta *gnocchi,* and a delicious dish made of white truffles, the local speciality. It was washed down with the local wine.

Elise, Umberto's wife, had worked in the vineyards when Joanne had been there eight years ago, and remembered her. She questioned her politely, and Joanne talked about her career and her work in Vito's house. Franco spoke to her courteously, but she had the feeling it was an effort. Nico said little, but sometimes she turned and caught him smiling at her.

It was like floating in a dream. Everything that was happening was unreal. She knew every inch of this place, yet it was as though she'd never been here before. She knew Franco, yet he was a stranger who wouldn't meet her eyes.

But then she looked up and found that he'd been watching her while she was unaware. And there was something in his eyes that wasn't cold and bleak. There was despair and misery, reproach and dread; but also anger. For a moment his iron control had slipped and she saw that Franco Farelli was possessed by a towering, bitter rage.

Rage at what? At fate that had taken the woman he loved? At herself, for coming here and stirring up his memories?

She felt suddenly giddy. Heat rose in her, and she was transported back years to the last time she'd sat at this table, trying to hide her feelings for a man who didn't love her. There was a roaring in her ears and she felt as though the world were spinning.

Then it all stopped. Everything was back in its right place. Franco was talking to someone else. It might all never have happened.

But the soft pounding of her blood told her that it had happened. Nothing had changed, and yet everything had changed. He was no longer the fierce stranger he wanted her to think, but a man at the limit of his endurance.

At last Umberto and his family departed. The sun had sunk below the horizon, leaving only a crimson lining on the clouds, and that too was fading.

Celia appeared bearing a small tray with a bottle of *prosecco,* a very light, dry white wine, that was almost a soft drink. Italians drank it constantly, and Joanne even recalled being offered a glass as she had waited to be served in a butcher's shop.

Celia placed the bottle and glasses on the table, and added a little plate of biscuits that she set close to Joanne with an air of suppressed triumph. While Franco poured the wine she tasted one of the tiny biscuits, then checked herself.

'Is something the matter?' he asked.

'I'm sorry, I can't eat these. I'm allergic to almonds, and I'm sure I can taste them.'

Franco took a biscuit, tasted it, and frowned as he

studied the sugar coating. To Joanne's astonishment his face grew dark with anger.

'Celia!'

The old woman came hurrying back. Franco asked her a question in Piedmontese, and Celia answered with a look of puzzled innocence. The next moment she backed away from his blast of cold fury, and hurried to snatch the biscuits from the table.

'What happened?' Joanne asked.

'It's nothing,' he said curtly.

'But you mustn't be angry with poor Celia just because I didn't like the food.'

'It wasn't that. Leave it.'

For the moment they'd both forgotten Nico, watching them with eyes that saw too much for a child. He moved closer to Joanne and whispered, 'They were Mama's favourite.'

Franco winced. 'Yes. I don't know what Celia was thinking of. They haven't been served in this house since—for over a year.'

'She must have thought that, since I'm Rosemary's cousin, I might like the same things,' Joanne said calmly, although she was feeling far from calm. She suspected what Celia was really thinking, and it was something far more eerie.

Franco seemed to pull himself together. 'Doubtless she thought that,' he agreed. He was very pale. 'Nico, it's time for bed.'

But at once the child squeezed closer to Joanne, smiling up into her eyes. Instinctively, she opened her arms to him, and he scrambled onto her lap.

'Let him stay,' she begged Franco. 'We used to cuddle like this when Rosemary brought him to visit me.'

'He was a baby then,' Franco said, frowning.

'He's not much more now. He's too young to do without cuddles.'

Franco sighed. 'You're right.'

Nico had dozed off as soon as he'd settled down, nestling against her. Joanne looked down tenderly at the bright head, and thought sadly of Rosemary who would never see her son grow.

'He's asleep already,' she murmured.

'He trusts you,' Franco said. 'That's remarkable. Since his mother died he trusts nobody, except me.'

'Poor little mite. Isn't there someone around here who can be a mother to him?'

'The servants make a fuss of him, but nobody can take his mother's place. Ever.'

Joanne turned her head so that she could brush her cheek against Nico's silky hair, and instinctively tightened her arms about him. Nothing was working out the way she'd thought. She'd been reluctant to see Franco again, fearing to be tormented by her old feelings. She hadn't allowed for the lonely child, and the way he would entwine himself in her heart.

'It's time he was in bed,' Franco said.

'Yes,' she said softly, rising with Nico in her arms. His head drooped against her shoulder as she headed for the stairs, and she smiled down at him tenderly.

Celia was upstairs, and darted away as soon as she saw her to open the door to Nico's room. Together they undressed the sleepy child, and slipped him between the sheets. He put his arms about Joanne again, and she hugged him back, her heart aching for the little boy who'd gone without his mother's embraces for so long.

'Will you sing to me?' he whispered.

'What shall I sing?'

'The song about the rabbit.'

For a moment her mind went blank. Then she remembered that Rosemary had written a little nonsense verse that she'd sung to Nico. Gradually the words came back to her, and she began to sing in a husky voice.

'Look at the rabbit, scampering home.
See how his tail bobs, bobs, bobs as he runs.
It's late and he wants his supper,
Then he'll curl up and go to sleep.
And he'll snore, he'll snore, he'll snore.'

Nico gave a small delighted chuckle. 'Sing it again,' he begged.

Obediently Joanne sang the little verse a second time, and then a third.

'Again,' he whispered.

From the corner of her eye she could see Franco standing in the doorway, keeping back, not to disturb them. He didn't move or make a sound, but she was aware of him with every fibre of her being, even while she concentrated on the child.

It was just as well that she couldn't see his expression. It was that of a man in unimaginable pain.

She sang the verse twice more. Nico didn't ask for it again, but nestled against her with a small sigh of content. Thinking only to comfort him, she murmured, *'Buona notte, caro Nicolo,'* as Rosemary had done.

'Buona notte, Mama,' he whispered, without opening his eyes.

'No, I—' she started to say, but fell silent, confused. *'Buona notte, piccino,'* she said after a moment.

There was no answer. He lay heavy in her arms, and

very gently she laid him back against the pillow and kissed his forehead.

Then she turned to Franco. But he was gone. She didn't know how long he'd stood there before slipping away.

She closed the door quietly behind her and went downstairs. There was no sign of Franco, and she went outside onto the terrace.

There was a faint trace of light in the sky, but the land was dark, and she could see shapes only in outline. The air was heavy with the scent of flowers, as it had been on that summer evening long ago.

Franco appeared on the terrace and watched her for a moment as she reached up to the trailing geraniums.

'What are you thinking?' he asked.

'I was remembering these flowers from the night of the dance. Renata couldn't come, so we were going together. You waited for me just here, and when I came down—we talked.' She ended lamely, wondering if Franco would remember what had happened. His eyes were glowing and a gentle smile touched his lips.

'I remember,' he said softly. 'And while we were there Rosemary arrived. She came out of that door, and I saw her for the very first time.'

He'd forgotten Joanne's part in that night. His memories were all of his beloved. Joanne guessed that his meeting with Rosemary was so vivid in his mind that he saw nothing else at this moment. Just as he'd seen nothing else then.

'I should apologize to you for the trouble after dinner,' he said. 'Celia served that dish because it was a favourite of my wife's, although she hasn't served it for a year. I was angry with her because she seemed to think you were Rosemary's ghost. But I overreacted and I'm sorry.'

'It's not me you should say sorry to,' she reproached him gently.

'Don't worry. I've made my peace with Celia. She's very forgiving of my moods.'

'I expect you don't like to talk about Rosemary.'

'On the contrary. I love to talk of her, because that keeps her alive. But how can I? Sometimes Nico and I speak of her, but he's a child. I can't put too much on his shoulders.

'But you, Joanne—you were there the moment I met her, the moment I fell in love with her. They were the same moment.'

'I know. I watched the two of you look at each other, and it was as if the world had stopped.'

'That's how we felt too,' he said at once. 'She said so afterwards—as though the world had stopped. Or perhaps I said it to her, I don't remember. We were one heart, one soul—at least, so I thought.'

He said the last words half under his breath, then looked up quickly and caught her puzzled look. Before she could question him he hurried on, 'We knew everything from the first moment. And you were there. You knew as well.'

'Yes. Everything,' she said, with a touch of sadness that she knew he wouldn't hear. He was lost in his own world where there was only himself and his beloved wife. Joanne was a privileged guest, but only as a witness. She herself had no reality, and nor did her feelings.

'She came with us to the party,' she said. 'And you two danced every dance together. Other men kept asking her, but you growled and drove them away.'

'Yes, I did,' he said, with a smile. 'She urged me to do my duty and dance with other girls, but I said, "Only with you. And you, only with me. Always."'

'You asked Rosemary to marry you that night?' Joanne queried.

'I never asked her, and she never said yes. We simply knew it would happen. Some things are inevitable from the first moment.

'My mother couldn't understand that. She urged me to wait, to marry "a girl of my own kind", a good Italian girl. But Rosemary and I were soul of each other's soul and heart of each other's heart. And what could be more akin than that?' He gave Joanne a reminiscent smile. 'You saw it. It's almost as though you were a part of our love.'

She knew it was madness to go on with this. After all these years it still hurt to know that he saw her only through the filter of Rosemary. But it was sweet to sit here in the fading light, talking with Franco, feeling him turn to her, even if it was for the wrong reason. And she couldn't make herself give it up just yet.

'Why did you come back now?' he asked suddenly.

Caught off guard, she stammered. 'I—I was working in the neighbourhood. I couldn't leave without dropping in.'

'You avoid us for eight years, then pay a brief visit. Why, Joanne? Whatever did we do to offend you?'

'Nothing, it's just that my life has been so busy. My career—'

'Yes, yes,' he said dismissively, and she knew how tinny and dishonest her words had sounded.

'I should be going,' she said.

'It's much too late for you to start your journey now.'

'It's only sixty miles.'

'Surely you can stay for one night? Nico thinks you'll be here tomorrow.'

'But I've no night things, no change of clothes, nothing. I can't—' She looked down at the badly fitting garments.

'That was ill-mannered of me,' Franco said. 'Celia wanted me to lend you something of Rosemary's. I should have done so, but I was still confused by the sight of you.'

'You still have some of her clothes?'

'Come with me.'

The house was quiet as they passed through it. Joanne followed Franco up the stairs and along the passage to the room she remembered his parents occupying. It had changed little. The huge bed still stood there, with its bedhead of polished walnut. Two great closets stood on either side of the floor-length window with its wrought-iron balcony.

Franco opened the door of one of them, and inside Joanne saw a rail of garments protected by cellophane. Part of the closet was taken up with drawers which he pulled open to let her see the contents. Here were Rosemary's underwear, her nightdresses, scarves, gloves.

'I've given most of her clothes to charity,' he said, 'but some I've kept. Perhaps I should dispose of these too. I keep meaning to, but the moment never seems to be quite right. Take something to wear tonight.'

He walked out abruptly, leaving her to sort through the clothes. Every nightdress was filmy, delicate and low cut and they gave Joanne a glimpse into her cousin's marriage. The woman who had bought these seductive garments had known that her husband worshipped her body, and had wanted to present it to please him, just as she, Joanne, would have wanted to, if—

She shut that thought off. Rosemary might be dead, but she was still here, and Franco belonged to her as much as ever.

She ought to choose something plain and modest, but there simply wasn't anything like that. In the end she selected a nightdress of white silk with a matching negligée. She held the dress against herself, looking into the mirror. To her eyes her own face seemed pale and dull, almost plain. She was sure that Rosemary had looked more beautiful, her features illuminated by happiness.

She was so lost in her thoughts that she didn't hear the door open and Franco enter, nor see him as he stood watching her. Only when he came up close did she become aware of him.

'You startled me,' she said breathlessly.

'I'm sorry. Have you chosen something? Good. Why don't you take these too?'

He reached into the wardrobe and pulled out a set of riding breeches and jacket.

'I want you to stay tomorrow,' he said. 'We'll go riding and I'll show you what the place is like now.'

'I should leave,' she said, torn between longing and a sense of danger. 'I said I'd be back tonight.'

'Call your employers and tell them you're staying a few days.' It was a command, not a request.

She looked at him helplessly, torn by longing.

'Please, Joanne,' he said more gently. 'I haven't been at my best tonight. You took me by surprise and I've been surly and unwelcoming. Let me atone by being a good host tomorrow. And Nico so much likes having you here.'

She would stay for Nico's sake, she decided. It was good to have a reason that she could justify to herself.

'All right,' she said slowly. 'I'll stay tomorrow.'

'Thank you with all my heart. Let me escort you to your room.'

At her door he said gravely, 'Goodnight, Joanne. Until tomorrow.'

There was a phone by her bed. She called Maria and explained that she wouldn't be returning that night. When she'd hung up she slipped out of her clothes and put on the beautiful nightdress. She went to stand before the long mirror, and Rosemary looked back at her.

How had she missed the fact that the years had emphasized their likeness, fining her down, making her features more delicate, until she was Rosemary's image?

She shouldn't have returned. This place was too beautiful and heartbreaking. She almost wished she'd never seen Franco again rather than see him as he was now. There was only pain left in her heart. She knew it had something to do with the tortured man she'd met today. But she wasn't yet sure what.

She also knew that if she was wise she would leave this house as soon as possible.

But she wasn't wise.

Franco was late going to his bed. He wandered through the silent house, stopping outside his son's door and opening it a crack to listen to the soft breathing coming from inside.

He went to another door, and stood in darkness and silence for a long time before turning away.

When he finally lay down, sleep eluded him. His brain was in turmoil from the events of the day. Images came and went. One face in particular tormented him. He tried to shut it out, but it was always there.

At last he rose with a groan, pulled on a pair of jeans and went, barefoot, downstairs and out into the yard. There was a full moon, and its brilliant beams fell straight onto the tall window of the guest room. He could see that it was open, and for a moment he thought he saw a woman's form in a long white nightdress. But then he realized it was only the gauze curtains billowing softly in the breeze.

He stood watching for a long time, but there was no movement. At last he went to the fountain and sat on the stone, plunging his arms into the cold water, and laving it over his face. He was trembling.

'God forgive me for my thoughts!' he murmured. 'Merciful God, forgive me.'

CHAPTER FOUR

JOANNE was awoken by the sound of a cock crowing. A glance at her watch showed her that it was three in the morning.

That cock, she thought. It must be the same one. There can't be two with that weird sense of timing.

Eight years ago she'd often been awoken at this hour by the cock, which had then proceeded to crow every ten seconds. It might have been maddening, but, once she'd grown accustomed to it, it had ceased to bother her. Now, as then, she slipped back into sleep, with the crowing still in her ears.

Two hours later she awoke again. The cock had finished for the day and all was silence as she pulled back the shutters and stood looking over the vineyards.

Everything was magic. A faint mist rose from the land, and the soft grey light of dawn gave the world a ghostly appearance. From somewhere far across the valley a bell was softly tolling. Gradually the shapes grew firmer, the outlines more clear, and she became aware that a man was standing beneath a tree, looking out over the valley. She couldn't see his face, but she didn't need to. His height, the breadth of his shoulders, the carriage of his head, all proclaimed Franco. He stood easily, gracefully, oblivious to everything but the scene before him, gradually coming into view.

He was as motionless as a statue. Even as a very young man, she recalled, he'd had the gift of stillness. She wondered what his thoughts were now.

She backed into the room, lest he should turn and see her watching him. But he didn't move, and at last she went back to bed.

It was Celia who awoke her the next time, bustling into the room with a tray of coffee, and saying that *il padrone* wanted to make an early start. Joanne hastily showered and dressed in the clothes he'd chosen for her the night before. She was a little nervous about riding. It was years since she'd mounted a horse, and even then she'd been a cautious rider.

Franco was drinking coffee as she descended the stairs. He looked up, smiling, and she had a twinge of surprise. In contrast to the tense, anguished man of the day before he looked fresh and relaxed, and there was warmth in his eyes. He too wore riding breeches, with a white shirt that emphasized his tanned skin. The early morning sun caught the blue-black in his hair, his fine, clean profile and the sensual curve of his lips. Joanne could have enjoyed watching him all day, but she pulled herself together and managed to seem casual.

'Have some coffee,' he said, pouring it out. 'And then we'll leave at once. We can stop for something to eat on the way.'

'Where are we going?'

'I want to show you how the estate has grown. I bought some more land.'

The horses had just been brought round to the front. Her mount was a chestnut mare called Birba. She was beautiful, and seemed gentle enough, standing there quietly while Joanne mounted. But as soon as she was seated Joanne felt a tremor go through the animal, and recalled that *birba* meant 'little rascal'.

But the mare seemed to be on her best behaviour. Joanne's spirits soared as she rode beside Franco, out

into the countryside, which was at its best. The sun
was still climbing the sky and the day was no more
than pleasantly warm. Across the valley she could see
cypress and poplar trees, the red-tiled roofs of cottages,
and acres and acres of vines.

'Franco, before we go anywhere,' she said, 'could
you show me where Rosemary is buried? Is she in the
churchyard?'

'No, we have our own burial plot. Come, I'll show
you.'

He turned his horse through the little plantation that
led from the garden at the back of the house, and down
a path under the trees. From some distance away she
could hear the gentle splashing of the stream, and suddenly they emerged into a small clearing.

Several graves stood here, but one was more recent
than the rest. It stood close to the trees, a simple white
marble headstone, surrounded by flowers. Willows
hung over the water. It was a beautiful place, gentle
and serene, where it was possible to believe that
Rosemary lay sleeping in peace.

They dismounted, and Franco stood back with the
horses as she neared the grave and dropped to one
knee, touching the cool marble. Tears filled her eyes.
Until this moment it had been almost as if Rosemary
had slipped away somewhere, soon to return. But there
was a finality about her resting place that brought the
truth home to Joanne sharply. Forgetting Franco, she
touched her fingers to her lips, then pressed them
against the marble, murmuring, 'Goodbye, darling.
Thank you for everything.'

When she turned around she saw Franco standing by
the stream a few feet away. He looked up at her approach.

'Do you want me to wait for you?' she asked.

He shook his head. 'She'll understand. She knows I'll return another time. Let's go.'

He helped her mount, and wheeled his horse to the north. The air was brilliantly clear and she could see the snow-capped mountains in the distance. She delighted in the beauty of the morning and the nearness of the man who still had a hold on her heart. It was a different feeling from the joy he'd once inspired in her. But it was very real.

He'd extended the estate by a good deal, buying up land and varying his crop. Isola Magia had always grown the Barbera grape, used to make a delicious dry red wine. But now there was also the darker Barolo and the lively Brachetto.

'This was her doing,' Franco explained, showing her the rich vines with their burden of almost black grapes. 'Rosemary had a gift for business. She went into the details of the trade, and persuaded me to expand.' He grinned. 'My mother was very cross. She said Rosemary should stay at home and cook, though how she should do that when Mama wouldn't budge from the kitchen, I don't know. Then Mama said it was an insult to Papa, because he was still officially the head of the business.'

'I remember your father,' Joanne said. 'He was the most easygoing man I ever knew.'

'You're right. Of course he wasn't insulted. As long as he was free to eat and drink with his cronies he didn't care what else happened. Besides, his health was failing. He'd earned his retirement.'

'And you didn't mind Rosemary making changes in the business?'

'We were like one person,' Franco said simply. 'Where did she end and I begin? I never knew.'

They stopped at a small *taverna* and drank wines the innkeeper assured them were made with grapes from Isola Magia. They ate *antipasto piemontese,* served from a vast trolley that contained raw meat served with lemon juice and grated truffles, trout in aspic and meatballs.

'I can't eat any more,' Joanne protested.

'But that was just the starter.'

'It was a whole meal.'

'All right, we'll stop again later.' Franco toyed with his food a moment, before saying, 'You really loved her, too, didn't you? I don't think I quite realized that until today.'

'Yes, very much. We were very close for a long time.'

'Rosemary would speak of you as a sister, sometimes almost as a daughter.'

'That's how it felt to me too,' Joanne said slowly. 'I was six when my parents died. She asked her mother to let me live with them. I don't think Aunt Elsie was very keen. She was a widow. But Rosemary wouldn't give up, and I went to live with them. When Aunt Elsie died, she was only eighteen herself, but she became my mother.

'She was a wonderful mother, too. She should have been rushing around, dating, having fun, but she put it all aside to care for me. She lost heaps of boyfriends because she had me in tow.'

'Then I'm in your debt,' Franco said, raising his glass to her. 'You kept her free for me. What is it?' His sharp eyes had seen a change come over her face. 'You've thought of something. Tell me.'

'I suddenly remembered her gift for writing little daft verses—doggerel, she called them. There was one by my breakfast plate on the day of an important exam. It made me laugh, but it also made me feel safe and loved. Maybe that's why I sailed through the exam. Rosemary could do that for you.'

'Yes,' Franco murmured. 'She could.'

'Did she write daft verses for you too?'

He smiled. 'They used to fall out of my socks, usually when I was in a hurry. I didn't always appreciate them as I should. I used to say, *"Cara, please,"* but now there's nothing. If you knew what I would give for a piece of paper to flutter out of my sock drawer. Nico misses them even more. She used to sing her songs to him at bedtime. I'm glad you knew one last night. It meant so much to him.'

'Did she ever tell you that she longed to write a "real poem" one day?' Joanne asked.

'Yes, she did,' Franco said. 'She really wanted to achieve that ambition, but in the end she didn't manage it. "A poem that really meant something," was how she put it.'

'Everything Rosemary did meant something,' Joanne said. 'If it wasn't for her, I'd have been taken into care, and probably shunted around foster homes. She saved me from that, and I always promised myself that one day I'd do something for her, to thank her for everything.'

A strange note in her voice made Franco look at her curiously. 'And did you ever do so?'

'Yes,' she said, thinking of the years when she'd kept away from him, for fear of clouding Rosemary's happiness. 'I did.'

'Are you going to tell me what it was?' he asked after a moment.

'No, I can't do that. It was between Rosemary and me, and even she didn't know.'

'How close you two must have been despite the distance. You keep your secrets about her, and she kept hers about you.'

'What do you mean?'

'When she returned from seeing you in England, she said something very strange. She told me that at last she understood why you'd never come to see us in all those years.'

Joanne grew still. 'Did she tell you what she meant?' she asked, not looking at him.

'No. But she seemed happy about you for the first time. It had made her sad that you didn't visit, but not after that. She said that all the best she'd ever thought of you was true. Why was that? What happened between you?'

'Nothing special. It was wonderful to have her and Nico there. We talked and went shopping, watched television. Ordinary things.'

'You must have told her why you never came here.'

'But I didn't. It was never mentioned. Not once.'

'Then what did she understand? And how?'

Joanne cast her mind over those happy few days, but all she could recall were hours of innocent chatter about the little things that made up their lives, the comfortable feeling that they'd never really lost each other. After all the years their sisterly love had still glowed undimmed. Rosemary had talked of Franco with joy and pride. Joanne had rarely mentioned him.

Was it possible that somehow her cousin had divined

the truth? Was that why she'd said all the best she'd thought of Joanne was true? The idea was breathtaking.

'What is it?' Franco demanded, watching her face. 'You've remembered, haven't you?'

'Franco, please, I can't talk about this. I may be wrong—'

'I don't think so. You two understood each other.'

'Yes, we did. I'm only just realizing how deeply.'

He gave a wry grimace, and shrugged as he saw her looking at him with a question in her eyes.

'It's nothing,' he said abruptly. 'It's just that—I'm jealous. It's stupid, but I'm jealous. I don't like her being close to anyone but me. Except Nico.'

'Do you know you talk of her in the present tense?'

'Do I? Perhaps. She's still very real to me.'

'Were you jealous when she was alive?'

'I'm a jealous man. What's mine is mine. Only she never gave me cause. And I never gave her cause. I claim no credit for that. I was never tempted.' He drained his glass. 'If you're ready, let's go.'

Birba skittered a little as Joanne mounted. She'd almost forgotten that she was nervous of the mare, but now Birba began to prance along, never quite out of control, but never calm enough for Joanne to feel easy.

'Are you all right?' Franco asked.

'Fine,' she lied valiantly.

They turned back towards home and rode for an hour before he stopped by a stream, saying, 'Let's rest here for a while. The horses will be glad of a drink.'

As he spoke Franco was swinging himself to the ground. Joanne was about to do the same when she became aware of an ominous buzzing. A wasp was circling her head. She swatted it frantically, but this sent it fizzing near Birba's head, and suddenly the mare reared, whinnying indignantly. The next moment she was off, with Joanne clinging on for dear life.

She heard Franco shout behind her, but knew that his chance of catching her was remote. He had to re-mount before he could give chase, and Birba was streaking over the ground at top speed. It was as though, after being on her best behaviour all day, she'd decided to shake off all restraint, and seemed to be going faster and faster, soaring over hedges and ditches as if they were nothing. Joanne was terrified, knowing that she would fall off at any moment.

From somewhere behind her she heard the sound of hoof beats and managed to turn her head just enough to see a young man on a black horse, galloping hard and gaining on her. Inch by inch he caught up, then his arm came shooting out to go around her waist and haul her off Birba and onto his own steed. She clung to him thankfully, feeling the animal slacken pace, while Birba tore on ahead.

'All right,' her rescuer said cheerfully. 'You're safe now.' He finally pulled up.

'Thank you,' she said breathlessly, turning to face him. The grin faded from his face, to be replaced by shock. *'Rosemary!'*

'I'm not Rosemary,' she cried.

The horse had come to a halt. The young man jumped to the ground and held up his arms to assist her down. He held her for a moment, looking into her face. He seemed to be in his late twenties, and was extremely handsome, with a merry, mobile face.

'No, of course you're not Rosemary,' he said at last. 'She was an intrepid rider, and would never have lost control like that.'

By now Franco had caught up with them. He flung

himself down from his horse and gripped Joanne's arm. 'Are you all right?' he asked hoarsely.

'I'm fine, thanks to—?'

'My name is Leo Moretto,' the young man said. '*Ciao,* Franco.'

'I saw what happened and I'm grateful,' Franco said, shaking his hand. 'It's good to see you back, Leo. Will you wait with Joanne while I recapture Birba?'

'Of course.'

When Franco had galloped away Joanne said, 'You knew her well?'

'I live around here. My father's land runs next to Franco's. We're old friends. And now tell me who you are, and how you come to be here in Rosemary's clothes, and with Rosemary's face? Am I seeing ghosts? Did I take a drop too much?'

His comical manner made her smile. 'No, of course not. I'm Joanne Merton. Rosemary was my cousin. I know we're very alike.'

'But only in your looks. What was Franco thinking of to let you ride Rosemary's horse?'

A shiver went through Joanne. 'Rosemary's horse?'

'Of course. That was her favourite mount. She often rode her when she went over the vineyard with Franco.'

'I see,' Joanne said in a colourless voice.

Franco was returning with Birba, now docile again. Leo hailed him. 'I was wondering what you were about, putting Joanne on that horse. She's only a moderate rider. Forgive me, Joanne.'

'No, it's true,' she said hastily.

'Of course,' Franco said. 'I should have thought. I had forgotten—a great deal.'

'We're close to my home,' Leo said. 'Come and

have some refreshment, and I can catch up with what's been happening while I've been away.'

'I don't think I want to get back on Birba,' Joanne said.

'Of course not, you'll ride with me,' Leo announced. 'Don't worry, you'll be quite safe.'

He sprang easily onto the animal's back, and drew Joanne up in front of him. At first she was nervous, but Leo's arm about her waist kept her safe.

The Moretto home was an old-fashioned farmhouse, sprawling and comfortable. Leo took them to a pleasant spot under the trees where there was a table, a couple of chairs and a swinging seat. He settled Joanne down on the cushions of the seat and promptly bagged the place beside her, leaving Franco to take the chair. The housekeeper brought out a tray with wine and cakes, and left them.

'Of course!' Joanne exclaimed suddenly. 'Now I remember you. At the *palio*. You and Franco collided.'

'*He* collided with *me,* and denied me victory,' Leo growled. 'There's a difference.'

'You rammed me to stop me passing you,' Franco said with a grin. 'But that's history. Now we're the best of friends.'

'Sure we are.' Leo smiled. 'And this year, I'm going to win.'

'If you don't lose your head,' Franco observed wryly. To Joanne he added, 'He's a madman when he gets on a horse.'

'I'm glad he is,' she said fervently. 'I've never seen anything like the way he galloped to my rescue.'

'The rescue of fair ladies is my speciality,' Leo said merrily. As he spoke he kissed the back of her hand with a flourish that was so gallant, and yet so droll, that she had to smile.

The two men, who evidently knew each other well, drifted into a discussion about crops, horses and wine. Joanne was feeling sleepy after her day in the open air, and she was content to sit there, letting the talk flow over her. When at last Franco rose to leave the light was fading fast.

Leo brought three horses out of the stables.

'You mustn't ride Birba again,' he told Joanne, 'so I've put your saddle on one of my own mares.'

'There was no need for that,' Franco said, sounding chagrined. 'I was going to ride Birba myself. Joanne would be perfectly safe on my horse.'

'She'll be even safer on mine,' Leo said smoothly.

They set off, Franco leading Birba, Joanne mounted on Leo's placid little mare.

'I'm sorry about that,' Franco said awkwardly. 'I gave you Birba without thinking. I'd forgotten that you weren't a confident rider.'

'It's all right,' she said hastily. 'After so long, how could you remember? And I managed her pretty well until she bolted, didn't I? Although not as well as—'

She bit the words back, regretting them as soon as they were out. A mood of contentment was enveloping her, and she wanted nothing to spoil this moment. As if he understood her thoughts, Franco nodded.

Riding home in the twilight, they began to talk of Rosemary again. Stories Joanne hadn't thought of for years came back to her, and strangely she found a measure of happiness in telling them, dwelling on Rosemary's memory. Franco said little, and once she fell silent, wondering if he could hear her, but he said urgently, 'Don't stop, I'm listening.'

'We're nearly home now. Nico will be waiting for us.'

'Celia will have put him to bed. Look at the time.'

'It's almost nine,' she said, astonished. Where had the time gone?

Celia was in the kitchen when they came in. 'Nico has been as good as gold,' she said.

'I'll go up and see if he's awake.'

Franco vanished upstairs and Celia indicated a spread of olives, meat, cheese and wine on the table.

'There is your supper,' she declared. 'And now, I go to meet my lover.'

She departed with dignity.

Franco came quietly down, smiling to himself. 'I looked in but he's sleeping like a log,' he said.

'Franco, Celia said she was going to meet her lover. At her age?'

'Don't be so prejudiced,' he told her with a grin. 'In this country we know there's no upper age limit to love. Celia's gentleman friend is a respectable man with a nagging wife who can't cook. Twice a week she goes to cook him a proper meal and "be friendly".'

'But where is his wife while Celia's doing this?'

'She goes to see *her* lover, of course. It's all very romantic.'

They laughed together and Joanne's heart eased.

CHAPTER FIVE

'LET'S eat next door,' Franco said, going into the next room, where the open fireplace had been stacked with wood. Now that the day's heat had faded there was a chill in the air, but he soon had a cheerful blaze going. Joanne carried in the food and laid it out on a low coffee table. They settled down on the huge sofa, and prepared to picnic.

'Oh, this is good!' she said, tucking into cheese and olives.

'Better than modern heating?' he teased, reminding her how she'd stared when she'd first seen the house's antiquated heating system.

'I wouldn't swap this for anything,' she said contentedly. 'I knew nothing in those days.'

He reached over and pulled a photograph album from a shelf, flicking through it until he found a large wedding picture, and gave it to her.

'Recognize yourself?'

'Is that me?' she asked, viewing the bridesmaid in horrified disbelief. 'I don't remember being as fat as that.'

'You weren't fat, just nicely covered.'

'I shouldn't have worn satin, though. Rosemary tried to talk me out of it, but the others were wearing satin, and I didn't want to be different.'

What did it matter what I wore when my heart was breaking? she thought. He had eyes for nobody but her, and poor Rosemary couldn't understand why I didn't care how I looked.

But the picture had explained something.

'I wasn't so like her then, was I?' she mused.

'You've grown more so with the years,' he agreed.

'No wonder you were shocked when you saw me yesterday. I shouldn't have appeared out of nowhere like that.'

'You gave us all a shock,' he admitted. He began to turn pages. 'Have you seen any of these others? I know she sent you some.'

She accepted his change of subject and went through the pictures. Some were familiar, but there were many she'd never seen before. She smiled as she went through page after page, but at the last page she stopped.

The picture showed Rosemary smiling with delight, her hands on her expanding waistline. She looked full of radiant health, yet the date underneath showed that the picture had been taken three days before her death.

'How could she look like that, and then—?'

'Her heart wasn't strong,' Franco said. 'Nico's birth weakened it. She should never have had the second child. God help me, I didn't know. If I'd known, I'd never have let her become pregnant again.' He added, so softly that she almost didn't hear, 'But she knew.'

'Rosemary knew she had a weak heart? And she didn't tell you?'

'She kept her secret until she had an attack on the day after that picture was taken. It was only a mild one, but the doctors told us that another could follow, and it would be fatal. On her deathbed she begged my forgiveness for deceiving me—' He broke off. 'As though there was anything for *me* to forgive. I longed to tell her of my gratitude for the years of perfect happiness, but no words would come.'

'I'm sure she didn't need the words,' Joanne said. 'When people are as close as you two were, they know, don't they?'

'I wish I could believe that she did. It has haunted me ever since.'

'Franco, Rosemary loved you with her whole heart. And she knew she had your love. If you could have heard the way she spoke of you when she came to England, if you could have seen what I saw in her eyes. But I can't believe you never saw that look. You must have seen it every day.'

'But you don't understand,' he said urgently. 'I thought I knew all this, until I discovered that she'd kept such a secret from me—from generous motives, I know. But I believed her whole heart and mind were open to me.'

'Is anyone's whole heart and mind ever open to anyone else, no matter how much they love them? Franco, people have to keep a little core of themselves *to* themselves. Sometimes even love can depend on that.'

'What a strange thing to say,' he said, looking at her.

'I know she loved you more than anything in the world, but she was Rosemary, a whole person. Not just one half of Rosemary and Franco. And that's how it should be. It's what made her special, made her the woman you loved.'

He seemed to relax. 'You're right, of course.'

It felt strange to be sitting here, explaining Rosemary to him, but nothing mattered now except to bring him some comfort. His sadness seemed to be her own, and if she could find some way to ease it she would. No matter what the cost to herself.

He finished the bottle and fetched another from the kitchen, refilling his own glass and hers. His eyes were a little wild.

'Do you do very much of this?' Joanne asked gently.

'Perhaps too much, at night, when there's nobody to see. I can handle the days, but the nights are very lonely. At first I thought I'd go out of my mind. A world without her was impossible, yet she was gone, so the world was mad. Or I was mad.

'They say time heals, but it didn't. The pain became different, that was all. For months I expected to meet her around every corner, and when she wasn't there she died for me all over again.

'I'd come home in the evening and listen for her voice in the silence, watch for her smile and know that I'd never see it again. I've wondered why I couldn't be like other men who put a dead love behind them. Why couldn't I let her go? What is the weakness in me that has clung on?'

'It's not a weakness to love faithfully,' Joanne protested. 'She was a special person. She deserved a special love.'

He was silent. He seemed to be struggling over a momentous decision. At last he said, 'I want to tell you something terrible, something I wouldn't admit to another living soul. I've actually blamed her for being better than other women, for giving me such happiness, then leaving me to spend my life in regrets.' He lowered his voice. 'I've almost hated her for leaving me. Can you imagine that?'

'Yes, I've heard of it before. It's natural—'

'Natural? To hate a woman because you loved her?'

'The greater the love, the greater the loss. You feel as if she abandoned you, don't you?'

'Yes. As she lay dying I begged her not to leave me, but she did. I know it wasn't her fault, but—' He clenched his hands as if fighting for the words. 'I blame her, and I blame myself for blaming her. In my mind, everything is tangled, and I can't see my way clear. I've just about worked out how to survive. And then you appeared…'

'I didn't mean to make it harder,' she said softly.

'I don't know whether you make it harder or easier. I don't understand anything that's happening.' He searched her face. 'Where did you come from?' he asked quietly.

'I told you—'

'I didn't mean that. I meant—' He drew a shuddering breath. 'Can you imagine what it was like to turn and find you standing there with *her* face? Like a ghost. Even now I'm not sure you're real.'

'I'm real enough,' she said, understanding him at last. 'Here, feel me.'

She stretched out her hand towards him, but he backed away, shaking his head, never taking his burning eyes from her. Impulsively she seized his hand, and held it firmly in hers. 'Feel me,' she repeated. 'Look at my hand. Hers were never like this. She had long, delicate fingers, like an artist, people used to say. But artists have powerful hands. Look how big and strong mine are. This is me, Franco, Joanne. Look and see *me*. Drive the ghosts away.'

He looked down at her hands in his, clasping them strongly. Joanne could feel the warmth from his body, sense the odour of earth and spice that was uniquely his. It affected her now as it had done long ago, and she wanted him now, as she had done then, so badly that it was an ache.

'Joanne,' he whispered. Then, more strongly, 'Yes, Joanne.'

He said it like a man awakening from a bright dream. She would have been hurt if she'd had any attention to spare for her own feelings. But they were lost in his. At that moment she would have made any sacrifice to give him a moment's happiness. Thinking only of that, she freed her hands and hugged him, holding him close as she would have done with Nico. And like his son, he held onto her for comfort.

'She's been dead over a year,' he said huskily, 'and every morning I wake up wondering how I shall endure the day. Only Nico keeps me sane.'

She stroked his hair. She was beyond speech. This was all she could give him.

'I begged her to return to me, and when I looked up and saw you standing there I thought—' A tremor went through him. 'I'm ashamed to tell you what I thought.'

'You thought it was her. And it was only me. I'm so sorry, Franco.'

'Don't be sorry. You gave me that moment, and it was more than I hoped for.' He ran a hand through his hair. 'What's the matter with me?' he said distractedly. 'Why can't I forget her?'

'Do you really want to do that?' Joanne asked softly.

He shook his head. 'Never. If the memory of her torments me to the end of my days, at least she's *there*. If I forget her, what would I do?'

Horrified, she searched his face, trying to find the words that would help his agony. But there was none.

Suddenly he burst out, 'Why don't you say it? You think I'm mad.'

'No, I—'

'The others do. They think I'm sick in my soul, as though a man must be mad to grieve for the love of his life. But they don't know—they can't understand—'

A shudder went through him and he seemed to control himself with an effort. 'I'm sorry. It isn't fair of me to burden you with this.'

'Why not? I'm here, and I only want to help you.'

Dumbly he shook his head, as though saying that there was no help for him. Forgetting everything but his need, she gathered him in her arms and held him tightly. His arms went around her, blindly seeking comfort, holding her to him fiercely.

It wasn't the way she'd dreamed of him holding her, but it was very sweet. She stroked his hair, murmuring incoherent words in which love and comfort were mixed. The years fell away. At this moment she was as much his as she had ever been.

'Hold onto me,' she whispered. 'Franco—Franco—'

He was quite still, as though trying to understand what was happening. When he moved, it was to draw back a little, just far enough for her to see his face, and the confusion in his eyes. He raised his hand tentatively, as if expecting a rebuff, and gently touched her face with his fingertips, the high cheek-bones, down the length of her face to the wide, full mouth, the resolute chin. She trembled at the touch she'd longed for and thought never to know. Looking into Franco's face, she saw something that made her catch her breath. Her heart was beating wildly. All the old bittersweet feeling welled up in her again, and it might have been yesterday that she'd stood close to him under the hanging flowers, longing for his kiss.

His hands were gentle, his fingertips featherlight. She trembled at the sweetness of that touch. The next moment his arms were about her and he was drawing her close. There was a look in his eyes she couldn't fathom, a look almost of desperation as he lowered his head and touched her mouth with his own.

Her very bones seemed to melt. She clung to him aching with desire and longing. After so many years her dream had come true, and it was as perfect as she'd known it would be. If only the world could stop at this moment.

She felt his arms tighten around her, his mouth become more urgent. His desperate hunger communicated itself to her through his lips, his skin, the heat of his body. After that nothing could have stopped her. The awareness of his need was like a match thrown among straw. She pressed closer to him, reaching up to put her arms right about his neck, eager and defenceless, giving everything, holding nothing of herself back.

'Franco,' she whispered, 'oh, yes—yes—'

He covered her mouth again, silencing words. There was nothing more she wanted to say anyway. There was only this glorious feeling, and this wonderful man for whom she'd waited so long.

His lips moved over hers hungrily, like a man who'd found his dream after a long search. Thrilled, she responded to his urgency. The stifled passion of years was welling up in her, making her press herself against him, seeking to be closer and then closer still, seeking to be one with him.

He wanted her. She could feel it in his movements and the touch of his skin. Whatever happened afterwards, at this moment he wanted her as much as she wanted him.

She reached for him, but he drew back a little, breathing hard. She could feel him shaking and thought she understood. But when she looked into his eyes, they were tortured. His hands were like steel, tensing against her, pushing her away.

'Franco—Franco—kiss me again—'

'No—I mustn't—I can't do this—forgive me—'

'There's nothing to forgive. Kiss me—'

'You don't understand,' he said hoarsely. 'I have no right—' He pulled away, staring at her with burning eyes. 'Forgive me,' he said again. 'I've behaved like a wretch. I'm worthless.'

'Franco, what are you talking about?' she pleaded, barely able to understand that this was really happening.

'I'm talking about my wife.' He rose abruptly as if he needed to put a distance between them, and turned away, running his hands through his hair. A terrible fear was growing in her.

'Don't you understand?' he said at last. 'Everything about today has been a fake. I've been with you, but I've seen *her*. It's her voice I've heard, her smile I've seen.'

She got to her feet and came closer to him. 'You mean I remind you of Rosemary, but I know that.'

'It's worse. *I've been pretending you were her.* I thought I'd learned to endure life without her, but when I saw you I yielded to a temptation so despicable that I'm ready to sink with shame.'

'But how could you pretend I was Rosemary? We talked about her. I said things she couldn't have said.'

'It's crazy, isn't it? But while we spoke of her, she was there with us. I could look at your face, and see hers. Tonight, I wanted to kiss you, to feel you kiss me—'

'Stop,' she cried desperately. 'I don't want to hear this.'

'But you must hear, so that you may know never to trust me. That's the only reparation I can make. Do you want to know how low a man can sink when grief has driven him to desperation? Then look at me, and despise me as I despise myself.'

'Wasn't I—there at all?' she whispered.

'Yes,' he said after a moment. 'When you were in my arms, you became yourself, and I understood the terrible thing I'd done. To let you think I cared for you when I cannot—when I *must* not—for pity's sake, go away before I do something that's a betrayal of all three of us.'

'You're talking in riddles. How could you betray all three of us?'

'I would betray you with deception. I would betray her if I cared about any other woman. I would betray myself by letting my heart be false.'

'But why can't you care for another woman?' she cried passionately. 'Rosemary doesn't need your love now. I—' She bit off the fatal words there, praying that he wouldn't have noticed. He seemed oblivious.

'We belonged only to each other, in life or in death. She needs my love now more than ever, when the world forgets and I'm the only one who truly remembers. I'm hers as I was when she lived, and I'll be hers until the day I lie beside her.'

Joanne could bear no more. Blocking her ears with her hands, she fled him. In her own room she locked the door and threw herself onto the bed, sobbing bitterly, and trying not to hear the terrible words, 'I'll be hers until the day I lie beside her.'

She'd thought Franco lost to her from the day Rosemary had come into his life. But since Rosemary's death he was more lost to her than ever.

She heard him coming up the stairs and forced herself to be silent. He mustn't know she was weeping for him. She'd already allowed too much of her feeling to show, and wanted to sink with shame. His footsteps paused for a long time outside her door, while she held her breath. But then they went on, and faded away.

She went to bed, and lay staring into the dark, bleak with despair. The day they'd spent together had been so happy that it had sent her a little crazy.

But then Rosemary had appeared, just like before, and taken him from her. Because Rosemary was his true love, and no other woman existed for him. There was only the memory of his lips to torment her.

She fell into a restless sleep, and awoke in the small hours, feeling thirsty. She remembered the jug of milk that was always kept in the fridge. Slipping out of bed, she pulled on the negligée and made her way quietly out of her room, along the corridor and downstairs. The first light was creeping in through the shutters, touching furniture, vases. It was like creeping through a ghost house. The quiet was so profound that she could hear the faint whisper of the negligée trailing on the ground behind her.

She found the jug and poured herself a glass of milk. It was ice-cold and delicious. She rinsed the glass and turned to leave, but gave a little start of alarm.

Franco was standing in the doorway. In the semi-darkness she could see little more than his outline, but she knew it was him.

'You startled me,' she said. 'I was thirsty. I came down for some milk.'

He didn't reply. He only stood watching her with a terrible stillness.

'Franco,' she said with a touch of alarm. 'It is you, isn't it?'

'*Sì,*' he said in a strange voice. '*Son io. E te?*'

Joanne drew a sharp breath. Franco had replied, Yes, it is I. And you? But he'd spoken in Italian, when they'd been speaking English all day. Why should he suddenly fall into Italian, unless—?

Franco had told her that he wanted her to be Rosemary, and now she saw what he saw, a woman with Rosemary's looks, the slight differences concealed by the darkness, wearing Rosemary's nightdress. A slight shiver went through her.

He took a step closer to her, moving into a patch of light. He wore only a pair of shorts. She could see his bare chest rising and falling under the force of some tremendous emotion, and his eyes burned with a fierce and terrible fire. A man might look like that at a vision of hell—or the ghost of his love.

'*Perché?*' he said hoarsely. '*Perché adesso?*' Why now?

'Franco—listen—'

He silenced her with a finger over her lips. His eyes devoured her. She tried to speak but the hypnotic gaze of those eyes was too much for her.

Her mind protested that she must stop his delusion, for his sake as well as her own. But his gaze held her spellbound. In a trance she swayed towards him, feeling his hands on her arms, drawing her closer until she was pressed against him.

'*Mi amore...*' he whispered.

She whispered, 'No,' but no sound came. Her heart couldn't say no. Not after so long spent in hopeless longing. She knew this was dangerous. He'd warned her, but she couldn't be with Franco without wanting to be in his arms, whatever the risk.

'*Mi amore,*' she murmured in return. 'Heart of my heart…' The rest was lost against his mouth.

He kissed her fiercely, moving his mouth over hers with driving purpose, and she responded in helpless delight. Loneliness and sadness were forgotten. They might return a thousandfold later, but she would seize this moment and live on it for ever. If it was all she ever had, she would bear that somehow.

His own words of love had been spoken, not to her, but to the ghost who, for him, was still the only reality. The love she'd stifled for years had always been there, waiting to be reawakened by a touch. She still belonged to him.

He rained kisses over her face like a man possessed. Before there had been gentleness, but now his arms seemed to hold her a prisoner as his mouth traced a burning path down her neck. Her heart was thumping wildly as his caresses grew more intimate, and she arched against him, inviting his lips further. Her heart and her body had been parched for so long, and she had no strength to deny him now. If she paid for it to the end of her days, she would claim her moment and say that it had been worth any price.

He tossed away the negligée, leaving only the night-dress covering her nakedness. Beneath the flimsy material she was burning up. He'd warned her not to trust him, but that seemed so far away, in another world. She'd forgotten why she should be wary. She only knew that the thrilling sensations that were coursing through her made her feel alive for the very first time, and she wanted them to go on for ever.

Time vanished. She was a young girl again, vibrant with her first passionate love, joyful that the man she loved had taken her into his arms at last. It was as sweet and glorious as she'd dreamed, and there was nothing else in the world.

'My love,' she murmured. *'Mi amore…'*

The words seemed to pierce his delirium. His hands gripped her arms hard, pushing her away, and she saw his eyes, full of horror.

'Joanne,' he whispered. *'Joanne*… Dear God, what am I doing?'

The brutal return to reality made her freeze with shock. She wasn't his beloved, but an unwanted woman invading his grief. She had no right to his love, his desire, or any part of him.

'Dear God, what am I doing?' His words, but they could have been her own. Appalled, she looked down at herself, the thin material pushed awry, and she could have cried out with the bitterness of shame and rejection.

Franco was shaking, his face livid.

'For God's sake, go,' he said harshly. 'Go while you're safe. Do you hear me? *Go!* Never come back.'

CHAPTER SIX

JOANNE laid down the brush with relief. Her arm was aching from long hours of work.

'Come in,' she called to Vito, who'd looked in, a question on his face. 'I've just about finished this one.'

The easel bore a copy of a picture by Giotto, so perfect that only the most refined techniques could have revealed the difference. Vito whistled in admiration.

'Maria has sent me to bring you to supper,' he said. 'Now we will make it a big celebration.'

'Vito, please,' she said in a strained voice, 'would you mind if I didn't? I'm very tired. I'd like to go straight to bed.'

'You say that every night,' he said, scandalized. 'Since you came back, you do nothing but work and sleep. Maria cooks you lovely meals, and you don't eat them.'

Joanne smiled wanly. The elderly couple were full of kindly care for her, but all she wanted was to be alone. She forced herself to go down to supper and talk cheerfully. But as soon as she decently could she pleaded a headache and went to her room.

She'd been back two weeks now, and however hard she'd tried to pull herself together she was as devastated as she'd been the first day.

After the traumatic scene with Franco she'd rushed back to her room and dressed hurriedly. She hadn't been able to stay another moment in that haunted place.

Despite the darkness she'd run out to the car. Franco, sitting downstairs with his head in his hands, had risen to run after her.

'Joanne—please—not like this—'

'Don't touch me,' she'd flashed, throwing off his arm. 'Just get out of my way.'

He hadn't tried to stop her again, but had stood wretchedly watching as she'd revved up the car and turned it away from the house. She'd driven until she'd been sure Isola Magia had been well behind her. Then she'd stopped in a lay-by, rested her head on her arms, and sobbed without restraint.

It had all been her own fault. She'd known that. She'd gone where she'd had no right to be, and stolen love that had been meant for another woman. She'd been well repaid for her shamelessness.

She'd cried until she could cry no more. Finally, drained, she'd started up and driven slowly back to the Villa Antonini. She'd arrived in the early hours, before her employers had been up, and managed to escape to her room without needing to answer their kindly questions. Even so, when they'd met a few hours later, they'd been shocked at the sight of her distraught eyes.

Joanne coped by plunging into work, trying to smother the thoughts and images that tormented her. But she was haunted by Franco's tortured face, and there seemed no escape from the humiliation she'd brought upon herself.

She knew that Nico's birthday was due, and she bought a box of colours and mailed it to him with a loving note. She wondered if Franco would contact her to thank her, or at least to say something that would help take the sting out of their final moments together. Even if it was only to say a proper goodbye. But it was

Nico who wrote, in a childish hand, politely thanking her for the gift. From Franco there was only silence. Joanne tried to be sensible, despite the ache in her heart.

She found that one part of her mind could stand aside from her misery and judge the quality of her work, observing ironically that it was excellent. Her strokes had never been so precise, her colouring so exact. In her mood of self-condemnation she thought bitterly that her function in life had been underlined. An imitator. Second best. Someone with no true existence or voice of her own.

With the Giotto finished, she began preparing for the Veronese. While she was getting the canvas ready Maria looked in on her to say, 'You have a visitor.'

'A—?'

'A very handsome young man. Hurry.'

Joanne flung down her brush and tossed aside her smock, trying not to let her hopes rise. But she couldn't stop her heart beating eagerly as she ran downstairs.

Franco had come looking for her. Somehow, all would be well. She was smiling as she threw open the door. Then she stopped in her tracks.

Her visitor was Leo.

'I was passing through Turin, and hoped you wouldn't mind if I came to see you,' he said, with his attractive, boyish smile.

She pulled herself together and greeted him warmly, for she really liked him, and it wasn't his fault he wasn't Franco.

'You don't mind my calling?'

'Of course not, Leo. I'm glad to see you.'

She accepted his invitation to dinner that evening, and surprised herself by enjoying it. Leo's honest ad-

miration restored some of her perspective, and although
her heart still ached for Franco she began to feel more
able to cope. She reached home at midnight, which
Maria told her was ridiculously early.

'You should enjoy yourself more,' she said indignantly.

'Maria, he's only a friend.' Joanne laughed. 'He's
leaving Turin tomorrow.'

'He'll be back,' Maria declared. 'I see how he looks
at you.'

Leo returned a week later, asking her out so casually
that it seemed silly to refuse. But when he dropped in
again two days later she began to realize that Maria
had been right. There was a growing warmth in Leo's
eyes as he looked at her, and at last, over a candlelit
dinner, he said, 'I think I could easily fall in love with
you—with a little encouragement.'

He accompanied the words with a quizzical, humorous look, and she suddenly knew whom it was Leo
resembled. It was Franco as he'd once been, a boy
taking his pleasures lightly. Franco as he never would
be again.

'Couldn't you encourage me just a little?' he asked.

'I don't think I should,' she said, speaking lightly.
'You're probably really in love with Rosemary.'

'Why should I be?' he asked in genuine surprise. 'I
wasn't in love with her when she was alive. And you
aren't really like her, you know.'

'You thought I was at first.'

'Oh, your faces came out of the same mould, true.
But you're such a different person. She never attracted
me as you do.'

She could almost have loved him for seeing her as
herself, and not the pale shadow of her cousin. The

next moment he disconcerted her by asking, 'Is that what's the matter with Franco?'

'What do you mean?'

'Can't he free himself from Rosemary's ghost? The day I arrived you were hoping to see another man, one who made you smile. But the smile faded when it was only me. No prizes for guessing who you were expecting.'

'I wasn't expecting him,' she said hurriedly. 'In fact, I don't suppose I'll ever see him again.'

'Does he know you're in love with him?'

'No—that is—I didn't say I was,' she stammered.

'Do you think you had to say it?'

'It makes no difference,' she said despairingly. 'You're right. He's still in love with Rosemary. He always will be.'

'Has he no eyes to see?'

'Not to see me.'

'Then there's hope for me yet,' he said with a smile. 'You can't always love a man who's blind and stupid. One day you'll turn to the one who adores you.'

His manner was so light-hearted that she easily fell in with his mood. It would be pleasant to flirt with this delightful young man who knew the score and wouldn't expect too much of her. And perhaps, after all, he really might have the answer to her sadness. To forget Franco, and love Leo, who admired her for her own sake. As the wine grew lower in the bottle, and the candlelight flickered romantically, it became a tempting prospect.

He drove her back to the villa in his sleek sports car, and hand in hand they ran up the steps and into the house. In the dark hallway he whispered, 'Don't I get a little kiss, on account?'

'I guess you do,' she murmured.

She let him take her into his arms, hoping against hope that the vital spark would leap between them, freeing her heart from Franco. He pressed his lips to hers, kissing her gently at first, then with increasing warmth. He kissed charmingly, as he did everything, but she felt nothing. His arms tightened, he grew more ardent, and Joanne made no protest, hoping against hope that he could inspire her.

'Joanne, *carissima,*' he murmured. 'I adore you— and you feel something for me too, don't you? I can feel that you do—'

But he was deceiving himself. Her body, so eager and passionate for one man, was cold and dull for all others. She tensed, ready to pull away and tell him she had nothing to give. But before she could do so the hall light snapped on.

Franco stood there watching them, a grim, ironic smile on his face.

Joanne freed herself with a gasp. Leo grinned, his composure undented. '*Ciao,* Franco,' he said cheerily. 'But how awkward of you to be here just now. We were just getting to know each other.'

'Leo,' Joanne said indignantly.

'Forgive me, *carissima.* That was vulgar of me. But who knows where the night might have ended—?'

'I'm not interested in where your night would have ended,' Franco said coolly. 'Joanne, I need to speak to you urgently.'

He stood back and indicated for her to pass before him into the main room. Maria appeared and hijacked Leo. As Joanne passed she hissed into her ear, 'He came two hours ago, and said he'd wait however long it took. He's been sitting there looking like a thunder-cloud.'

Thundercloud was right, Joanne realized as she went to find Franco. Just why he should be angry was a mystery, but he regarded her low cut evening dress and glamorous make-up with hard eyes. She was deter-mined not to flinch before his disapproval, and she walked past him into the room, tossing aside her eve-ning cloak to reveal her bare shoulders. Then she faced him, hoping her inner disturbance didn't show in her face.

'What did you want to say to me?' she asked, and to her relief her voice sounded cool and in control.

'A great deal,' he replied, looking her up and down. 'But much of it has gone out of my head. It's a surprise to find you in Leo's arms.'

'Then you've got a nerve,' she said with a flash of temper. 'It's no business of yours who I go out with, or who I kiss.'

'Of course. I merely thought you had better taste.'

'But Leo's a friend of yours.'

'That doesn't make him a suitable friend for you. He's a playboy, a Lothario—'

'He's fun. We have a great time together.'

'Evidently,' he snapped.

'Franco, I don't know why you came, but if it was just to criticise my friends you can leave again.'

'I came to take you back to Isola Magia. Nico has set his heart on having you there for his birthday to-morrow. I've cleared it with your employers.'

She drew a long breath as the memory of the last few miserable weeks rose. He'd ignored her, then felt he could snap his fingers for her return. Joanne seldom lost her temper, but she lost it now.

'I'm sorry you had a wasted journey, Franco,' she said firmly, 'but I'm very busy for the next few days—'

'I told you I'd cleared it with your employer—'

'But you neglected to clear it with me. I do have some feelings.'

'And evidently they're all tied up in Leo Moretto,' he said in a tone that was almost a sneer. 'What a pity you don't have your cousin's clear sight. Rosemary always said he was so shallow that you could see right through him.'

'Rosemary was in love with you,' Joanne said defiantly. 'But I'm not her. I'm Joanne, and my tastes are my own.'

Franco gave her a strange look, and she guessed he was remembering how she'd betrayed herself in his arms, wondering how much her actions had meant then, how much her words meant now.

'I don't ask for myself,' he said at last, 'but for my son. You won Nico's heart. Do I have to tell you how precious a gift that is? Did you delight him only to amuse yourself, and to throw him aside when it suits you?'

'Of course not. That's a wicked thing to say.'

'Then come back with me now. It will mean the world to him—and to me.'

'To you?' she echoed uncertainly.

'Nico is all I have left to love. Last year his birthday was sad, coming so soon after his mother's death. This year I want him to enjoy himself as a child should, and you can give him that.' When she hesitated he burst out, 'Do you think it was easy for me to come here and see you again?'

'No, I don't. Any more than it's easy for me to see you.'

'Yes, it's hard for both of us, but can't we put our differences aside for the sake of that little boy?'

'Of course we must,' she said after a moment. 'I'll come with you first thing tomorrow.'

'I'm afraid we can't wait until tomorrow. I promised Nico you would be there when he awoke.'

'You *promised* him—?'

'I knew I could rely on your kindness.'

'You knew nothing of the sort,' she said indignantly. 'You relied on being able to steamroller over me. Obviously Rosemary let you dictate to her—'

'Rosemary would never have argued where Nico's happiness was concerned,' Franco told her quietly.

That silenced her.

'It hurt him to awake and find you not there that morning,' Franco said. 'He kept asking why you'd gone without saying goodbye.'

'I wonder what you told him,' Joanne flung at him.

He had the grace to redden.

'Please, Joanne, let's forget that. What happened was my fault, and you have every right to be angry with me. But if I promise you that it won't happen again— please, for Nico's sake.'

She knew his words were meant as reassurance. It was as well that he didn't know the hurt he was giving her. How could she have thought there could ever be anything between her and Leo when Franco could affect her like this?

She thought of returning to Isola Magia with him, being close to him, knowing that he was keeping his distance, having to hide her feelings. And her mind cried that she couldn't do it. But her heart couldn't resist another day with him, even on these bitter terms.

And there was Nico, the bright-faced little boy

who'd come so trustingly into her arms. How could she disappoint Rosemary's child?

'All right, I'll come.'

'Thank you,' he said fervently. 'We'll leave as soon as you've changed. Can you hurry, please?'

'I'll need time to pack an overnight bag.'

Franco look awkward. 'I hardly know how to tell you this, but Signora Antonini is very kind-hearted, and when I told her the reason for my urgency she packed your bag herself.'

'Really,' Joanne said, almost bereft of speech. 'Well, you've certainly left me nothing to do.'

It seemed that Maria was not merely kind but romantic. She met Joanne on the landing, her eyes shining.

'Two lovers,' she pronounced triumphantly. 'How exciting!'

'He's not my lover,' Joanne protested.

'Nonsense, of course he is. When you were so late getting home he was very upset. You take him. He's worth ten of that other one.'

It was pointless arguing. Joanne changed out of her glamorous evening dress and went downstairs. Franco was waiting impatiently by the front door. Leo lounged around in the hallway, regarding Franco ironically.

'What a shame our evening ended so abruptly,' he said to Joanne. 'But I'm going home myself tomorrow, so I dare say we'll meet again soon.'

'I won't be there long,' Joanne said quickly. 'Maria, I'll hurry back to work.'

'You stay away as long as you like,' Maria told her. 'A pretty girl like you should enjoy herself with all her lovers.'

'Shall we go?' Franco asked.

He had a large, heavy-duty four-wheel-drive car, useful for the estate, and totally different from Leo's showy sports car. He put Joanne's bag in the back, asked if she was comfortable, and started up.

When he'd driven for some time in silence, she said, 'I can't help Maria talking like that. I've told her we're not lovers, but she is the way she is.'

'You don't have to explain Maria to me. I have several aunts just like her.'

'I didn't want you to think that I gave her the impression that we—'

'I probably did that. I was annoyed not to find you there, and I'm afraid it showed, especially when you were so late. I was beginning to think you'd be out all night.'

'It's not as late as that.'

'You came in at nearly two in the morning.'

'Goodness, I hadn't realized.'

'No, I understand Leo can be charming company. We shouldn't find too much traffic at this time of night. We'll be there soon and you can get some sleep.'

She didn't react to his abrupt change of subject. She sensed that beneath his courtesy Franco was angry. But he had no right to be.

The world seemed to be whirling around her. Only a short while ago she'd thought she would never see him again. Yet here she was, sitting beside him as they drove through the night.

They were soon off the main roads and out into the country, where there were no street lamps, and little passing traffic. By turning her head slightly she could see his face, almost in darkness, except that the lights from the dashboard threw him into relief. He looked like a man made of bronze. His only movement was the occasional turn of the wheel. He stared straight ahead, almost as if she weren't there.

Her annoyance returned. She'd fought so hard to put him out of her mind. But when he turned up, practically commandeering her, she knew that all the work had been in vain. She was as much in love with him as ever. And he ignored her.

'I'm sorry you had a long wait,' she said coolly. 'Perhaps if you'd called me first—'

'I couldn't. Nico asked for you tonight, as he was going to bed. I didn't know where you were. You left no address. You'd mentioned only your employer's name and that he'd made his money in engineering. I had to do some fast detective work.'

'And tomorrow wouldn't have been good enough?'

'That's right.'

'Franco, are you sure this is a good idea? You know why Nico wants me, to fantasize that his mother's returned. Is it wise to indulge that fantasy? He could suffer for it later—'

'You're wrong,' he interrupted her. 'It's "Aunt Joanne" he wants. You can talk to him about Rosemary. He's thrilled about your connection with his mother, but he knows who you are. Nico is less confused about you than—than anyone else.'

He stopped talking abruptly, as though afraid of what he might be betrayed into saying.

As they neared Isola Magia he slowed, and by the time they approached the gate the car was crawling along. Once inside he stopped the engine while they were still some distance from the house.

'I'm afraid we have to walk from here,' he said. 'If I drive closer Nico will hear us. I told him he'd simply wake up tomorrow and find you there, like magic. If he knows when you arrive tonight it will spoil it for him.'

'But surely he knows why you went out?'

'I left after he went to sleep. With luck he may never know I was gone. I promised him that you would appear "like magic", and that's what I want to happen. He's lost so much. I want to please him.'

She was touched by the imaginative way he'd thought himself into the child's mind. Beneath the hard shell with which Franco protected himself, there was still a loving heart, even if it was only for a little boy.

A moon had appeared, and by its light Joanne could see the house, a dark bulk, a few hundred yards away among the trees. She could just make out the path at her feet.

'Be careful, the ground is uneven,' Franco said.

She trod carefully, wishing she could see more clearly, but then the moon went behind a thick cloud, and suddenly she was in total darkness. Her foot went down into a rut. She gasped and staggered, almost falling. But strong hands came out of the darkness, to hold her. She clasped him frantically back and felt herself held firmly against his chest.

'Steady,' Franco said in a ragged voice. 'Are you all right?'

'Yes—yes, I'm all right.'

Silence fell between them. He didn't release her, and suddenly she knew that he couldn't make himself do that. He was trembling, and beneath the thin material of his shirt she could feel the thunder of his heart.

She looked up. She couldn't make out his face, but she could see his eyes glittering strangely, and heard the sharpness of his breathing. He wanted to kiss her, wanted it desperately. She knew that because it mirrored her own desire. His hands on her arms tightened, drawing her closer. In another moment he would lower his head.

'The moon's appeared again,' he said raggedly. 'You'll manage better now.'

She was still standing with him, yet nothing was the same. As though a curtain had been ripped aside she saw the truth behind his outward calm. He wanted her, yet he was determined not to want her. He'd vowed to set a distance between them, and he would keep that vow, no matter how it tormented him. He saw her only as the reincarnation of his dead wife, and there would be heartbreak—for both of them—in pursuing that delusion.

She understood this as she stood there, held against his chest, feeling the heat from his body, and her anger with him grew for the way he could provoke her feelings without returning them. She pulled herself free.

'I can walk, thank you,' she said coldly.

Luckily the moon appeared again and she was able to make her way to the house unaided. As they neared it they saw a light coming from Nico's room.

'Quickly, come into the trees,' Franco whispered. 'He mustn't see us.' He put out a hand to guide her, but immediately drew it back.

They moved into deep shadow, looking up at the window where the light still glowed.

'He must have awoken,' Franco said. 'I hope he hasn't discovered that I've gone. Celia promised not to go to bed until I returned.'

They were still, waiting, holding their breaths. Overhead the stars swung in silent majesty, and all the world seemed to be still.

'Try not to hate me, Joanne,' he said sombrely. 'You

have every right, after the way I behaved. But don't let Nico be hurt, I beg of you.'

Hate and anger were only different sides of love. Being with him had taught her that, but she couldn't tell him so.

'I'll never do anything to hurt that little boy,' she said. 'That's why I'm here.'

'That's all I ask. His light's gone out. Let's get inside quickly.'

They crept noiselessly into the house and up the darkened stairs. A floorboard creaked, and they stood petrified. Then they heard footsteps from behind Nico's door. At once Franco moved forward and opened the door. Joanne heard Nico's glad cry of 'Papa!' and a grunt as though they'd clasped each other vigorously.

'You should be in bed,' came Franco's voice.

'I was coming to see you. Is Aunt Joanne here yet?'

'She'll be here when you wake up tomorrow. My word on it!'

'Why not now, *now?*'

Franco spoke in a strange, constricted voice, 'Is it so important that she comes here?'

'But you like her too, don't you, Papa?'

'Go to sleep, my son,' Franco said heavily after a moment. 'Wait for the morning, and see if I've kept my word.'

'Will it be my birthday soon?'

'It'll never be your birthday if you don't go to sleep,' Franco said firmly.

'I'm asleep now,' Nico insisted at once.

To her surprise Franco chuckled. It was a rich sound that touched her senses. Keeping well back, she moved across the door until she could see inside the room.

Franco had lifted Nico in his arms and was setting him down on the bed. 'Snuggle down now,' he said.

His voice was gentle, patient, full of love. Nico wriggled down in the bed and Franco tucked in the sheets around him.

'You're not cross because I was awake?' Nico asked sleepily.

'No, my son. I'm not cross with you.'

He leaned down and kissed the child. Joanne moved back slowly, careful not to make a noise. At last she gained the room that had been hers last time, and slipped inside. Just before she closed the door she saw Franco come out into the corridor and stand in a patch of moonlight. As she watched, he dropped his head and covered his eyes with one hand. He looked like a man at the end of his tether.

If only she could go to him now, put her arms about him, tell him that she loved him and longed to comfort him. But she knew he couldn't cope with that.

He raised his head, and for a moment she thought she saw the glint of tears on his face. Joanne backed silently into her room, and closed the door.

A moment later there was the sound of a soft tap and she heard Franco's voice. 'May I come in?'

'No,' she said quickly. 'I've gone to bed.'

'Is there nothing you want? Some refreshment?'

'Nothing,' she said, trying to keep her voice steady. 'Please go away, Franco. Please.'

CHAPTER SEVEN

JOANNE was up early, ready and dressed before Franco came for her.

'Thank you,' he said. 'After that late night, I'm impressed.'

Joanne smiled. 'I know what children are like on birthdays.'

Franco was dressed in jeans and an olive-green vest. His brown arms were glistening as if he'd already been outside working. To the casual glance he looked as if he didn't have a care in the world. Only a certain tension around his mouth hinted at the truth.

They were just in time. Further along the corridor they heard Nico's door open and a small voice say, 'Papa?'

'Here!' Franco called cheerfully.

The next moment Nico saw Joanne and his face lit up. Still in his pyjamas, he raced at her full tilt, almost knocking the breath out of her as they collided.

'*Zia, zia!*' he squealed. 'You came!'

'Of course I did,' she said, laughing. 'Oof! Don't strangle me.' Nico had leapt up into her arms, hugging her tightly around the neck. She kissed him back and rubbed her cheek against his shining hair.

'Happy birthday, little one,' she said.

'You weren't here when I went to bed?' he said, making the statement a question.

'I came in the night, when you were asleep,' she declared dramatically.

'But what made you come?' he asked, taking her by surprise.

Joanne thought fast, dropping down on one knee to look the child in the eyes. 'I knew you wanted me,' she said. 'That was all I needed to know.'

'But how did you—?'

'Shh!' She put a finger over her lips. 'It's magic, and we mustn't talk about it.'

He beamed at her. 'This is going to be the best birthday *ever.*'

'Don't I get a kiss too?' Franco demanded, laughing.

Nico hugged his father, bouncing eagerly and carolling, 'I'm seven, I'm seven.'

'Almost a man,' Franco teased.

'Will I be a man next year, Papa?'

'Very soon,' Franco promised.

'*Zia,* come and see my puppies,' Nico begged, seizing her hand and pulling her downstairs.

'How about getting dressed first?' Franco called.

'I must see the puppies first, Papa.'

'How long have you had them?' Joanne asked, following him breathlessly downstairs.

'Celia gave them to me yesterday.'

The little dogs were older than Joanne had expected, being about four months. Both were female. One was covered in long fur and looked like a mop. Nico had named her Zazzera, shock of hair. Zaza for short. The other was smooth-haired with an excitable temperament, so Nico called her Peperone. And she became Pepe.

'Celia's brother has a little farm near here,' Franco said, catching up. 'As a sideline they breed dogs, to sell in the markets. But males sell faster than females.

These two have been to market and back seven times, and nobody was going to give them an eighth chance.'

'They were going to kill them,' Nico said earnestly. 'So I asked Papa and he said I could have one. But I couldn't take just one and leave the other one to die, could I, *Zia?*'

'No, you couldn't do that,' Joanne agreed, regarding him tenderly.

Without warning there were tears in her eyes. She rose hastily and went out onto the terrace. Nico was embracing his pets again and didn't notice, but after a moment Franco followed her.

'What is it?' he asked urgently.

'Nothing, I just—I suddenly remembered Rosemary, when she telephoned me to say she was pregnant again. She was so happy, and she said she was glad Nico would have a little brother or sister before he was seven. I can hear her saying, "That's just the right age gap. He'll be old enough to learn by being close to a small, helpless creature." She'd be so proud of him today.' She wiped her eyes. 'I'm sorry.'

'Don't be sorry for loving her,' Franco said. 'How could anyone not do so? I only hope I can raise her son to be worthy of her.'

'You're doing a wonderful job with him. He's a splendid little boy.'

'Yes, he is, isn't he?' Franco's eyes shone with love and pride. Joanne looked away, realizing that today was going to be harder than she'd thought.

But despite her fears, breakfast was a cheerful meal, out under the trees, with Pepe, Zaza and Ruffo crouched beneath the table, poised for titbits. Celia served it hastily, for she was already deep in preparations for Nico's birthday party that evening. Even

Franco, venturing to look into the kitchen, had been driven out by Celia's indignation.

Nico ate his breakfast in a state of suppressed excitement, throwing his father significant looks.

'Have I forgotten anything?' Franco asked at last, all bland innocence.

'Papa!' Nico protested indignantly.

'Oh, your present. Well, let me see, it's a bit late to be thinking of anything—' His eyes were full of mischief.

'*Papa!*'

Franco laughed. 'Let's see what's hiding around the corner of the barn.' He raised his voice. 'All right, you can bring him out.'

A grinning young man came around the barn, leading a small, fat pony. Nico's shriek of delight made everyone cover their ears. Leaving the rest of his breakfast untouched, he bounded over to throw his arms around the pony in an ecstasy of love.

'He's so like his mother,' Franco said in a low voice. 'She too was always full of eagerness.'

'I remember you as just the same,' Joanne said impulsively. 'When I first met you all those years ago you seemed to regard all life as your own to be enjoyed.'

'I was a heedless boy then, taking everything because I thought my own pleasures mattered. She taught me better.'

Nico's eager shouts recalled him to the present. Smiling, he helped his son into the saddle, and led the pony around the yard. Nico sat holding the rein with the confidence of a child who had already learned to ride, while the pony ambled placidly along. Pepe and Zaza gambolled at his heels, but he ignored them.

'Papa says we can all go riding together,' Nico said, scampering back to her.

'I promise you a slower horse today,' Franco said instantly.

'So I should hope.'

'Can we go *now?*' Nico begged.

'Just as soon as we've changed,' Franco promised.

'I'm going to change,' he called, already halfway to the house.

Left alone, Franco gave her a wry look. 'You don't mind, do you?'

'I'm here to do whatever pleases Nico.'

When she came down a few minutes later, wearing Rosemary's riding things, she was glad to see that she did indeed have a quieter-looking horse. Nico was already mounted and eager to go. He flapped the reins and urged his mount on, but the placid little pony moved at a sedate pace.

'Papa, he won't go fast when I tell him to,' Nico cried indignantly.

'Thank heavens!' Franco declared wryly. Under his breath he added to Joanne, 'The man who trained him promised me that.'

She chuckled and they shared a smile. Franco seemed to be growing more relaxed, almost contented when his eyes rested on his little son.

They descended into the valley and began to climb the other side, passing through little villages. In one of these they found a small inn and sat outside at a table beside a wooden rail, looking down into the valley, where they could see Isola Magia, basking in the sun. At this distance it looked peaceful and content.

The landlord brought Nico a milk shake. The others drank *prosecco* with sweet biscuits.

'What is it, Nico?' The child was tugging at his sleeve. He whispered something that made Franco frown and shake his head. 'No, *piccino*. Not this year.'

'But we didn't go last year, either,' Nico pleaded. 'And *Zia* could come too—'

'No,' Franco said, more sharply than Joanne had ever heard him speak before. He softened the effect by squeezing the child's shoulder, but Nico still looked upset.

'What is it?' Joanne asked.

'Nico wants to go to Lake Garda,' Franco explained. 'I have a little villa there and we've always visited it in summer, except for last year. The time isn't right yet, Nico.'

'I'm sorry, Papa,' the little boy said, with a gentleness that made him seem much older than seven. He squeezed Franco's hand between his own small ones. 'It'll be all right, Papa. Truly it will.' For a moment it was he who was offering comfort.

And it was there again, the echo of Rosemary saying, 'Don't worry, I'll look after you,' as Rosemary had said so often in the past. 'Don't worry, I'll take care of you—I'll be your sister, your mother—'

And she'd repaid Rosemary's bounty by wanting her husband. Driven by the need to get away from the other two, she rose quickly and went to stand by the stone wall, looking out at the view.

After a while there was a touch on her shoulder.

'I'm sorry to force that on you,' Franco said. 'Please believe I didn't plan it. I've commandeered your day, but I couldn't ask for a whole week.'

'I don't mind if it will make Nico happy.'

'If I could persuade him to choose somewhere else—'

'But he wants to go there,' Joanne said. 'He was happy there, with the two of you. You're right. It's not a good idea. You should take him there some time in the future, but without me.'

He was silent so long that she turned to look at him, and something she saw in his eyes made her heart beat rapidly.

'Without you?' he echoed quietly.

'What do you think I am?' she demanded. 'Just a doll with Rosemary's face? I'm Joanne. You want me to be a copy of Rosemary, like the imitation pictures I paint. On the surface, everything looks the same, but it's all false. At least Leo—'

'Must we talk of him?' Franco demanded sharply.

'Leo sees me as *me*. I like him for that.'

Franco's lips tightened. 'I think we should return home now.'

They made their way back slowly, Nico riding between them. He talked non-stop, relieving them of the task of appearing normal. It was a relief to them both when the house came into view.

Everything was ready for the party, and soon the guests and their parents began to arrive. Joanne was swept up in the merrymaking. She helped serve the refreshments, took part in the games, and met many of the neighbours, trying not to see the strange looks they gave her and Franco.

But, although she seemed oblivious to him, she was acutely aware of Franco all the time. He too played games and joined in the songs, apparently enjoying himself. Joanne guessed what it must cost him to appear cheerful when he must be recalling other parties, with his wife. But he allowed no sign of his own sadness to appear.

As the light faded coloured lamps came on in the trees, and those who could do a turn were pressed into service. An old man played an accordion, two little girls did a dance, a boy did a recitation, all to great applause. Someone called for Nico to sing, but the little boy refused bashfully.

'He must sing,' Celia confided to Joanne. 'He has a lovely voice.'

The calls grew. Nico continued to shake his head, and hid his face against his father.

'It's your birthday, my son,' Franco chided him gently. 'Your guests have brought you gifts. Now you must do what pleases them.'

'I can't sing alone, Papa,' Franco pleaded. To Joanne's amazement he added urgently, 'Only if you help me.'

'All right,' he said. 'We'll sing together. What shall we sing?'

'The two brooms,' Nico said.

Franco sat down on a bench with Nico standing between his knees. The accordionist struck up, and Franco began to sing in his pleasant, light baritone. After one short verse, Nico took over. The song was about two brooms having an argument.

'The mistress wrote this for them,' Celia said in an undervoice.

'Yes, I guessed that,' Joanne said with a smile. 'It's her style.'

She could hear Rosemary's voice through the comic words, as the brooms squabbled about which one cleaned the best. The song ended on a yell, but then the two singers hugged each other. It was a real hug, arms wide and tightly enveloping.

Two against the world, Joanne thought wistfully. They don't really need me.

An impromptu dance followed. Franco did a series of duty dances before approaching Joanne. 'Will you dance with me?' he asked.

'I think I should help Celia with the washing-up,' she said hastily.

For answer he held out his hand. His eyes were fixed on her face, demanding that she yield. She was swept by temptation. It would be sweet to dance with him, feeling him hold her close. And surely she could allow herself this one indulgence?

But there were some pleasures that were not for her. She would leave first thing next day, and forget this enchanted interlude. She backed away from him, smiling but firm. 'It's better if we don't,' she said.

'Are you angry with me, Joanne?'

'No, I'm not angry. But I don't really belong here.'

'How can you say that? Who belongs here more than you?'

'I don't think so. The sooner I leave the better.'

He laid his hand on her arm. His touch seemed to burn her. 'Do you think I'll let you just disappear?'

She couldn't answer, he affected her so powerfully. She'd tried to resist, but he would not be resisted. He took one of her hands in his and drew her into the shadows. 'They won't miss us for a while,' he said.

He led her on through the trees, until they reached a clearing on the far side. The valley stretched out before them, almost in darkness, for the moon was hidden behind clouds. But at that moment the clouds parted and the scene was flooded with brilliant silver moonlight. They stood watching it for a moment, awed by its ghostly beauty.

'The light appears like that,' Franco said at last. 'Suddenly, when you least expect it, driving away the darkness. And then you understand that this was why you clung on when all hope seemed to be gone. Because one day this moment would come.'

She couldn't speak for the beating of her heart. His words seemed to promise so much, if only she dared believe them...

'Dance with me,' he said again.

She could no longer resist what her heart longed for. She went easily into his arms and felt him draw her close. The party was so far away that even the lights were hidden by the trees, but they could still hear the sweet wail of an accordion, playing the yearning notes of a waltz.

He moved her gently this way and that, swaying to the time of the music. She followed his lead, feeling the warmth of his body against hers, the movements of his limbs. They danced as one, lost in the same dream, or so it seemed to her. They might have been alone on a distant planet, the first man and woman, existing before time began, dancing to the music of the spheres. She longed for it to last for ever.

But she knew that nothing so sweet ever lasted. She must cherish the precious moment, for it might be all she ever had.

'Joanne,' he said softly, 'look at me.'

She looked up and found his mouth very close. His eyes held hers for a moment, before he tightened his arms and touched her lips with his own.

She felt herself flower into life under the kiss she'd longed for. This was the man she loved, no matter how hard she tried not to. She'd fought her feelings for years, but he was her destiny, and she was in his arms, feeling his lips move softly over hers.

It was a kiss such as a young boy might have given, uncertain of his welcome, fearful to offend. But as he grew more sure of her his lips became ardent, purposeful, thrilling her with the intent she could feel. She pressed closer to him, eagerly seeking deeper caresses, and he responded by teasing her lips apart.

She was ready at that moment to yield him all of herself, heart, soul and body. She would give everything for one night of happiness and never count the cost. But in the same moment a little demon spoke in her head. It had Franco's voice and it said, You must hear, so that you may know never to trust me.

His warning had cast a shadow over every kiss, every gentle word. It ruined this moment which might have been so beautiful. The spell was broken and, try as she might, there was no way to bring it back now.

She could feel Franco's passion growing, his arms tightening about her. The ardour in his kisses made it hard to think but she knew she mustn't succumb. Putting out all her strength, she broke free.

'Joanne…'

'Please,' she begged. 'Let me go. We must stop this.'

'Why?' he demanded urgently.

'We have to get back. They'll notice we've gone.'

He let his hands fall, but she could still sense the trembling that shook him. 'Is that the only reason?' he asked raggedly.

'O-of course,' she stammered.

In a voice grown suddenly harsh he demanded, 'Are you sure it has nothing to do with Leo Moretto?'

For a moment she couldn't think whom he meant.

She was so caught up with the enchantment of being with him that no other man existed.

'What do you mean?' she asked.

Franco turned away from her as if wrenching himself by an effort. She saw him run both hands through his hair. His whole body radiated tension. At last he seemed to feel that it was safe to speak.

'I saw you together last night, saw how ardently you kissed him. I heard what he said, "*Carissima,* I adore you." He adores, but he doesn't know how to *love.* Loving a woman is when she gets under your skin so that you can't forget her however hard you try. It means watching her face to know what pleases her, what hurts her. It means lying awake, thinking of her in the arms of another man, wanting to—'

He stopped and drew a sharp breath. A rider who'd reined his horse back from the edge of a precipice might have made that sound.

'Franco, what is it?' she asked, not daring to believe that he was speaking of herself.

'Nothing! I only meant—you implied that I'd driven you into his arms,' he said awkwardly, 'and I didn't want that on my conscience.'

She longed to ask, 'Is that all it is?' But it was too much to hope that he might be jealous. Things were moving too fast, leaving her in a whirl. He raised his head to look at her and she saw in his eyes something that might have been her heart's desire. But then again she could be deceiving herself. His next words would tell her.

'Papa! Papa!'

The sound of Nico's voice seemed to fall between them. Whatever Franco had been going to say, he wouldn't say it now. She saw the shock on his face as he returned to the real world, and guessed that it mirrored her own. She forced herself to turn to where Nico was running through the trees.

'Papa, people are getting ready to go,' he cried. 'Everyone wonders where you are.' He looked innocently from one to the other.

Joanne recovered first. 'Your papa was showing me the view of the valley,' she said. 'It's very beautiful.'

Franco spoke up before Nico could ask any questions. 'But we should go back now,' he said hastily. 'I should never have neglected our guests.'

'Zia?' Nico held out his hand to her.

'I'll stay here a little longer,' she said. Returning with Franco would be too obvious, and there must be enough knowing looks going around already.

She gave them a head start, then followed to where the party was coming to an end. She managed to slip into the kitchen without being noticed. Celia was there, washing up, and Joanne picked up a towel. To her relief Celia asked no questions.

From outside Joanne could make out Franco's voice, raised in farewell, the sound of car doors slamming. Soon it was quiet. Nico ran in, followed by Franco, and gave Celia a smacking kiss. 'Thank you for my party,' he said.

He kissed Joanne too and said, 'Are you coming up with me?'

'I think it should be just your papa tonight.'

'Come, Nico,' Franco called. 'Whoah! Don't choke me. Come away to bed with you!'

'You go with them,' Celia urged.

'No,' Joanne said stubbornly. 'I'll stay here and help you.'

Celia fell silent. There was no arguing with the look on Joanne's face.

When everything was done Celia looked around. 'Where are those puppies?'

'They went into the garden a few minutes ago,' Joanne said. 'You go to bed. I'll find them.'

Celia departed and Joanne wandered outside. The coloured lamps were still on, casting a magic glow over the house and the garden.

'Pepe,' she called softly. 'Zaza.'

She heard a faint rustle in the bushes and went to investigate. Two bright eyes gleamed at her through a shock of hair.

'Zaza, there you are. Come on, it's time for bed.'

She picked up the furry bundle and looked around. 'Pepe, where are you?'

'I have her here,' came Franco's voice.

She made her way back to where he was standing with Pepe tucked under his arm. He took Zaza from her, set both pups down and shooed them into the house.

'Don't run away,' he said. 'I have things to say. I promise not to touch you.'

He thrust his hands in his pockets and headed away under the trees, the lamps throwing their lights on his black hair. Joanne followed, keeping a few paces away, not allowing herself to catch up when he stopped and leaned against a tree. He seemed to be having trouble finding the words.

'You're upset with me,' he said at last. 'And I can't blame you. I had no right to kiss you. I don't know what came over me. I apologise.'

'You don't need to apologise,' she said, trying to muffle her disappointment.

'But I do. My only excuse is that, after all this time, I'm still a little crazy.'

Joanne went closer to him, moved by the bleakness in his voice. She'd resolved to put a distance between them, to keep herself safe. But now her own safety counted for nothing, and all she cared about was to comfort him. If only she knew the way.

'I walk and talk like a normal man,' Franco said, 'but inside here—' he touched his breast '—there is still confusion, words that I can't speak, thoughts that I'm afraid of.'

Joanne put out her hand and found it clasped fiercely in his.

'You don't need to tell me about those thoughts,' she said. 'You've already warned me about them. I can cope.'

'You're very generous with my selfishness,' he said with a faint touch of bitterness.

'Franco, I—' Joanne stopped, amazed by the idea that had come to her, and by the strength of the impulse to put it into words. They didn't seem to be her own words. She wasn't sure where they'd come from, but the need to say them was overwhelming.

'I think there has to be a place for you where the sadness ends, and life is worth living again,' she began hesitantly. 'And perhaps I can be the bridge to that place. It troubles you to look at me because I'm half Rosemary and half not. If the half that's her can be any help to you, then—then use it. And when you reach the other side of the bridge, you'll be safe.'

'And you?' he asked, looking at her curiously. 'What about you when I've made use of you like this?'

'Well, that's the idea of bridges. You leave them

behind. I'm not suggesting anything that I can't cope with.'

'And where does Leo Moretto come in all this?'

She was about to say that he came nowhere, when it occurred to her that if Franco thought she had another man to turn to in the end he would find her offer easier to accept.

'Leo's my problem,' she said. 'He knows where he stands with me, and I know where I stand with him.'

'And where exactly is that?'

'It doesn't matter.'

'Meaning, mind my own business? In that case, I might ask why you kissed me back there, but I know the answer. You were always a very kind person.'

Before she could speak they heard the sound of a car approaching.

'Who can be arriving at this hour?' Franco mused. '*Damn!* Talk of the devil!'

Leo came to a sharp halt and hopped out of the car. '*Ciao*, Franco,' he called, waving cheerily. '*Ciao*, Joanne.'

'What a surprise,' Franco said in a tight voice. 'Was I expecting you?'

'You should have known that I wouldn't miss Nico's birthday. I came to bring his present.'

He held up a parcel, tied up in brown paper.

'That's very kind of you,' Franco said politely. 'I'm afraid my son's in bed.'

'No, I'm not,' came Nico's voice from overhead. 'Hallo, Uncle Leo.'

'All right, you can come down,' Franco said in a resigned voice in which Joanne could detect an undertone of anger. But the anger was for Leo, not his son.

CHAPTER EIGHT

FOR two days after Franco's surprise announcement Isola Magia was abuzz with preparations. Celia set herself to launder practically every garment in the place, despite Franco's insistence that they would need very little.

His own time was taken up giving instructions to his foreman. Joanne spent hours shopping for clothes in Asti. The overnight bag Maria had packed for her contained only the basics. There wasn't enough there for a vacation, and Joanne was determined not to wear anything of Rosemary's.

She agonized for ages over suitable swimwear, unable to choose between a bikini or a sleek one-piece. She'd been invited mainly for Nico's benefit, which meant the one-piece. But then she remembered how her invitation had come about. She would have sworn that Franco had had no such intention a moment before. It had been said to drive Leo off. When she thought of something that had flashed in his eyes as he'd spoken, she felt that a bikini might be the right choice after all.

But perhaps she was reading too much into that look. Maybe she'd only imagined the enchanted dream when they'd danced in the moonlight. She bought the one-piece.

She returned to Isola Magia laden down with parcels, but with spirits buoyed up at the prospect of a week at Lake Garda, close to Franco.

As she entered the house she could hear the telephone ringing. There was no sign of anyone about, so she answered it.

'So you are there,' said a sour voice.

'Sophia?'

'I still have friends there, and they tell me what is happening,' said Franco's mother. 'I heard that you'd returned.'

Her tone was unpleasant, but Joanne remained determinedly courteous. 'I'm working in Italy now, quite near here. Naturally I came to see Rosemary's husband and child.'

'And to see if you could take up where you left off?'

'If that's what the gossips are telling you, they're wrong,' Joanne said firmly. 'I'm here mainly for Nico's sake. Yesterday was his birthday—'

'Don't tell me my own grandson's birthday.'

'I was only trying to explain that Franco felt—since Nico knows me—'

'It's just because you look like her. Oh, yes, I know all about that. "Rosemary came back to life." That's what they say. Franco's using you. Have you no pride?'

Joanne drew a slow breath and chose her words carefully. 'I don't think my pride matters. I'm needed. I'll help in any way I can.'

Sophia's voice hovered on the edge of a sneer. 'And that's why you're going to Lake Garda with them? To help?'

'That's right.'

'Well, my dear, I very much admire you.' The silky words made Joanne apprehensive as the open rudeness had failed to do. 'You know, of course, that the villa is where they spent their honeymoon?'

'I don't—see that makes any difference,' Joanne said

resolutely. The news made her heart sink, but she strove not to reveal how much she minded.

'Of course not. They rented it the first time, but their honeymoon was so happy that Franco bought it for her. They went back every year to rediscover their happiness. He really didn't tell you that?'

'Why should Franco tell me? It's none of my business.' To her relief she saw Franco entering. 'He's here now. Goodbye.'

She handed him the phone and escaped.

Their honeymoon villa! Why should he tell her? She'd assured herself that none of this mattered as long as she could give them what they needed. But it shocked her to discover how much she minded.

Celia had just returned from buying food. Joanne went to help her unpack the shopping in the kitchen. Franco's voice could be heard faintly, speaking in a placating tone.

'The Signora?' Celia said in a half-whisper.

Joanne nodded. 'I answered the phone. She wasn't pleased to find me here, or about me going to the lake with them.'

'She's not pleased, ever,' Celia said with a snort. 'When the mistress die she come here and take over. Order me out of the kitchen. Everything must be done her way, until Signor Franco said she should let me get on with my work. Then she make a big scene.

'She try to change Nico's life. Everything his mother did was wrong, she say. He's just a little boy. He's lost his mama. His father's going about in a daze, and suddenly this woman is trying to turn him against his mama.'

'That's inexcusable,' Joanne said.

'*Sì*. Is an *infamia*. So Signor Franco say no, she must

not do this. Another big scene. And we're all hoping
she go back to her own home, but she stay and she
stay and she stay. I think she stay for ever, but then
her husband come here and say she must go back to
Naples with him.

'Signor Franco try to keep the peace. He respect his
mother. Also he love her, but she don't wanna believe
that. She think—if you love her, you gotta do everything she say. If you don't, is not love.'

Joanne nodded. 'People like that are very frightening, because their minds are closed.'

'*Sì!* So now, she hear about you, and she get mad,
because she think Signor Franco marry you, and she
don't like that. Everyone else like it, though.'

'Celia, please, don't talk like that,' Joanne said urgently. 'I'm only here to help Nico.'

'Yeah, sure!' Celia said, lapsing in slang in her disconcerting way.

Joanne wandered out of the house, sunk in thought.
She remembered Rosemary saying that Sophia had
hated her, and she had no doubt that it was true. Franco
was her darling, and she'd never forgiven the woman
who'd won his heart. Now it seemed that resentment
had been transferred to herself.

She found Nico and joined in a romp with Pepe and
Zaza, but they only had half her attention. The other
half was wondering when Franco would come off the
phone.

He was away for a long time, and when he appeared
he wore an expression of displeasure that told its own
story.

'Go and give those pups a bath,' he commanded,
tweaking Nico's hair. 'Otherwise we won't take them
with us.'

'Papa, you promised!'

'Go and clean them up, then.'

When Nico had raced away, his two boon companions lolloping at his heels, Franco said, 'What did you mean when you told my mother that it was "none of your business"?'

'She asked if you'd told me about your honeymoon at Lake Garda,' Joanne said lightly. 'But why should you?'

Franco ran a hand distractedly through his hair. 'That's why I originally refused to go. I should have told you—'

'But why?' she asked with a cheerful shrug. 'We're doing this for Nico. How can the details matter?'

Franco frowned, uncertain how to read her tone. But Joanne had anticipated this, and she'd had enough time to get her reaction precisely right. As she'd intended, her smile and her manner gave nothing away.

'My mother—' he began '—she means well, and she wants only the best for me.'

'I'm sure she does, like all mothers,' Joanne said brightly. 'Now, perhaps I should go and help Nico bath those dogs.'

Nothing more was said on the subject, and the preparations continued. Joanne lovingly unwrapped her new clothes and packed them away in a suitcase. The sight of them made her feel better.

She wondered what had been said between Franco and his mother, but he never mentioned it, and by the next morning they were ready to leave. Nico and the puppies piled into the car, Franco stowed the last of the baggage aboard, and they were off.

'It's about two hundred miles,' Franco said. 'We should be there by late afternoon.'

It was an enchanted journey, through the most beautiful scenery she'd ever seen. Had there ever been such a fertile country? she thought as they travelled past silvery olive groves, beneath palm trees and cypress. In the distance she could see mountains, covered in snow that looked almost blue, although down here the summer heat was growing fierce.

Franco drove with the windows down, one arm resting on the edge, the other hand controlling the wheel with light movements. Joanne was glad to see that he looked relaxed.

She spent the first part of the journey sitting beside him while Nico sat in the back explaining everything to Pepe and Zaza. They stopped for a coffee, and when they resumed the journey Joanne sat in the back and chatted to Nico. He was eager to tell her about where they were going.

'It's in a little fishing village called Peschino, and the villa is right at the edge of the lake, so we can run out onto the beach and into the water. And all the fishermen are our friends, especially the Terrinis, who live near. There are lots and lots of them. And the house is called the Villa Felicità.'

'The Villa of Happiness.' Joanne tried the words.

'It used to be called something else, but Mama and Papa were so happy there that they renamed it,' Nico said innocently, unaware that he was turning a knife in her breast.

Joanne heard Franco take a sharp breath, and spoke quickly. 'Those hills are so beautiful, as if they were covered in gold.'

'Those are orange and lemon groves,' Nico said. 'And over there—look, *Zia*—'

He prattled on happily and the dangerous moment passed.

Joanne's first impression of Lake Garda was of flowers. Camellias, azaleas, rhododendrons, geraniums everywhere, spilling over the banks, their brilliant colours rioting in the sun.

To get to Peschino they had to drive right around to the west shore, so the last part of the journey was spent with the lake in view. She drank in its beauty, the impossible blue of the water, the red-tiled villas that nestled against the hills, flanked by fruit and olives.

'We're nearly there,' Franco told them as he drove into the little town of Bardolino. 'Shall we stop for a coffee?'

Joanne was about to say that she'd love one when she realized that Nico was crossing his fingers.

'Do you want to?' he asked her politely.

'I think we should just get straight on,' she said, ruffling his hair.

'Yes, *please*,' he cried in relief, and Franco shouted with laughter.

'You said the right thing,' he told her.

'I remember when I was a child, and we were going to the seaside, and when we were on the last lap some wretched adult always wanted to stop and make you wait for the treat,' she said.

Nico nodded vigorously, pleased at her understanding.

Half an hour later they reached Peschino, a tiny place out of a picture book that Joanne loved on sight: the roads that ran down straight onto the sand, the little fishing boats bobbing on the water, the cafés with their tables and chairs outside, the tiny population who all seemed to know each other. Franco told her that this was literally true.

'There aren't more than eight hundred people here and over the years they've intermarried. Somehow everyone is related to everyone else. Weddings, funerals and baptisms are great occasions.'

The villa was an enchanted place, with cool *terrazzo* floors and huge windows. Gina Terrini, who cared for it in Franco's absence, came, smiling, to welcome them. She was a plump, middle-aged woman, who hugged Nico and greeted Franco as an old friend. Her eyes briefly flickered over Joanne, but she showed no surprise. She'd put her and Franco in separate rooms, and Joanne guessed that he'd briefed her well.

Joanne's room had a tall window that overlooked the garden, and then the lake. It was dark from the closed shutters, but she pushed them open and breathed in the fresh, glorious air. When she'd unpacked she went to find the others, and found them in the kitchen, seated around the table gossiping nineteen to the dozen. Nico was drinking milk and munching almond biscuits. Gina and Franco were drinking *prosecco,* and she immediately set one in front of Joanne.

'Now I go,' she declared. 'But tonight, you come to us for supper.'

'Gina comes from the family Nico was telling you about,' Franco explained. There are plenty of them, including five children.'

'Six,' Gina said at once. 'Since last year. And my brother's wife is pregnant.'

'Which brother?' Nico asked.

Gina shrugged. 'One of them.'

'That little house is going to burst with all of you,' Franco protested.

'Oh, no, we've got the house next door now, so we can stay together.'

Nico clamoured to be allowed to go with Gina and meet his friends again.

'You do your unpacking first,' Franco told him. 'And put everything away tidily. Don't leave it all to Joanne.'

Nico seized Joanne's hand, putting his whole heart into the one word, *'Please.'*

'Nico, what did I say?' Franco asked firmly.

'I take good care of him,' Gina put in.

'Let him go,' Joanne begged. 'Let him enjoy himself.'

'OK, I'm outvoted,' Franco said with humorous resignation.

Nico's shriek of joy made them all cover their ears. The next moment he was out of the door, bounding along the beach with the pups gambolling beside him, and Gina trying to keep up.

'Thank you,' Franco said. 'He's happy now. Do you think you can be happy here for a week?'

'I think it's the loveliest place I've ever seen. And you? How will you manage?'

'It's time I laid my ghosts. And I'm in good company.'

She wasn't quite sure what he meant by that, and he didn't explain.

'I should tell you some more about the Terrini family, because you'll probably find them a little overwhelming. There's Papa and Mama Terrini, their two sons, and Gina, their daughter, their sons' wives, a couple of teenage boys, and lots of children.'

'I should think they do need the house next door,' Joanne said. 'Why must they all stay together?'

'Italians believe families belong together. Besides, the men are all fishermen. It's a family business, and it's more convenient to live beside the boats.'

He carried their cases upstairs and Joanne did her own unpacking, then Nico's. On her way back from his room she passed the open door of Franco's room. The sight of him struggling to keep things in order took her back over the years and she stopped to watch. Her chuckle made him look up and he grinned ruefully.

'Let me do it,' she said, coming inside. 'You always were the most untidy man in the world.'

'Only for some things,' he defended himself. 'I keep the estate books in perfect order.'

'Yes, but get you inside a house and things just seem to rearrange themselves into a mess,' she said, taking clothes out of his case and hanging them up. 'I remember your mother saying that.'

'And I remember her telling me to get my room tidy in half an hour, and you doing it for me. I took you out to a meal as a thank you, didn't I?'

'No, you were going to, but you forgot,' she said lightly. 'Where do you want this shirt?'

'Anywhere will do.'

'That's the attitude that got you into a mess in the first place,' she told him severely. He grinned with a touch of sheepishness, just like the old days. And her heart did somersaults. Just like the old days.

When she'd finished he took her out to show her the village. Peschino was little more than five streets, converging around a bustling market. There were a few tourists' shops and cafés, but it was still mostly a working fishing port.

He'd told her that it was like a huge family, and wherever they went they were pursued by cries of,

'Franco! *Hey, Franco!*' People remembered him and called him from doors and windows, running out to shake his hand and exult.

There was one awkward moment when a man cried, 'And Signora Rosemary. We heard a rumour you were dead. How nice to see you alive and well.'

Appalled, Franco explained, the man made hasty apologies and faded away. They looked awkwardly at each other.

'I'm sorry, Joanne.'

'Will you buy me a cup of coffee?' Joanne asked. 'We should talk.'

They settled at a table outside Luigi's, a small café where the owner greeted him lustily. When their coffee had been served, Joanne said, 'We've got to face this ghost and stop running away from it.'

'I had no right to impose such burdens on you,' he said heavily.

'You let me worry about that,' she replied briskly. 'I knew what I was doing when I took this on, and I'm not going to collapse like a wilting violet every time someone calls me Rosemary. Anyway, nobody will, now. After what just happened, it will be all around the village.'

'True.'

'Nico's got it clear in his head,' Joanne said. 'And I've sorted myself out about it.'

It was a lie. Her ghost was the thought of their honeymoon. But she was determined to banish that one too.

'You're the one who's still troubled,' she said. 'I'm afraid it will be harder on you than anyone.'

After a moment he said, 'At first I looked at you and saw her, and there was a cruel moment when I faced the truth all over again. Not any more. Now I see you. Your voice is different, and you say things she would never have said. And I'm glad to be here with you.'

Because he'd said that, the sun was brighter, the air more clear and pure. But all she said was, 'That's what I meant about being your bridge. Now, come along, we're all going to enjoy ourselves.'

They returned to the house to shower and dress. She put on a bright blue linen dress and brushed out her hair, letting it fall naturally about her shoulders. Franco wore jeans and a white shirt, open at the throat. He'd meant to visit a barber before they'd left, but there hadn't been time, and now his hair curled about his collar and fell over his forehead. It made him young again, less severe, and ten times as attractive.

When it was time for supper they went the few yards along the beach and were engulfed in the family. Franco introduced her to everyone but she soon lost track of husbands, wives, children in a tidal wave of hospitality.

But then she discovered a snag. This side of the lake belonged to the Veneto region, and Joanne, whose ears were just becoming used to Piedmontese, found herself among people who didn't use it. *La madre lingua,* as Italian was known, was useful for watching television and dealing with officials, but at home civilized folk spoke Venetian.

At first she was sure she'd never fit in, but with these cheerful people being a wallflower just wasn't an option. Between two languages, a dialect and a lot of laughter, they all found a way to understand each other.

The problems of living in two houses had been solved very simply. The fences between the front and back gardens had been removed, and it seemed as if no doors were ever closed. Folk wandered in and out as they pleased, and soon Joanne stopped trying to work out who lived where, who was called what, who was married to whom, or who was whose offspring. After all, what did it matter?

She even found herself giving the characteristic Italian shrug with its implications of not worrying about trifles. She was with the man she loved, in a closeness that would once have seemed an impossible dream. All else was a trifle.

Supper was mussel soup followed by fillet steaks with brandy and Marsala, cooked in the first kitchen. This was followed by caramel oranges and *asiago,* a mountain cheese from the region, both prepared in the second kitchen. Joanne found that all her hosts and hostesses wanted a share of her, and she went back and forth between kitchens, slicing garlic in one, and adding kirsch to syrup in the other, struggling to understand and make herself understood, and laughing a lot.

The meal was served outside on two small tables pushed together to make one large one, so that everyone could see everyone else's face, and all shout together. Papa Terrini produced bottles from an apparently inexhaustible supply of Raboso and Soave, clapped Franco on the shoulder, kissed Joanne's hand and yelled, 'Eat! Eat!'

Italy was a country of plenty, and never more so than when entertaining guests. The Terrinis were poor but they ate and drank with gusto, laughed and loved with vigour and took no thought for the morrow. Joanne, who spent too much time worrying about the morrow, found her cares slipping away from her in a riot of colour, wine and pleasure.

Best of all, Franco seemed affected the same way.

From across the table he raised his glass to her. She saluted him back, drained her glass, and immediately found it filled again by Tonio or Plinio or Marco or whoever…

They strolled home in the moonlight, Nico between them, too sleepy to talk. When they'd put him to bed Joanne yawned. 'I'm not used to all this riotous living,' she murmured. 'I can hardly keep my eyes open.'

'It was a very long journey,' Franco said. 'And the wine was very potent.'

'And very plentiful,' she added with a slight chuckle. 'I really drank more of it than I should.'

'You certainly are a trifle flushed,' Franco agreed, considering her face and smiling. 'The sooner you go to bed the better.'

He escorted her to her door, and opened it for her. 'You can sleep late tomorrow, if you wish. Goodnight, Joanne.'

She fully expected to take advantage of his offer, but the air of the lake was stimulating, and she awoke early, feeling fresh and ready to enjoy herself. There'd been a hint of admiration in Franco's eyes when he'd smiled at her last night, and something in his voice as he'd said her name—

She told herself to stop this. She was building on nothing. But she could no more prevent herself examining every look and word for hope than lovers had ever been able to do.

Over breakfast the others were full of plans to take a boat trip one of Gina's brothers had offered them. Joanne hastily declined.

'I'm not good in boats. I get queasy very easily. You two go.'

'But you must come,' Nico protested.

'Not if it's really going to make you feel bad,' Franco said. 'But we can't go off and abandon you.'

'Nonsense, I shall have a wonderful time exploring. There are some ruins near here. Someone told me about them last night—'

'But you can't remember who,' Franco said wickedly.

'No, I can't. But I do remember about the ruins. I shall take my sketch-pad, and have a fine time.'

She resisted all attempts to persuade her. She felt that father and son should have some time together without her, and she really was unhappy in a boat. When Franco saw that she meant what she said he gave her his car keys, bid her enjoy herself, and followed Nico out to the beach.

She did enjoy herself, roaming the picturesque ruins, making sketch after sketch, and finally driving back in the late afternoon.

She stopped in the village to buy some sun cream, and dawdled, looking at the shops. Suddenly the tasteful clothes she'd bought for this trip seemed a waste of money. She wanted something colourful and crazy; the crazier the better. She found a shop selling beach wear and beach equipment, and purchased a gaily coloured, wide skirt and matching scarf. Then, in a moment of madness, she chose a bikini. As bikinis went it was rather modest, but buying it felt like an act of liberation.

She almost danced out of the shop and immediately collided with someone coming in.

'I'm sorry,' said a young male voice. 'I was just about to catch your attention.'

'Leo!'

CHAPTER NINE

'Leo!' Joanne repeated. 'What are you doing here?'

'You don't say that as if you were delighted to see me,' he said sadly. 'Startled, yes. But not delighted. Let me buy you a coffee.'

They went to Luigi's and sat outside. Leo ordered coffee for them both. 'I was about to go and knock on your door,' he said. 'What luck to run into you when Franco isn't there looking daggers at me.'

'What are you doing here, Leo?' she asked wryly. She was becoming suspicious of him.

'What do you think I'm doing?'

'I think you've come to make mischief.'

He grinned sheepishly. 'Well—I'll admit I enjoy doing that. Come on, aren't you a little glad to see a man who adores you?'

His words made her face the fact that she wasn't glad at all. In fact she was rather annoyed with him for threatening to spoil this magic time.

'Of course you are,' he persisted. 'Maybe not very glad, since you're idiotically hung up about Franco. But a little bit.' His manner was teasing but confident, like a small boy who knew he could get away with anything.

'Not even a little bit,' she told him.

'You could be very depressing for a man without a lot of self-confidence,' he complained.

'What would you know about lacking confidence?' she asked with a reluctant smile.

'Let's put it this way. If you said you didn't like me at all, I wouldn't believe you. Because I still remember that smoochy kiss you gave me in the Antoninis' house that night. If Franco hadn't turned up—who knows?'

'I did like you a little,' Joanne said wryly. 'You reminded me strongly of someone, although I couldn't think who. Since then it's come to me.'

'Aha! That's better! Who do I remind you of? Mel Gibson? Warren Beatty?'

'Franco. As he was, years ago.'

For once Leo was really taken aback. He opened and closed his mouth, and let out a long breath.

'Well, I guess he's done it again,' he said at last.

'Done what?'

'Years ago he balked me in the *palio.* Now it's the same story. I just can't win against him.'

'It depends what you're trying to win. You don't really want me. You're just playing games.'

'And you don't want to play games with me?'

'No, I don't.'

'So you won't have dinner with me tonight?'

'No, but I'll invite you home to dinner with Franco and Nico and me.'

He made a face. 'Thank you, but I'll decline that charming invitation. I've just about time to drive home. There's nothing to keep me here, is there?'

'No,' she said firmly. 'There isn't. Goodbye, Leo.'

On the way home she debated whether to tell Franco about Leo's visit, but decided not to. He might read the wrong thing into it.

She found the others already there. It had obviously been a tiring day, for they didn't have much to say about what they'd done. Franco seemed a little distracted, and refused Gina's invitation to come over for dinner.

'Thank you, but not tonight,' he said with a brief smile. 'We'll eat out.'

They found a little *trattoria* and ate pasta and fish soup. Joanne was puzzled. A malaise that she couldn't explain seemed to have fallen over them. They were all glad when the evening was over.

Last night she'd slept like a log. Tonight she was restless, tossing until two in the morning. At last she got up, threw on a robe meaning to go downstairs.

But once in the corridor she heard her own name spoken and stopped. The sound was coming from Nico's room. Through the open door Joanne could see Franco sitting on the bed, listening to Nico who was talking earnestly.

'But why didn't Aunt Joanne just tell us she wanted to see Uncle Leo, Papa? Why pretend she didn't like boats?'

'Perhaps she thought we wouldn't like her seeing Uncle Leo.'

'Does Aunt Joanne like Uncle Leo better than she likes you?'

'Maybe. She likes us differently. We don't own her, you know.'

'But aren't you going to marry Aunt Joanne?'

She'd been about to push open the door, tell them what she'd heard, and set right the misunderstanding. But at this question Joanne stopped, frozen.

The silence seemed to go on for ever before Franco said, 'I don't know.'

'Wouldn't it would be lovely if you did?' Nico said wistfully.

'Yes, it would be lovely,' Franco agreed in what sounded to Joanne like an awkward voice.

'Couldn't you make Uncle Leo go away?'

'Suppose he won't go?'

'He will if you tell him Aunt Joanne likes you best.'

Silence. Then Franco's voice, sounding rather heavy. 'That's enough for tonight, my son.'

Joanne backed away. She'd heard too much and too little. Enough to know that Franco knew of her meeting with Leo and thought she'd arranged it. Enough to know that he minded. But not enough to know why he minded, or how he really felt about her. She wanted to laugh and cry.

Franco tucked his son up, kissed him, and went to the door. He stood there a long time, watching the sleeping child. As he stepped out into the corridor he paused, wondering if he'd really heard a sound. But the corridor was empty, and the house was silent.

At breakfast next morning Joanne took the first chance to say casually, 'By the way, Leo was here yesterday. I bumped into him in town, and we had a coffee.'

'Why did he have to come?' Nico asked in a rebellious voice. 'We don't want him.'

'Nico, that's very rude,' Franco reproved. But he spoke without heat, as if he secretly agreed with his son.

'Well, he's gone again, so we don't have to have him,' Joanne said cheerfully. 'He was only passing through.'

'Are you sure he won't come back?' Nico demanded.

'If he does I'll tell him we don't want him,' Joanne promised.

Nico looked happier, and Joanne was relieved. The worst thing would be to have the child thinking she'd deceived them to meet Leo secretly. Franco gave her a grin, as though he too was free of a load, and she suddenly found that she was having trouble breathing.

It was absurd to be acting like a fluttery teenager after all this time. But the man she loved had smiled at her with meaning, and she wanted to sing for joy.

'Can we go to the beach?' Nico demanded.

'We can do whatever you like,' Franco told him fondly. 'The beach it is.'

In her own room Joanne had a final dither between the one-piece and the bikini. At last she took a deep breath and put on the bikini, slipping the gaily coloured skirt over it.

The other two were waiting for her impatiently downstairs. 'Nico says if you don't hurry the water will have gone away,' Franco assured her. The three of them went out in high spirits.

They were spotted at once by the Terrini family, who joined them boisterously. Nico went off to play with the children, while two of the Terrini sons, both in their mid-teens, settled down to admire Joanne.

Yesterday they'd treated her with distant respect, as befitted the wife of an older man. But they'd obviously discovered that she and Franco weren't married, plus Gina had probably gossiped about the separate rooms. Now they felt free to throw themselves at her feet.

When she tossed aside the skirt for a swim they whistled in admiration, and jostled each other to keep near her in the water. Afterwards, as they all had a snack, the boys rushed to anticipate her every wish, doing antics trying to make her laugh, squabbling with each other for the privilege of sitting beside her. They were like innocent puppies, and she was entertained.

But later the fun got out of hand when they announced their intention of going out in the little dinghy, and taking her with them.

'No way,' she said, trying to pass it off with a laugh. 'I'm nervous in boats.'

'But we will keep you safe,' they protested. 'You come with us.'

For a few minutes they squabbled, the boys demanding, Joanne protesting, until finally they seized her hands and began to pull her down the sand to the water's edge.

'No!' she cried, beginning to be alarmed.

'It's all right. We look after you.'

'*Basta!*' Franco's voice was like the crack of a whip. 'Let her go.'

The boys stared, amazed by his transformation from a cheerful companion to a man with alarming anger in his eyes. To underline his point Franco put his arm about Joanne's waist and pulled her firmly against him, snapping out something curt in Venetian. She couldn't make out the words, but the boys released her and backed off, looking shamefaced.

'Are you all right?' Franco asked, still holding her.

'Y-yes, I'm fine,' she stammered, hoping she didn't sound as breathless as she felt. The bikini didn't feel so modest now that her skin was pressed against his.

'They're only children,' he said. 'They mean no harm, but they don't know when the joke's over.'

'Yes, of course.'

He touched her face lightly. 'Are you sure you're all right? You still look a little upset.'

She wasn't upset, but her heart was thumping from

being held so close to him. How could he hold her like
this, half naked, in front of all the world, and stay so
calm?

Then she saw a little pulse beating at his throat, and
understood that he wasn't calm at all. Suddenly he
tightened his arm and laid his mouth on hers. It was
only for a moment, and he pulled away at once, laughing and slightly self-conscious.

'They won't trouble you again now,' he said softly.
'I've made the matter plain.'

'Is the matter plain to you?' she whispered back.

He drew a ragged breath. 'No, not at all. It grows
more confused every moment.'

He let her go and turned away quickly. Joanne was
left feeling as if her whole body was blushing while
the Terrini clan looked on, exchanging nods and smiles
of understanding.

There was no chance of a private moment with him
after that. The boys' mothers converged on her, full of
apologies for their sons' behaviour. To make them feel
better she went into the house for a coffee and a chat,
where they all laughed at their language difficulties and
had a good time. But she knew they were thinking of
the little scene on the beach, and regarding her curiously.

Without warning, Mama Terrini demanded to know
if she could do Italian cooking. And, when she said no,
insisted on teaching her the secrets of *linguini* with
walnuts. Joanne concentrated, and the other women
pronounced her first attempt excellent.

To her embarrassment, Mama Terrini trumpeted her
achievement as she served the linguini that evening.
Everyone cheered, pronounced it delicious, and toasted
her. It would have been delightful if she hadn't been

growing more self-conscious by the minute. It was so obvious that these good-hearted people had decided she was to be Franco's wife. But what was he thinking? He was swapping cheerful insults with Papa Terrini, and seemed oblivious.

She was relieved to be able to slip out of the spot-light after that, except for the awkward moment when the boys apologised, their eyes nervously on Franco. She told them to forget it, and they hightailed it out of the house.

Nobody would have dreamed, from the lateness of the hour, that this was a family who had to rise early to catch fish. The party went on and on, always picking up with a fresh batch of coffee or wine. Children fell asleep in the arms of their parents, aunts or uncles, or simply whoever happened to be nearest, for in this warm-hearted country everyone was at ease with children, and children belonged to everyone.

Joanne sat cuddling a little girl whose name she hadn't caught, until the child's mother lifted her gently out of Joanne's arms, with a whispered *grazie,* and bore her off to bed.

On her other side, Nico was leaning against her, doz-ing with a smile on his face. 'It's time he was in bed, too,' she said, gathering him up into her arms.

She bid the others goodnight in a whisper, and they responded likewise. Franco watched her with softened eyes as she carried his little son away, the child's head drooping against her shoulder. After a moment he re-alized that Papa Terrini was speaking to him.

'I'm sorry,' he said hastily.

'I only asked if you want some more wine.'

'No—yes—thank you.'

'Is that a yes or a no?' Papa asked patiently.

'Er—no, I think.'

'My friend, you're in a bad way.'

'Yes, I think I am,' Franco murmured. He forced himself to sound bright. 'I mean, thank you, I'll have another glass.'

Joanne set the little boy down on the bed and began pulling off his shirt and jeans. He helped her like someone moving in his sleep, and when she pulled the duvet over him he still hadn't opened his eyes.

But some part of his mind was still with her, for he clung onto her hand. So she sat down on the bed and waited. When his regular breathing told her that he was asleep Joanne gently released her hand. Leaning down, she kissed his forehead too gently to awaken him, and crept out of the room.

Gina was there in the kitchen, having followed her home. Joanne smiled at her and slipped out of the house. She badly needed a walk in the cool fresh air.

On the beach she kicked off her shoes and strolled at the water's edge, letting the peace of the lake wash over her. It was a blessed relief to be where she could hear only the lapping of the water, and the sweet sound of an accordion floating along the shore from Bardolino.

'Is he asleep?'

Startled, Joanne turned and found Franco sitting on an upturned dinghy. She hadn't known he was there.

'Nico? Yes, he didn't really wake up to get undressed.'

'He trusts you. I'm glad.'

He gave her a glance of invitation, and she went to sit beside him on the boat, leaning back a little to look at the stars. In this clear air they seemed almost impossibly brilliant, and she felt giddy at the beauty.

'Careful, don't lean back too far,' he said, supporting her shoulders with his arm.

She didn't move, enjoying the feeling of his nearness. At this moment she wasn't thinking about passion, only the sweetness of being here quietly together.

Further along the beach a young couple strolled hand in hand, totally absorbed in each other. The young man turned and rested his arms on the girl's shoulders, his forehead against hers. Smiling, she put her arms about him, and looked directly into his eyes. His lips moved.

'I wonder what he's saying,' Joanne mused.

'Te voja ben,' Franco said.

'What's that?'

'It's Venetian. It means, I wish you well.'

Joanne smiled. 'No, I think he's saying something a little more significant than that.'

'To a Venetian there is nothing more significant than that. It means, I love you.'

'Oh, I see.' She didn't know what else to say.

Franco gently removed his arm and sat with his hands clasped, staring across the water. He spoke without looking at her.

'And what about Leo, Joanne? Does he wish you well?'

'I told you, Leo was just passing through.'

'That story will do for Nico, not for me. He drove all this way for a purpose. Did you exchange the words of lovers? I have no right to ask, of course. But I'm asking anyway.'

His voice and his attitude gave nothing away, but she could sense his tension, and she wondered if his heart was beating as urgently as her own.

'You don't answer,' Franco said at last. 'Perhaps that *is* my answer. Will you be leaving with him soon?'

'Of course not. As though I'd just abandon Nico like that!'

'And me, Joanne?' he asked quietly.

'No, I wouldn't abandon you, either.'

'Did you tell Leo to go away and come back later?'

'No, I just told him to go away.'

He turned his head to look at her. 'Only that?'

'Only that. There never was anything in it.' She smiled. 'He's still mad at you for making him fall off in the *palio*.'

'I know. He always will be. We're friendly, but he keeps trying to find ways to upset me. And this time he managed it.' He took her hand in his. 'I mind. Maybe I have no right to, but I mind.'

'There's nothing to mind about, Franco. Truly.'

He didn't answer directly, but sat looking down at her hand clasped in his. 'I've found myself remembering things about you, from eight years ago. The way you nursed Ruffo for me. Once I had to be away, and you stayed up with him all night. You saved his life.'

'You saved him, getting him away from those louts.'

'That was only the start. You gave him love. I saw how he greeted you, after all this time. He remembers, you see. Just as I remember.'

He fell silent. Joanne had a strange feeling that Franco was half in and half out of a dream. How much of what he was saying was memory, and how much projection back from now? Whatever the answer, it was very sweet to sit here, holding his hand.

'What do you remember, Franco?'

'About you? Lots of things. The way you were always rushing around, full of eagerness, wanting to do everything at once. You were so young and untouched. All the possibilities of the world seemed to be there in you.

'And then sometimes I'd see such a strange look in your face, as though you had a secret that made you sad. Why was that?'

'I can't remember,' she said. 'Everything seemed so important at that age.'

'And then you grow up, and the same things aren't important?'

'Well—some of them are. Some of them even more important.'

He raised his eyebrows in query, but she backed off. It had gone as close to the truth as she dared, but she would go no further.

'We used to be able to talk, as friends, didn't we?' he asked.

She chuckled. 'Most of our conversations consisted of you making me promise not to tell your mother about something you'd done.'

He grinned. 'That's true.'

'But if you need a friend now, I'm here for you.'

'And is that all you'll be to me, Joanne?'

'I don't know,' she said softly. 'Let's wait and see.'

'How wise you are. At first I was reluctant to bring you to this place, where I was happy with her. I thought it wouldn't be fair to you, and I was afraid of the memories. But now the memories are all kindly ones. Tonight I feel peaceful for the first time in a year, as though the world were once more a good place, where I could find a home. And that's your doing.'

Still holding her hand, he rose and led her back to the house. They bid goodnight to Gina, and while Franco locked up Joanne slipped upstairs to look in on

Nico. He was sleeping soundly, still in the same position she'd left him. Franco came in behind her and they stood watching for a moment, before backing out silently.

At her door he stopped. 'Joanne,' he said softly. 'Joanne...'

His kiss was gentle, one hand cupping her face while he explored her mouth with slow, tentative movements. When he felt her sway against him he let his arms slide right around her, holding her close.

This wasn't like last time, when he'd kissed her with fierce urgency. Now she could feel his uncertainty, as if every step were a minefield. They were both uncertain, wondering what lay just ahead, but wanting to search out the way to each other.

'Am I crazy?' he whispered against her mouth.

'If you are, I'm crazy too.'

'I've wanted to kiss you all day—and yesterday— when I saw you with Leo I could have—'

'Hush, I've told you about that.'

'I warned you, I'm a jealous man. Now tell me I have no right to be jealous. Tell me that what you do is none of my business—if you can.'

It was hard to think of words while his lips were trailing a path of fire along her jaw. His words teased her, but his mouth teased her more. She drew a long, trembling breath.

'You have no *need* to be jealous,' she murmured with difficulty.

'I'm jealous of every man who looks at you. If I'd had my way I'd have knocked those boys' heads together.'

'But they're just children,' she said, reminding him of his own words.

'They looked at you with the eyes of men, and I wanted to carry you off out of their sight. All I care about now is you, and how good it feels to have you in my arms. Say it's the same with you.'

She answered him, not in words, but with her mouth and the movements of her hands. She was where she longed to be, and there was nothing but this man and her love for him. No talk now, no arguments, just the wondrous feel of him close to her, wanting her with all his being. And the glorious certainty that she could give him what he needed.

Quietly she pushed open her door and took his hand to lead him inside. The room was dark, save for the moonlight coming through the tall window. It was open, the long gauze curtains whispering in the soft breeze. Outside the lake lay still, gleaming under the moon like a scene from a beautiful, alien world. In here was all the world she would ever want.

Franco put both his arms right around her, imprisoning her own arms between them, holding her gently while he laid his cheek against her hair.

'Are you sure?' he whispered.

'I'm quite sure. Hush, don't ask questions.'

He cupped her face in his hands, regarding her with searching intensity. He kissed her, not on the mouth but on the forehead, then the eyes, so lightly that he was barely touching her, yet she felt every movement as a delight. At last he laid his lips on hers, enfolding her in his arms and kissing her as though he were laying claim to her. She gave herself up to him without reservation. She was his to claim if only he wanted her.

She was still dressed in the flowing skirt over the bikini. She felt his fingers moving on the straps, drawing them gently down, releasing the clasp behind. Her breasts were full from the strength of her desire, the nipples proud and peaked. She knew the sight and feel of them would tell him of her passion. She drew a trembling breath as he let his hands drift slowly down to cup the fullness.

His gentleness was a revelation. He caressed her as though she were breakable, or perhaps it was the spell being woven between them that he feared to break. He pulled off his shirt and drew her against his bare chest. The feeling was so good that she gasped.

Lost in sensation, she hardly knew when he released the fastening of her skirt and let it fall. He gently removed the rest of her clothes, and his own, and led her towards the bed, drawing her down beside him, then leaning back to look at her. Her body was slim and elegant, the waist tiny, the breasts firm and generous. She was glad of it for his sake, because she wanted to make him a perfect gift.

His own naked body was a delight to her. She'd seen him in shorts, and knew the broad torso and muscular thighs. But the promise in his lean, powerful hips made the blood rush to her face and warmth engulf her. She wanted him to make love to her now, but yet how sweet it was to lie here, letting him prepare her slowly and tenderly for the joy to come.

He seemed awed by her, and caressed her almost reverently. Wherever she felt his touch she came newly aware with sensations she'd dreamed of but never known before, and she gave herself up to them eagerly. He pressed his face between her breasts, loving her tenderly with his lips and tongue. She clasped her hands behind his head, arching against him, seeking deeper pleasure from his skilled hands and mouth. With every flickering movement she felt fire stream along her nerves, until she was one pulsing, throbbing centre of desire.

She'd feared her own inexperience, but the strength of her love dispelled all doubts and made everything come naturally with him. She knew when he was ready to come over her, and she was eager to welcome him. At the moment of their union she sensed, rather than saw, his shock as he discovered that she was a virgin, but then everything was lost in the fusion of sensation and emotion.

She was moving easily and naturally in his rhythm, letting him guide her forward. She moaned softly with pleasure, wanting more yet content to trust in him for what was to come. Looking up into his face, she saw his smile of reassurance, and answered it with one of her own. Her heart was in that smile. If her life was a desert after this, still she'd had her moment of joy.

Her lips moved but no sound came. The pleasure was spiralling upwards, carrying her with it. Her breath came rapidly as she felt herself caught up in a force beyond her control. When the explosion of pleasure came she felt his arms strong about her, holding her safe as they reached the peak and plunged down, far down in a swirling abyss.

But he was there still, keeping her safe as she trembled. She closed her eyes and clung to him, feeling ecstasy turn into contentment. She'd come home at last, and it was a wonderful place, as she had always known it would be.

CHAPTER TEN

WHEN Joanne awoke she lay for a while with her eyes closed. She was sure that when she opened them she would find herself alone. Franco would have left before the light came, pursuing whatever delusion was sustaining him.

But when she looked he was sitting by the window, clad in a towelling robe, gazing out over the lake. One arm rested on his raised knee, and his head was thrown back against the wall. He looked the picture of contentment.

She made no sound or movement, but something seemed to tell him that she was awake and he turned to smile at her. That smile eased her heart. It was without strain, almost happy.

'Good morning,' he said.

'Good morning,' she replied, smiling back at him.

He came towards the bed, holding out his hands. She took one of them in hers as he sat down beside her. Her flesh was still alive with the feelings of last night.

'You should have told me,' he said gently. 'I never dreamed that it was possible. You're so beautiful, so warm. How could I be the first man to discover it?'

'I've done so much travelling around,' she said quickly. 'There's been no time to get to know people.' She kept her voice light. 'Always another picture to copy on the next horizon.'

'Yes, your life has been full of imitations,' he said. 'But last night—was no imitation.'

She looked at him steadily. 'No?'

'There was only you in my arms, and in my heart. Believe it, Joanne. Surely your own heart knew that before I told you?'

'I think so. But perhaps—' she lay a hand over his lips '—perhaps it doesn't matter right now.'

'You're right.' He leaned down to kiss her. 'Some things are too fragile to be talked about. But we must talk—some time.'

'Yes, some time,' she agreed. 'But not yet.'

At breakfast Nico was loud in his pleas to go swimming again. Franco agreed, but added, 'Not here, where we'll be overrun with Terrinis.'

They drove along the shore as far as Bardolino. Here the beach was more geared to tourists, with loungers and ice-cream sellers. But nobody knew them, and they could think only of each other.

Franco and Nico went off to buy ice creams, while Joanne stretched out on the sand. She needed time to think, time to come to terms with the new person she was this morning.

She felt more physically alive than ever before. The colours of the world had a new vividness, the air was like champagne, and she knew what she'd been born for.

She could see now that if Franco had been frozen in time, so had she, frozen to her love of many years ago. From her new perspective it seemed more of a teenage infatuation with its emphasis on being chosen and loved. But now she loved him as a woman and wanted to give more than to receive. There was nothing she wouldn't do for him, no matter what the cost to herself.

The others returned. She accepted an ice cream and joined in the conversation with half her attention.

Inwardly she was considering her lover, the length of his legs, the straightness of his back, the proud carriage of his head and shoulders. From here she passed to his narrow hips, flat stomach and powerful thighs, but these evoked too many memories from the night before, and she began to blush.

She blushed ever harder when he caught her eye, and she knew he'd guessed her thoughts. But his own thoughts were the same. His reflective smile told her that.

'Please, Papa, can we go into the water now?' Nico pleaded.

Franco rose. 'Are you coming with us?' he asked Joanne.

'No, I'll sunbathe a bit longer,' she said, stretching out comfortably. She wanted some more time to herself, and they too needed to be without her sometimes.

She watched fondly as they ran into the water, the child's hand clasped firmly in the man's. They began to romp together, Franco tossing his son into the air, letting him fall into the water with a splash, but always there with his strong hands to hold him again. Each time Nico would beg eagerly, 'More, Papa.'

The sun was brilliant, gleaming off the water and dazzling Joanne, so that she had to squint to see them. The details disappeared and the two figures became shapes moving against the light. Glittering droplets of water cascaded over them.

Then something occurred to her that made her smile fade, to be replaced by a look of intense concentration. She reached for her bag and pulled out her sketch-pad. She began to make strong, dramatic strokes, seeking to capture the essence of those fast-moving figures.

She became oblivious to her surroundings, oblivious

to everything but the excitement mounting in her. She knew what she was doing was good. It was full of life and conviction, and it was infused by her love for the man and the child. She covered page after page, carried away by a creative urge such as she hadn't known since her student days, when she'd still thought of herself as an artist.

At last she looked up to find Franco and Nico running up the beach. Some deep instinct made her hide the sketch-pad. She wasn't ready to talk about what had happened, even with Franco.

'Shall we go and get some food?' Franco asked when they reached her.

'No, I think I'll take a dip myself now,' Joanne said, getting quickly to her feet. 'There's no need to come with me.'

She wanted to be alone to think, so she swam strongly out into the water, then turned to face the shore. Father and son were tossing a large ball to each other. The light was behind her now, and she could see them clearly. She trod water, her eyes fixed on them, while her brain acted like a camera, the shutter going fast. Click! Franco dived for the ball, his bronzed body graceful against the sand. Click! Nico raced along the beach, hopping and skipping with glee. Click! They were running side by side, the man pulling back to let the boy win the race. Click! Click! Click! Picture after picture imprinted itself on her brain, while she went dizzy with the thrilling thing that was happening.

They had lunch at a little *trattoria*. She ate and drank whatever was put before her, and took only a mechanical part in the conversation. Her mind was filled with bright pictures. Her two menfolk regarded her in consternation. They were used to having her whole attention.

'Is anything wrong?' Franco asked.

'No, everything's wonderfully right,' she told him. 'I've been doing some drawing, and I'm pleased with the way it came out.'

But she wouldn't tell them any more. It was too soon, and she wasn't yet sure.

But Nico's interest had been caught, and before they returned to the beach he dived into a newsagent and begged Franco to buy him a sketch-book. 'Like *Zia's*.'

'I'll get it,' Joanne said, delighted.

They spent the afternoon sketching together. As she'd thought, Nico's drawing showed signs of real skill.

'What's that?' he asked, watching her bring a face to life.

'That's my grandfather, and your great grandfather,' she told him. 'He was a talented artist, and we both get it from him.'

'You look like him,' Nico said, studying the picture.

'Yes, I inherited his looks too. So did your mother.'

'Did you and Mama live together when you were little girls?' Nico asked.

'Not until I was six.' She related the story of her mother's death and how Rosemary had virtually adopted her, and he listened eagerly.

From there she passed onto other memories of their childhood. Nico listened with shining eyes to the tale of the gang that had bullied her at school until Rosemary had come to the rescue, and their kitten who'd gone missing, so that they'd had to hunt for him all night.

'We found him on a patch of waste ground, in a big

pipe,' she remembered. 'We called him, but he was too scared to move, so she had to crawl in and get him. It was a terrible squeeze.'

'But Mama said that was you,' Nico objected. 'She told me about the kitten, and she said she was too big to squeeze through the pipe, so you had to do it.'

'No, it was her,' Joanne protested. 'I'm sure it was—wasn't it?' She covered her eyes, trying to picture the scene. 'I remember her crawling in—maybe she did have to come out again—I don't know, I thought it was her.'

'Does it really matter?' Franco asked gently. 'You were both prepared to do it to save the little cat.'

'No, it doesn't matter at all,' she agreed. 'I do remember that Aunt Elsie was mad at both of us for being out so late. Rosemary insisted that it was her fault, because she was the elder. She was always protecting me.'

'Me too,' Nico said. 'I broke a window once, and she told Papa it was her, because I shouldn't have thrown the ball so near the house.' He took a quick glance at his father. 'Sorry, Papa.'

'I guessed,' he said with a grin. 'I used to get mad at her. I'd say, "How can I teach him to do right if you always shield him?" And she'd say, "If he knows he's loved, he'll know how to do right."'

He held out his arm and Nico scrambled into the curve, to be held tight against his father's body. Joanne watched them contentedly. Something had happened this afternoon, something for which there were no words, but which made everything better.

They drove home slowly, arriving in the dusk. This time Franco declined the Terrinis' hospitality, choosing to cook part of the supper himself, and giving Joanne a chance to show off what she'd learned.

She lay awake for a long time that night, waiting for Franco to come to her, but he didn't, and her heart sank. Of course, with Nico there, they had to be circumspect, but she couldn't help feeling that he would have managed somehow, if he'd really wanted to. She fell asleep feeling despondent.

She awoke very early. Dawn was creeping across the lake, creating silhouettes, dark at first then tipped with silver. She watched, motionless, thrilled by the play of light and shade, until she couldn't bear to sit still any longer. Pulling on some clothes, she took her sketchpad and slipped away.

On the beach she plunged into an orgy of sketching, while her mind's eye saw the pictures that would result. The fishermen were emerging from their houses, preparing to start up the boats. A few strokes caught the sweep of their powerful movements. She could fill in the details later, now that she'd caught the essence. When she was satisfied she crept back into the house, returned to bed and fell instantly into a contented sleep.

She awoke to the feel of Franco's lips on hers, and his arms around her.

'Good morning,' he whispered against her mouth.

The room was full of warm light, as though the day was far advanced.

'Franco—'

'Hush, not now.' He pulled back the sheet, which was all that covered her, and drew her naked body next to his.

'But Nico—' she said urgently.

'Nico has gone fishing. He'll be away all day. I had to have a day alone with you. Did I do right?'

'Mmm, yes. You did exactly right.'

It was hard to speak for he was caressing her already, exciting her with subtle movements. She understood the message of those movements now, knew the pleasure that was to come, and responded with eager anticipation. He understood and laughed at her gently.

'Not so fast,' he teased. 'We have all the time in the world.'

'We can't be sure,' she said urgently. 'Maybe there's only now.'

'You're right. We must treat every moment as the last. Come to me, my love.'

My love. Her heart treasured the words. She was his love, as he was hers. She gave herself up to him with joy, offering all the love in her heart, for now and for ever. And it was given back to her a thousandfold. Now the union of their flesh felt like the union of their hearts.

When passion was slaked and they lay contentedly in each other's arms he asked, just a shade too casually, 'Did you miss me last night?'

'Not a bit,' she said with dignity.

'Little liar! At least, I hope you are. I wanted to come to you, but Nico was restless and I had to be with him. This morning I almost begged the Terrinis to take him out, so that we could have the day alone together.'

'I'm so glad you did,' she murmured, snuggling against him, and immediately dozing off.

She awoke first, and slipped gently out from under his arm. Franco was sprawled across the bed, his big, relaxed body speaking eloquently of the satiety of love. She knew a passionate urge to capture that on paper, and began sketching madly.

Again she felt the thrill of being mistress of her own creation. It was different from the excitement that had so recently possessed her, but just as satisfying in a different way. She became so absorbed that she didn't notice Franco had woken and was looking at her with interest.

'Can I see?' he asked.

'You moved!' she cried in anguish.

'I'm sorry.' He lay down again.

'No, further to your left,' she said, frowning. 'Bit more—bit more. That's it!'

After a while he said, 'Am I allowed to speak?'

'As long as you don't move.'

'I saw you slip out onto the beach this morning. I kept thinking you'd look up and notice me, but you never did.'

'Uh-uh!' She was making rapid movement.

'Did you hear what I said?' he asked. There was a slight edge on his voice and she looked at him quickly.

'I'm sorry,' he said at once. 'I didn't mean to snap. It's just that—' he wore a self-mocking grin '—I'm not used to being with a woman who ignores me.'

'But I'm not ignoring you,' she protested. 'I've been drawing you for ages. I mean—'

'Quite. You've been drawing me, but as a man I haven't existed. Light and shade, yes. But as a man, no.'

'Oh, dear,' she said, mortified. 'I hadn't realized. I got so excited with this—'

'Never mind. It's probably good for my vanity,' he said with a touch of ruefulness. 'Now may I see?'

She put the sketch-pad into his outstretched hand and he studied the pictures.

'Who are you being this time?' he asked after a while. 'Leonardo, Michelangelo—?'

'This time I'm being me,' Joanne said.

He made an alert movement, and she knew that he'd immediately understood the true meaning of her words. He began to go through the pictures again, seeing them with new eyes, nodding as what had happened became plain to him. When he looked up at her his eyes mirrored her own sense of triumph.

'E miracolo,' he said.

He'd said it exactly. A miracle. Something that happened without apparent reason, at a moment of its own choosing. Beyond logical understanding. The dream she'd longed for all these years had finally come true. And the best thing of all was sharing it with him, knowing that he felt its full significance to her, because of the understanding that was growing between them.

'But why now, at this moment?' he asked.

She could have told him that it was because their love had completed her as a woman, and therefore as an artist. That it was this completeness that enabled her to sing in her own authentic voice, instead of echoing the voices of others. But she kept silent for the moment. There were secrets that must wait for another time, and secrets that could not be told at all. She wasn't yet sure which one this was.

He cooked the lunch himself, serving her with a flourish. Afterwards they went back to bed and lay in each other's arms, not making love but talking in slow, contented voices. 'You have recalled me to life,' he said. 'I was in a dead place, and glad to be so, because the one I loved was there. But now, another one I love has shown the path back, and the world is beautiful again.'

'Another that you love?' she whispered longingly.

'Will you believe me when I say that I love you? *You,* not a shadow. There are no explanations, just the feeling. And what I feel is that I love you more than my own life.'

'I want so much to believe you.'

'When you went away—when I drove you away—I cursed myself for my own stupidity. You'd filled the house with grace, and brought a peace to my heart I'd thought never to know again.'

'But that was because I reminded you of her.'

'I thought so at first. But as time went by I found my memories were all of you, things you'd said and done that weren't like her at all. I couldn't stop thinking of you, wondering if you hated me, whether I'd thrown away any hope for us.

'It all came back from years ago. You were just a kid. But you were delightful, and I was very fond of you.'

'You never noticed me.'

'I never tried to seduce you,' he corrected. 'That's different. You were too special to be one of my light-o'-loves. And you don't need to tell me that I had too many—'

'*Far* too many.' They laughed together.

'Yes, but I was already growing up, seeking a woman I could truly love. If I hadn't met Rosemary, I think it would have been you, one day. But not then. You were too young, and we weren't ready for each other as we are now.

'But I did meet her and loved her, and thought of nobody else while she lived. Not even you.'

'I'm glad. I wouldn't have wanted to take anything away from Rosemary.'

'You didn't. But now—' A shadow crossed his face. 'What is it, Franco?'

The shadow flickered and was gone. 'They say that a man who loves more than once somehow chooses the same woman every time. I love you for the things you share with Rosemary—not your face, which grows less like hers the more I know you; but your sweetness and compassion, the way your arms open to welcome life, the way you love without thinking of yourself.

'But I love also the things that are different in you, even your ''other world'', the place you go to when you take up a pencil and forget I exist.'

'And you don't mind? I don't believe that.'

'I mind,' he admitted with a grin. 'I don't say I like it, but I can love it, because it's you. But that's recent. While you were away, and I was coming to my senses, I began to realize what a fatal mistake I'd made. And yet I couldn't come to you because my thoughts were still confused and I didn't know what to say.

'It was true that Nico wanted you for his birthday, but—' his grin mocked himself '—if it hadn't been that, I'd have found something else. I had to get you back, and start again. I was a little too sure of myself as I drove to Turin. And I found you in Leo's arms.'

'I've told you about that—'

'I know, but at the time it gave me a nasty shock. And he kept turning up.'

'He won't turn up again. I don't think he really cares about me anyway.'

'To hell with what he cares about! Tell me again that *he* means nothing to *you*.'

She slipped her arms contentedly about his neck. 'How would you like me to tell you?'

'In whichever way you think will be most convincing.'

'You could always listen while I telephone him,' she teased.

'I was thinking of something much more convincing than that. Come here and let me show you...'

She responded passionately, rejoicing to be in his arms, forgetting all else. Now that her dream had come true she wanted to savour it every moment, and rediscover her joy with every sweet caress. He loved her gently, patiently at first, then with vigour and purpose, and finally with a tenderness that almost made her want to weep. The world held nothing better than this.

It was only much later that she listened to the haunting, uneasy echo in her head. It came from the shadow that had crossed his face, and it warned her that in the midst of their happiness there was something ominously wrong.

A few days later they packed everything into the car and headed for home. By the time they were on the last stretch the sun was setting, casting a coral glow over the land. Nico and his two canine friends were sound asleep in the back. Joanne turned slightly in her seat, drinking in the sight of her lover. She was filled with wonder at the marvellous thing that had happened to her.

He loved her. It was unbelievable, but he loved her. Not a pale echo of another love, but her, Joanne. He had said so, and he was a man of his word.

Without taking his eyes off the road, Franco reached over and took her hand, to draw it to his lips.

'Will you marry me soon?' he asked.

'As soon as you like, my darling. I must finish my work for the Antoninis, but that won't take long.'

'I long to have you as my wife.'

'I'm almost frightened,' she said. 'Nobody is allowed to be this happy. Something will spoil it.'

'I don't believe it,' he said firmly. 'We will make a world together that nothing can destroy.'

She remembered that he knew all about seeing his joy snatched away in a moment, and decided to say no more. But her uneasiness persisted.

The last mile. The light was fast fading, but she could recognize the way home. *Her* home now, a place that was warm and welcoming to her. Franco was right. It was foolish to give way to groundless fears.

The car slowed to a crawl and glided between the gate posts. There up ahead was the house, ablaze with golden light. As they drew up they could clearly hear the sound of two female voices, raised in dispute. One of them belonged to Celia. The other, Joanne recognized instantly.

She tried to ignore the cold hand that seized the pit of her stomach. Her fears had come rushing back and she knew that something terrible was about to happen.

She understood why when they entered the house, and Franco's mother rose to greet them.

CHAPTER ELEVEN

'GOOD evening, my son,' Sophia said, smiling coldly.

She was older, thinner, harder. Her face was a little more lined and a lot more sour. When Franco went to her, her arms closed around him possessively.

He greeted his mother affectionately, and Sophia seemed to return the affection, but her eyes on Joanne were cold as stones. She enveloped her in a formal embrace.

'It's delightful to see you again, after so long,' she said. 'And dear little Nico. Put that dirty dog down and give your grandmama a big hug.'

She pulled the reluctant child against her. Nico returned her hug obediently, but without enthusiasm, and afterwards he slipped away quickly, scooping up the pups as he went.

'I'll do Nico's unpacking,' Joanne told Franco.

'There's no need.' Sophia restrained her with a chilly hand on her arm. 'It isn't the job of a *guest* to unpack for my grandchild.'

'Joanne is being kind,' Franco said. 'She knows that you and I wish to be alone together. How are you, Mama?'

He opened his arms to her again, but Sophia evaded his embrace. 'One moment.' She waylaid Nico before he could mount the stairs, and removed the pups from him. 'We don't allow dogs upstairs. In fact dogs belong outside.'

She took Pepe and Zaza to the door and shoved them out.

'Papa lets me keep them indoors,' Nico said indignantly.

'Not now, Nico,' Franco said. 'Go upstairs.'

Nico stuck out his lower lip rebelliously, but Joanne calmed him with a touch on his shoulder. His answering smile wasn't lost on Sophia whose eyes became, if possible, harder than ever.

'I don't like her,' Nico muttered as they unpacked.

'Shh, Nico, you shouldn't say things like that.'

'But she didn't like Mama. She doesn't like anybody.'

Joanne soon learned that Sophia had arrived two hours earlier and contrived to upset the entire estate. The meal Celia had lovingly cooked for their return had been pronounced unsuitable and a new menu drawn up.

'She stands over me in the kitchen as though I'd never cooked before in my life,' Celia seethed. 'Everything has to be done her way. But her way is not my way, and it's my kitchen.'

'Why did she come here now?' Joanne asked.

'She telephone yesterday, and when she find that Signor Franco is at the lake with you, she say, "I see", in a special way that mean she is angry.'

'I remember the way she used to say that,' Joanne said with foreboding. 'It used to send shivers down everyone's spine.'

'*Sì*. Shivers,' Celia agreed, but then became more cheerful. 'But, after all, if you and Signor Franco— well, what can she do?'

'I wish I knew,' Joanne murmured. Her uneasiness was increasing by the moment.

Supper was a tense meal. Celia had done her best to change everything to Sophia's orders, but it had been a last-minute rush. Sophia praised every dish in a tinkling, silver voice, but always with a suggestion for improvement that turned praise to blame.

Franco tried hard to give his mother's thoughts a more cheerful direction, asking about her husband and her two stepchildren.

'They are all well, my son. None of them gives me a moment's anxiety. It seemed the right moment to pay a visit to my true family.'

'That's good of you, Mama, but you've no need to be anxious about Nico or me.'

'That, perhaps, is a matter of opinion. But we can discuss the matter later. *Signorina,* did you enjoy yourself at Lake Garda?'

'Mama,' Franco protested, 'you can't suddenly start calling Joanne "*signorina*". You've known her for years, and she's part of the family.'

'Oh, yes, of course. Forgive me, *signorina,* but it's been so long since we met that I'd forgotten that you are, in some slight way, connected with us. In fact, you've been away for so long that I wonder why you returned now.'

'My career has often taken me to the other side of the world,' Joanne said, determinedly polite.

'Ah, yes, your career. I remember how determined you were to be a great artist. These days a woman must decide which is more important to her: her career, or a family.'

'She doesn't always have to make a choice,' Joanne said, speaking politely and refusing to let herself be needled.

'Really? I would have thought that there was always

some sort of choice to be made. Nobody gets everything in this world, do they?'

'No, *signora,* they don't,' Joanne said with a small flash of temper. The words might have meant nothing, but the goaded look she gave Sophia contained a challenge, and the flash in the older woman's eyes showed that she understood.

It had been a long day, and Nico's eyes were beginning to close. As soon as supper was over Joanne said, 'Come on, darling. Off to bed.'

'I won't put a guest to so much trouble,' Sophia said, rising instantly.

'Let Joanne do it, Mama,' Franco said. 'She's been looking after Nico while we were away.'

'But now his Grandmama is here,' Sophia said with a smile that was like the drawing of battle lines. Her claw-like hand fixed itself on Nico's shoulder.

'Let Joanne take him,' Franco said firmly. 'We so rarely see each other, Mama, that I don't want to lose a moment with you.' He took her hand in his, a gesture of affection that nonetheless prevented her from interfering with the others.

When she'd put Nico to bed Joanne returned downstairs long enough to say, 'I think I'll retire now. You'll wish to be alone. Goodnight.'

She left before Franco had the chance to kiss her, knowing it would only make Sophia worse if he did, and triumphant if he didn't. But she gave him a smile to show that she understood his predicament, and knew that Sophia had seen that, too.

Through a restless night she tried to believe she was worrying about nothing. Sophia could throw all the tantrums she pleased. Franco had dealt with them before, and knew how to ride out the storm.

But this time there was something different, and she was beginning to be afraid that she knew what it was.

In the early morning she slipped out and made her way on foot through the garden and down the path under the trees. She plucked some wild flowers along the way, until she had a pretty bunch in her hand.

Rosemary's grave looked peaceful in the early morning light. Joanne dropped on one knee to brush some of the long grass away, and laid the flowers down. She spoke to Rosemary, not aloud, but silently, in her heart.

I love him, darling. He loves me, and I know I can make him happy. It's only that—you don't mind, do you?

She heard a step behind her and turned to see Sophia watching her coolly.

'I followed you here,' the older woman said, 'to find out how much of a fool you really are. I wanted to see you offer flowers to the woman who took him from you—oh, yes, I knew you loved him.'

'She didn't take him from me,' Joanne said. 'He was always hers, from the moment they met.'

'And he is hers still,' Sophia said bitterly. 'He'll be hers for ever. There was never anything so strong as her grip on his heart. She even turned him against his mother.'

'Rosemary wouldn't have done that.'

'No? I tell you he drove me out of his house to please her. His own mother!'

Sophia came nearer. Her eyes were glittering. 'Don't ever delude yourself that he loves you. To him you're an imitation, nothing more. His heart is still in there.' She flung out an arm to the grave. 'She bewitched him, and he will never be free.'

'I don't believe you,' Joanne said breathlessly. 'I

knew Rosemary. She was a wonderful, generous woman who gave all of herself.'

'She was a woman who took everything, because she could never be satisfied. And she wants everything still. You can't fight her. *She will never give him up.*'

Tight-lipped, Joanne turned to leave.

'That's right, run away from the truth,' Sophia jeered.

'I'm not running away, but I won't stay and argue with you, Sophia. Franco loves me, and I love him. And I'm not going to become the victim of your hate.'

She walked away without a backward glance. Her head was held up at a proud angle, and she didn't look back. But she was trembling.

'I don't believe it,' she said to Franco later that day. 'Your mother says Rosemary made you throw her out, but that can't be true.'

'Of course it isn't true,' Franco said wryly. 'Mama was the only person I knew who didn't like Rosemary. I think she was jealous because I loved her so much. And then—two women in the same kitchen—it was the old story.

'Rosemary did her best, but Mama made a fight of it, always trying to bully her, saying things to needle her. Once she made a great fuss over something that wasn't really important. I tried to calm her down but she demanded that I take her side. I couldn't do that. Rosemary was my wife, and besides, she was in the right.

'When I wouldn't speak the words Mama wanted to put into my mouth, she declared that since there was no place for her in her son's home—which wasn't true—she would "seek refuge" with her sister in Naples.'

'I can just hear her playing it for all the drama it was worth,' Joanne said wryly.

'I replied that a visit to Naples might be a good idea. I thought she'd stay away a few weeks to clear the air, then return and we could start again.

'But she never returned. In Naples she met Tonio and married him. Now she runs him, his house, his children and his servants, for he's a wealthy man. Tonio dotes on her and gives her everything she wants. But whenever she wants a stick to beat me with I become the heartless son who threw her out of her home.'

'I thought it might be something like that.'

'But—I wish I knew how women's minds work. Why does she tell you how much I loved Rosemary, when she tried to make Rosemary believe that I didn't?'

'Because she's using her to push us apart. She'll say anything she thinks might work, whether she believes it or not.'

Franco slipped an arm about her waist. 'Don't worry, she won't stay long. But while she's here it's best to let her do as she pleases. Then you and I will be free to start our life together.'

'Have you said anything to Nico yet?'

'No, I want to wait until this is over. Mind you, I think he's guessed, and he's thrilled.'

'I'll try to make him happy, Franco.'

'Hey, what about making me happy?' he asked with a smile. 'I'm not doing this for Nico. I'm doing it for me.'

'Sure?'

'If you doubt me I'll have to spend my life making the matter plain to you. Come here, my love.'

He drew her into his arms, and in the tenderness of his kisses she managed to put her fears aside.

The storm didn't break until next day. Joanne went riding with Nico and stayed out with him as long as possible, unwilling to face the atmosphere that Sophia seemed to carry with her. When they returned he raced off to play with his friends. As she went indoors she could hear the old woman's angry voice carrying.

'What you're proposing to do is a scandal. Everyone is shocked.'

'I don't think so.' Franco was speaking in the easy-going way that he habitually used to cool her down. 'Everyone on the estate is pleased at what's happening.'

'They're pleased that you're making a fool of yourself over a girl who happens to look like your wife?'

'It's not her face,' Franco said at once. 'Joanne is only herself, and it's Joanne that I love. Don't try to convince her otherwise. She knows me too well.'

'And why does she look so like Rosemary?' Sophia snapped. 'Because she's her cousin. Have you thought what you're doing, marrying another from that family? Suppose she too has a weak heart? These things can be hereditary.'

'That's true,' Joanne said, stepping into the room. 'Rosemary inherited her weakness from her mother. But she and I were related through our fathers, who were brothers. I'm not connected to her mother at all. And I'm perfectly strong.'

'Strong enough to step into a dead woman's shoes, where you have no right,' Sophia sneered.

'That's for Franco to say.'

'You're very confident. You might not be so sure of yourself if you could have seen him when she died. He was dead himself, inside. He told me everything was ended for him. He swore he would never love again, that he had no *right* to love again. He still has no right. And he knows why.' She turned on Franco. 'How can you forget your wife so soon, *when it was you who killed her?*'

Franco's face had a ghastly pallor. 'I didn't kill her,' he cried out.

'As good as. It was you who wanted more children, you she was trying to please.'

'As God is my witness,' he said harshly, 'if I'd known she was weak I'd never have asked for another child. She was everything to me. Would I have risked her life if I'd known?'

'And why didn't you know? Why did she hide the truth? Because she knew you didn't want to hear it.'

She waited for his answer, but he only looked at her with eyes that had seen hell. Joanne bit back a cry. She longed to help him, but even her love couldn't conquer his demons for him. Only he could do that.

'She gave her life to please you,' Sophia said with a kind of triumph. 'How can you make her sacrifice count for nothing? If you were dead, would she love again, in a year? Ten years? Ever? You know that she wouldn't.'

'For God's sake!' Franco whispered. 'What are you trying to do?'

'Trying to make you see the truth of what you're doing, before it's too late.'

'No,' Franco said in a firmer voice. 'You want to make trouble between us, just as you tried to make trouble during my marriage. Understand me, Mama, I won't allow it. I don't know why you feel you must tear things down, but I won't let you do it.'

Sophia regarded him with pity. 'Do you think you can silence the truth like that?'

Franco's voice was steady. 'I want you to leave, Mama.'

Sophia met his eyes, and gave a very thin smile.

'Very well, my son. I will leave at once.'

Joanne was surprised by this easy capitulation, but only for a moment. She'd seen the hint of triumph in the older woman's manner, and it told her the worst.

Sophia was leaving because she had no further need to stay.

When Franco returned from seeing his mother off at the airport he went in search of Joanne, and found her in her room. What he saw there made him stop on the threshold.

'What the devil are you doing?' he demanded, staring at the open suitcases that were filling up.

'I'm getting ready to leave.'

'Yes, of course,' he said after a moment. 'You must return to the Antoninis and finish your work for them before we can be married.'

'No, I'm leaving for good.' She looked up at him with a ravaged face. 'We can't be married, Franco. Not now, or for a long time. Maybe not ever.'

'That's nonsense!' he said violently. 'Of course we're going to be married. I thought you had more sense than to believe what my mother said.'

'It's you that believes it. She's done what she meant to. You feel guilty, just as she wants.'

It was just a fraction too long before he spoke, and then his voice was forced.

'That's absurd. You heard me tell her that she was wasting her time trying to make trouble between us.'

'Yes, I heard you tell her. And you're right. She can't really make trouble between us, because I'll always love you, and I think you'll always love me. But we can't marry, because whatever you say, whatever you try to believe, your mind is troubled because of Rosemary.

'I've seen it, in odd moments when you thought I wasn't noticing. We've been happy, and you've suddenly remembered that *her* happiness is over for ever. Then you've told yourself it was your fault, and you've wondered what right you have to be happy.'

The look he gave her was one of desperation. 'Why do you talk like this?' he demanded. 'Why don't you help me fight it?'

'Because I'm not sure it can be fought. You're not to blame for Rosemary's death, but the rest is true. You did share a remarkable love. You felt like two halves of one person, which means that if she's dead you should be dead too. But you're not dead. You've returned to life and you're ready to move on, except that part of you doesn't believe you have any right to. Sophia exploited that. But the real problem is in there.' She tapped him gently on the breast.

He turned away and leaned his arm against the window, resting his forehead on it. Joanne was torn apart, longing to help him. It would be so easy to give in and marry him quickly. But they would never have a peaceful moment.

'It's just a mood,' he said at last. 'It was bound to cross my mind, but it'll pass. Do you doubt that I love you?'

'No, I know you love me. In a way, that may be just the problem—'

'Yes,' he said, picking up her thought instantly in the way she found so lovable. 'If I loved you less, I'd have less cause for guilt. It's because my love for you is so total, so overwhelming, that it feels like a betrayal.' A shudder possessed him. 'It's true that I killed her,' he said in agony.

'No, it isn't true.'

'She died trying to please me. I didn't know that her health was so bad, but I should have known. Many times I asked her, "When will we have another child, beloved?"'

'And she kept her secret. That was her decision.'

'Because she thought only of me, of my wishes. Perhaps if I hadn't pressed her she could have told me it was impossible. Why did she feel she couldn't tell me? How did I fail her? I loved her so much, and yet I failed her. And because of that failure she's dead.

'You're right. I've asked myself many times how I can put her sacrifice behind me, and find a new life. I've lain with you beside me, listening to your breathing, and I've kissed you in your sleep, longing to be shown the way, because to part from you would break my heart.' He seemed to shake himself out of an unhappy dream. 'But that will pass,' he added quickly.

'I don't think so. I think you loved her too much for it to pass. But, my darling, there's something else. It isn't just you that feels guilty, but me too. I'll tell you something that I've kept a secret until now. I fell in love with you years ago, but you loved Rosemary, and married her. When she died I still loved you, but I couldn't come here then. Don't you see why?'

'I think so...' he said slowly.

'I would have felt wrong to come rushing out here trying to take what was hers. That's how I thought of you—hers. In a way, I still do. All these years I've envied Rosemary because she had you, and then when I could have—well, I just couldn't. And even now—' she sighed '—it feels like stealing. I know it's crazy—'

'Then we're both crazy,' he said heavily.

'Maybe when someone's been given such a precious gift, it's something that can only come once, and they mustn't ask for more—' Joanne broke off because her voice had become thick with tears. What she was doing was tearing her apart, but something stronger than herself told her it must be done.

'And what about Nico?' he demanded suddenly. 'How will we explain to him that he's losing you? I told you I wasn't marrying you for his sake, and it was true. But now I'll say to you, marry me for Nico's sake. Forget all we've said here today and think only of him.'

'It's no use, my darling,' she said helplessly. 'The problem would still be there, and we'd end up tearing ourselves and each other apart. Nico would see that, and he'd suffer more than if I went now.'

She couldn't bear the hurt in his face. She opened her arms to enfold him, and he came to her blindly. They stood for a long moment holding each other, silent, motionless.

'I can't let you go,' he said at last. 'Don't ask me to do that.'

'It might not be for ever. One day—'

'You don't get a miracle back once you've thrown it away. If we part now, it will be for ever. I feel it.'

'But there's no way out. What we're really asking is for Rosemary to give us her blessing. And even she can't manage that.' Suddenly she was shaken by the misery of what she had to do. 'Hold me, my love. Hold me and love me…just once more.'

They loved gently, with tenderness greater than passion, storing memories for the long years apart. When they became one she told herself that she would always be one with him, always belong to him, body and heart and soul, although she might never see him again.

'My love,' he whispered. 'Always…always…'

And her heart answered, *Always.*

She was glad now that they hadn't told Nico of their marriage plans, so there was no need to tell him that the plans were shattered. He took her departure calmly, evidently assuming that she would be back soon, as had happened before. Some time Franco would have to tell him that she would never return, but by that time perhaps his bond to her would have loosened a little.

When they said goodbye Nico gave her a picture he had drawn, showing a man, a woman and a little boy.

'It's us,' he explained. 'So you don't forget us.'

'I'll never forget you, darling,' she told him, trying not to break down.

Franco drove her to the station and waited while she boarded the train. She felt as if she were dying, and his eyes told her that it was the same with him.

When the train was ready to depart it swept over her with awful finality, what she was doing, that it was for ever.

'Franco—' She reached out to him wildly.

'For God's sake, go!' he said in a shaking voice. 'Leave me alone with my dead.'

CHAPTER TWELVE

'JUST another week,' Maria pleaded. 'Please, we want you to stay.'

'But I've finished all your pictures,' Joanne said. 'And you've paid me. I've no excuse for staying.'

'Except that we want you. I give a party next week and show the pictures off, and you must be there to explain them,' Maria said, triumphant at having finally thought of an excuse.

'All right, I'll stay until then.'

'*Bene*. And by then, who knows? He may have called.'

'He isn't going to call, Maria. It's over. And it was as much my decision as his. More perhaps.'

'If you gave up such a man as that, you are *stupida*.' Maria declared, leaving the room indignantly.

'Yes,' Joanne murmured. 'I am *stupida*. But I can't help it. It would never have worked. Not without Rosemary's blessing. And she can't give us that now.'

She'd returned to Turin three weeks ago, and many times since then she'd pictured herself going back to Franco, marrying him, forgetting all for love. And they would be happy for a while. But then the shadow hanging over them would grow bigger until it destroyed them. Rosemary had given her husband everything, and then sacrificed her life. And he couldn't accept such a sacrifice with a shrug. He was a man of honour, with an overgrown conscience. The more he loved Joanne, the more guilty he would feel.

Maybe one day he would feel that his debts were paid and he was entitled to be happy. But that day would be a long time coming.

Now that the Antoninis' pictures were all done she had only her own painting to pass the time. Once this had been a dispiriting process, underlining her limitations. But the inspiration she'd discovered at the lake had stayed with her. It was as if her love for Franco had completed her, not only as a woman, but as an artist.

It made no difference that they'd lost each other. The love they'd shared had been deep and passionate, giving each of them an extra dimension, and nothing would ever be the same for either of them. If she never saw him again, never heard his voice or saw his eyes soften as they rested on her, still he'd left his legacy in her life. And because of it, she would endure and be stronger.

But then she wondered about what she had left him. Was there any way their love could be a strength to him through the years apart, or had she merely abandoned him to more bitterness? When she thought of that it took all her strength not to call him.

She completed the pictures of him and Nico. Then, half fearing, she began work on the fishing village, and found that the charm was still powerful even when Franco wasn't the subject. The pictures took shape under her skilful fingers: confident, imaginative, but above all her own.

She was a true artist at last. And Franco's love had done this for her.

An art expert came to the villa to inspect her reproductions. He turned out to be her old tutor from the academy in Turin. He pronounced the copies excellent, and then, at Maria's insistence, examined Joanne's own paintings. After a long silence he looked up at her with a curious smile.

'So! You found the missing "something" at last?'

'Yes, I found it,' she agreed.

'And now it will never leave you.'

He told her to contact him when she had more work to show, promising to speak to a friend in Rome who owned a gallery. Joanne tucked his card away in a safe place. A new part of her life was just beginning. But most valuable of all were the words, 'now it will never leave you.' As long as she lived, she would have something of Franco's, although he himself might never know.

As she'd promised, she stayed for Maria's party, and every time the telephone rang she flinched. Then told herself to be sensible, when it wasn't him.

Leo rang her, and she finally managed to convince him that he was wasting his time. Two days later she watched the Asti *palio* on television, and saw him speed to his long-delayed victory.

At the party she did her hosts proud. She was approached for another commission in the area, but she declined. She could never come back here again.

She finished her packing late next afternoon and took a last look around her room. Vito and Maria were driving her to the airport to catch the evening plane to England, and she must go down to them at any moment.

Somewhere in the house she heard the shrill of the phone, but by now she'd trained herself not to react. Vito looked in to help her with her baggage, and they went down the stairs and out to the car.

'Where is Maria?' he demanded with husbandly exasperation. 'Isn't she coming with us?'

'I think she's on the phone—no, there she is.'

Maria came flying out of the front door, her face wreathed in smiles. 'It's him,' she shrieked triumphantly to Joanne.

'Maria—who?'

'Signor Farelli. He must talk to you, very urgent. Hurry.'

Joanne ran back into the house and snatched up the phone. When she'd said 'Hallo,' she held her breath. She would surely know from Franco's tone whether this was good news or bad.

But he sounded strange and unlike himself. 'I'm sorry to trouble you,' he said stiffly, 'but I must ask you to return here.'

'Franco, what is it?'

'I can't tell you over the phone. Can you come at once?'

'Of course I will.'

'Thank you.' He hung up.

'Well?' Maria demanded in agony.

'He wants to see me, but he won't say why.'

The old couple were as overjoyed as if she were their own daughter. They almost pushed her into the car, Vito handed her the keys and told her to be off.

'Invite us to the wedding,' Maria called.

But, try as she would, Joanne could extract no message of reassurance from Franco's voice. If anything he'd sounded curt. And yet he wanted her to come back, and the ache of misery in her heart seemed to lift a little.

She resisted the temptation to drive fast, but she was eager to see him again at the first possible moment. As she rounded the last bend into the valley she saw a figure standing on the peak, watching the road by which she must come. It was too far away for the man's face to be clear, but her heart told her it was Franco. As soon as he saw her car he mounted his horse and galloped off in the direction of the house. Whatever was the matter, he was so anxious for her arrival that he had been watching for her.

He was waiting by the front door as she drew up, his face dark and full of tension. He didn't open his arms, attempt to kiss her, or give her any kind of welcome. They might have been distant acquaintances, except that he looked pale and ill, as though the weeks apart had tortured him too.

'Forgive me for demanding you at a moment's notice,' he said, 'but something has happened, and I need you.'

'Nico—'

'Nico is well. He's staying with friends today. I have to talk to you alone.'

'Franco, don't keep me in suspense. What is this all about?'

'Come with me.'

He led her into the house and upstairs to his room. A large box stood in the middle of the floor. It was open, and the contents were scattered all around, as though someone had been going through them hastily.

'They were her things,' Franco said. 'When she died I locked them away. I couldn't bear even to go through them. But today Nico asked me about them, and I opened the box. I found this.' He held out a cream, sealed envelope. Taking it, Joanne could feel that it contained several sheets of paper. Her own name was written on the outside in Rosemary's hand.

'She wrote that just before she died,' Franco said.

'You've read it?'

'Of course not. It's sealed. But that paper is used by the hospital. It has the hospital name stamped on the envelope. She wrote it while she was there.'

His eyes burned her.

'Don't you see what it means? She knew she was dying. She must have meant that letter to be given to you after her death. For God's sake, read it. And if you can, tell me what it says.'

With shaking hands Joanne opened the envelope, and read aloud Rosemary's last words to her.

'My darling Joanne,

If you ever read this, it will be because I'm not here to talk to you any more, and there are things I so much want you to know.

I took a gamble with this pregnancy, but every day I've been afraid it wouldn't come off. Yesterday my heart began to give out, and they brought me here, to this hospital. I know they expect me to have another attack.

I dreamed of growing old with Franco and seeing our children become strong and wise. Now I think it will never happen, and I must take care of him in the only way I can.

I want you to come out to Italy, and look after Franco, and Nico. You see, darling, I know your secret. I know you love him, and that's why you've stayed away from us. I've known ever since I visited you in England. You never told me in words, but the truth shone from you whenever I spoke his name. You love him, and you are the only person I can entrust him to.

Nico, too, will be all right with you. I used to watch him snuggle happily in your arms, and I know you'll keep him safe.

I hope Franco comes to love you, and that you will marry. He'll resist, because he's a man of honour, and he'll feel he's betraying me. But that's not so. He gave me all his love while I needed it, and when I need it no longer I want him to be free to love again. Perhaps you can teach him to understand. I hope so.

I thought of writing all this to him, but it wouldn't do. He needs to come to the idea gradually, when he's ready. I leave that to you. You'll know how to pick the moment.

Goodbye, my dearest. I entrust my two most precious treasures to your safe keeping. Be happy, and teach my poor Franco that it isn't wrong for him to find a new life with you. I know I'll always have my own corner of his heart, and you're too generous to grudge it me. The rest I gladly give to you.'

Joanne's voice faltered, and for a moment her eyes were blurred with tears as she thought of great-hearted Rosemary, whose generosity had never faltered, right to the end.

When she could see again she looked at Franco. He was sitting with his face buried in his hands. She wanted to go to him, but she must wait. There was one last thing.

Rosemary had written:

'You'll find my thoughts to Franco enclosed with this letter. When you think he's ready to hear them, I want you to read them to him yourself.'

'What are her words to me?' Franco said huskily.

It was growing darker. Joanne rose and sat by the window to catch the light. From here she guessed she must present a silhouette to Franco, and probably she seemed more like Rosemary than ever before. She hadn't planned it, but perhaps it was for the best. For one more time she must 'be' Rosemary for him, giving him the last message from the wife he had loved, and whose love for him reached out from beyond the grave.

'It's a short verse,' she said, glancing at the paper. 'It seems that she managed that poem at last. It's called—it's called "Goodbye".'

A tremor went through him. 'Read it to me.'

Softly Joanne began to read. As she did so, she felt as though Rosemary were there in the room with them, a strong, tender presence, making her last and greatest gift to those she loved.

'Remember me a little while,
Pause in the orchard where we often walked,
When days were longer and the world was ours.
Say, *"Cara, please!"* one last time, and smile.

From beneath the apple tree,
Glance up to where I once looked down at you.
Wear, just once more,
The look that said I was your love,
And you were mine until my end.
I knew it all the while.

Miss me, but not for long.
I was your joy,
Don't let me be your woe,

So remember me, and smile.
Then let me go.'

When she had finished there was silence. Joanne sat with her head bent, tears falling silently down her cheeks. It was all there, everything that had made Rosemary the person she was: the understanding and compassion, above all the love, stronger than self, stronger than death.

At last Franco rose and came to her. He dropped on his knees beside her and put his arms about her, resting his head against her. He was weeping, and she joined her tears to his, stroking his head. Just now they had no thoughts for themselves. This was Rosemary's moment, and they would give it to her in full measure.

'She loved you so much,' Joanne whispered.

'She loved us both,' he said huskily. 'All this time— I could have sent you that letter when she died.'

'It wouldn't have been the right moment, my darling. We were neither of us ready then.'

He lifted his head to look at her. 'I feel as though a huge weight has gone from my heart.'

'That's how she meant it,' Joanne said. 'That was her gift. We wanted her blessing, and now she's given it to us.'

'To be granted two miracles in one life,' he said softly. 'No man has the right.'

'You have the right to all the best the world has to offer,' she told him. 'And I'm going to give it to you.'

'The best is you. If I have you, I have everything.'

'And you'll have me always. I'll never leave you again.'

He rose to his feet and drew her up and into his arms. 'Promise me that your life is mine, as mine is yours.'

'I promise,' she said. 'Yours. Always. And Rosemary was right. I don't grudge her a place in your heart. That's where she belongs, just as I do. Keep us both safely there, my darling. Now and for ever.'

EPILOGUE

THE trees hang over the marble headstone, their branches heavy with blossom. A winter has come and gone, and the earth is full of new life and hope.

There are fresh flowers there today. Two bouquets of roses lie side by side, one red, one white. A card nestles between them. It bears no name, and contains only two, heartfelt words.

Thank you.

Modern Romance™
...seduction and
passion guaranteed

Tender Romance™
...love affairs that
last a lifetime

Sensual Romance™
...sassy, sexy and
seductive

Blaze Romance™
...the temperature's
rising

Medical Romance™
...medical drama on
the pulse

Historical Romance™
...rich, vivid and
passionate

27 new titles every month.

*With all kinds of Romance for
every kind of mood...*

MILLS & BOON®

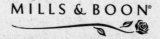

MILLS & BOON

the $\heartsuit$other's Day collection

Margaret Way Kate Hoffmann Helen Dickson

Money Off Voucher
see inside for details

Available from 21st February 2003

*Available at most branches of WH Smith,
Tesco, Martins, Borders, Eason, Sainsbury's
and all good paperback bookshops.*

0303/024/MB65

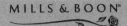

dark angel
LYNNE GRAHAM

Knight in shining armour
or avenging angel?

Available from 21st March 2003

*Available at most branches of WH Smith,
Tesco, Martins, Borders, Eason, Sainsbury's
and all good paperback bookshops.*

0403/135/MB68

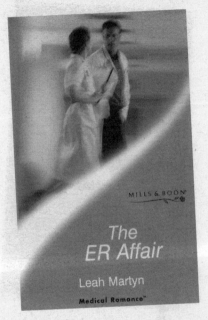

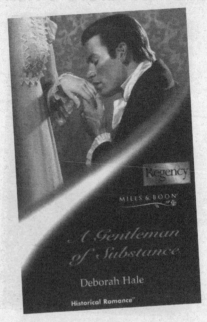